Lyle
College
Mona Hall
Albuquerque, N.M.

Robert Chambers
111 Carver St.
Madison, Illinois

$$x = \frac{-b \pm \sqrt{b^2 - 4ac}}{2a}$$

INTERMEDIATE ALGEBRA

INTERMEDIATE ALGEBRA

Paul K. Rees

Professor of Mathematics
Louisiana State University

Fred W. Sparks

Professor of Mathematics
Texas Technological College

SECOND EDITION

McGRAW-HILL BOOK COMPANY, INC.

New York   Toronto   London

1957

THE MAPLE PRESS COMPANY, YORK, PA.

PREFACE

The chief purpose in the preparation of the second edition of "Intermediate Algebra" was to provide a selection of problems greater in number and more carefully graded than those in the first edition. Few changes were necessary in the text material, and no changes were made in the order of the chapters. Hence all features of the first edition have been preserved.

The book is designed for the student who has completed only one year of high school algebra and includes the basic material necessary for further work in mathematics, for the required courses in science, for statistics and for mathematics of finance. It is planned for a three-semester-hour course but contains sufficient material for use in longer courses in which the student requires more drill.

The authors are aware of the fact that most students who have completed only one year of high school algebra have forgotten most of the content of the course by the time they become college freshmen. However, most of them are familiar with the use of the formula and remember something about the basic methods for solving simple equations. Hence the formula, simple operations, and the solution of simple equations were chosen for the subject matter of the first chapter. With this as a springboard, the discussion moves through fractional equations, systems of linear equations, quadratics, and systems of quadratic equations. In the course of this development, it was necessary to discuss the fundamental processes of algebra, factoring, and fractions before presenting fractional equations. Furthermore, it was necessary to discuss functions and graphical methods before simultaneous equations and to present exponents and radicals before quadratic equations. The last four chapters deal with ratio, proportion, and variation; logarithms; the progressions; and the binomial formula.

Every effort was made to prepare a book that the average student can read, and we believe that the following features help to achieve this goal:

1. The book is written in an informal style, and the use of long and involved sentences is avoided.

2. The introduction of new concepts and definitions is postponed until they are needed. Important definitions are stated as concisely as possible and are printed in italics as separate paragraphs.

3. Every process is illustrated by carefully explained examples so arranged that they may be used by the student as models in the preparation of his papers.

4. Numerous notes are included which call attention to common errors. These notes point out the causes of such errors and suggest methods for avoiding them.

5. The use of the equation to solve stated problems is a stumbling block to many students. The authors have attempted to help the student over this difficulty by providing detailed directions for the method of setting up the equation and by including numerous fully explained illustrative examples. The problems deal with situations familiar to the student and are so constructed that the equation is not difficult to obtain. There are many problems that will give the student confidence, rather than discourage him.

6. In the chapter dealing with simultaneous quadratic equations, special methods have been avoided, and the method of solving by substitution is emphasized. The authors feel that this method is generally sufficient for the future needs of a majority of students.

Since, in a course in intermediate algebra, a considerable amount of drill work is necessary, the selection and organization of problems is very important. For this reason, especial attention was given to the preparation of the exercises, and the authors believe that the following salient points are worthy of consideration:

1. Approximately 3000 carefully graded problems are provided.

2. In the selection of problems every effort has been made to avoid triviality and at the same time provide problems in which a mass of tedious computation does not obscure the principle involved.

3. The problems in each exercise are arranged in groups of four that are on about the same level of difficulty, and the difficulty increases gradually through the exercise. A good coverage of each exercise may be obtained by assigning every fourth problem. This

makes it possible for the book to be used in several sections simultaneously or for several semesters without repeating assignments.

4. The exercises are so spaced through the book that the text material between two of them, together with the exercise that follows, constitutes a good assignment. If the book is used for a four- or a five-hour course, more time can be spent on the exercises.

5. More difficult problems are placed at the end of each exercise to serve as a challenge for the better students.

6. Answers are provided for all problems except those whose numbers are divisible by four.

PAUL K. REES
FRED W. SPARKS

CONTENTS

CHAPTER 1

THE FORMULA, FUNDAMENTAL OPERATIONS, AND SIMPLE EQUATIONS

1. The formula. In arithmetic, a student learns to express relations and rules of procedure in handy and compact formulas which assist the memory and are convenient to use. Although he may consider this practice a type of shorthand, he is actually using algebra for one of its intended purposes, that is, as a symbolic language. Every formula is a symbolic statement which can be translated into words, since the letters represent numbers and the signs stand for arithmetic operations or relations. A formula strips the worded statement of its confusing verbal trappings and presents it in bold relief in which the essential relations and procedures are easily apparent.

The verbal rule for finding the amount to which a certain sum will accumulate at simple interest is "The amount at simple interest is equal to the principal plus the product of the principal, the rate, and the time." This cumbersome statement expressed as a formula becomes merely

$$(1) \qquad A = P + Prt,$$

and then the procedure is clearly indicated. If one knows the values of P, r, and t, he needs only to perform the indicated multiplication and addition in order to obtain A.

After one has learned to handle formulas so that he can place any one symbol alone on the left with all the others in proper positions on the right, he can use one formula for many different situations. For example, (1) can be placed in the form

$$(2) \qquad t = \frac{A - P}{Pr},$$

1

and then by use of (2) one can find the time required for a given principal to accumulate to a given amount at a specified rate. In fact, if a person is familiar with the laws of algebra, (1) is sufficient for all simple-interest problems which involve the amount.

EXAMPLE

Find the time required for a principal of $300 to accumulate to $336 at 4 per cent per year.

Solution

We shall use (2) since A, P, and r are given and t is to be found.   If we substitute the given values in (2), it becomes

$$t = \frac{336 - 300}{(300)(.04)}$$
$$= \tfrac{3\,6}{1\,2} = 3.$$

Hence, the required time is 3 years.

The formula for obtaining the amount at compound interest is

(3) $$A = P(1 + r)^t,$$

and it is harder to handle than (1).   Generally speaking, the more complex the situation is, the more complicated the formula for dealing with it becomes.   Then more algebraic skill is needed for handling it.   Although work with formulas usually constitutes a person's first experience with algebra, it is only a gateway to this important field, some knowledge of which is indispensable to anyone who wishes to live intelligently in this scientific age.

2. Some definitions.   Before going further, we need to define some of the terms we shall use.   The numbers we employ in introductory algebra are those used in arithmetic, two classes of which are the integers and the rational numbers.   These are defined below.

DEFINITION I.   *An **integer** is a number used in counting.*

DEFINITION II.   *A **rational number** is a number that can be expressed as the quotient of two integers.*

It is evident at once that the common fractions are rational numbers.   Furthermore, since a common fraction whose denominator is one is equal to an integer, the integers are also rational numbers.

In order to classify numbers further and to understand certain of their properties, it is helpful to associate each number with a specific point on a straight line.   This can be done by the method we shall next describe.

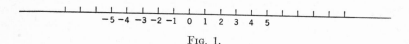

Fig. 1.

We shall consider the straight line segment in Fig. 1 as a portion of a line of unlimited length and shall designate the point marked 0 as the starting, or zero, point.   Furthermore, we shall select the length from 0 to 1 as the unit length.   Next, starting at 0 and going in both directions, we lay off on the line intervals equal to this length.   Now we assign to the right ends of these intervals, taken in succession to the right of 0, the integers $1, 2, 3, \cdots$ and to the left end of the intervals, taken in succession to the left of 0, the numbers $-1, -2, -3, \cdots$.   By properly subdividing each interval, we may locate a point representing each of the common fractions.

It can be shown that there are points on the line which cannot be associated with any of the rational numbers.   Some of these points can be found by ruler and compass constructions and others by methods too difficult to discuss here.   As an example of the former type, we shall show how to obtain the point corresponding to $\sqrt{2}$.   If we construct a right triangle whose sides are equal to 1, its hypotenuse is equal to $\sqrt{2}$.   This number is neither an integer nor a common fraction.   However, it is a definite length, and with a compass we can lay off this length on the line from 0, and its extremity represents $\sqrt{2}$.   Numbers of this type are called *real numbers*, and at this stage we are not in position to define them rigorously.   However, the following definition will suffice for our present purposes.

DEFINITION III.   *A real number is a number that can be associated with a point on a straight line.*

We are now in position to state three additional definitions.

DEFINITION IV.   *An irrational number is a real number that cannot be expressed as the quotient of two integers.*

DEFINITION V.   *A positive number is a number which represents a point located at the right of the zero point on a straight line.*

DEFINITION VI.   *A negative number is a number which represents a point located at the left of the zero point on a straight line.*

Definitions V and VI impart a directional property to each number which indicates the way it is measured from zero. Most people are familiar with at least two instruments which use both positive and negative numbers: the thermometer, and the ammeter on the instrument panel of an automobile. The latter indicates the rate at which the battery is being charged or discharged.

EXERCISE 1

1. The per cent of gain realized on the sale of an article is given by the formula $P = \dfrac{s - c}{c} (100)$, where s is the selling price of the article and c is the cost. Find the per cent gained on an article that cost $250 and sold for $300. What per cent is gained if the selling price is twice the cost? Three times the cost?

2. The income tax paid by a person whose net income is between $4000 and $6000 is given by the formula $T = 840 + .26E$, where E is the excess of his net income over $4000. Find the amount of the tax that must be paid by a person whose income is $5000; $5750.

3. The number of gallons that a rectangular container will hold is given by the formula $n = \dfrac{lwh}{231}$, where l, w, and h represent the length, width, and height, respectively, expressed in inches. Find the capacity of a vessel 30 in. long, 22 in. wide, and 14 in. high. How will the capacity be affected if each dimension is multiplied by 2?

4. The corresponding readings on a centigrade and a Fahrenheit thermometer are given by the formula $C = \frac{5}{9}(F - 32)$, where C and F represent the centigrade and the Fahrenheit readings, respectively. Find the centigrade reading that corresponds to 140°F.; 212°F.; 32°F.

5. The area of the walls of a rectangular room is given by the formula $A = 2h(l + w)$, where h, l, and w represent the height, length, and width, respectively, of the room. Find the number of square feet in the walls of a room 15 ft. long, 12 ft. wide, and 10 ft. high. What will be the effect on the area of the walls if each dimension is doubled?

6. The principal P invested at simple interest that will amount to A dollars in t years at r per cent per year is given by the formula $P = \dfrac{A}{1 + rt}$.

Find the principal that will amount to $1500 in 10 years at 5 per cent. How much would the principal be decreased if the time were extended to 20 years?

7. The circumference c of a circle is given by the formula $c = 2\pi r$, where $\pi = 3.1416$, approximately, and r is the radius. Find the circumference of the earth at the equator if the radius is 4000 miles. How much would the circumference be increased if the radius were increased by .1 in.?

8. The area A of a trapezoid is given by the formula $A = \frac{1}{2}h(b_1 + b_2)$, where b_1 and b_2 are the lengths of the parallel sides and h is the altitude. Find the area of the trapezoid in which the parallel sides are 18 and 10 in. long and the altitude is 8 in. in length. What would be the effect on the area if each of the parallel sides were increased 1 in. in length?

Identify the numbers in each of Problems 9 to 12 according to definitions I to IV.

9. $\frac{2}{3}$, $\sqrt{3}$, 3, $\frac{8}{2}$.

10. 3π, $\dfrac{2a}{a}$, $a + a$, $3a \div 4a$, where a is an integer.

11. $\frac{2}{3} + \frac{1}{3}$, $\frac{1}{2} + \frac{1}{4}$, $3 \times 3\frac{1}{3}$, $4 \div 3$.

12. The hypotenuse of a right triangle whose perpendicular sides are respectively 1 and 2 ft. in length; the circumference of a circle whose radius is 3 in.; the side of a square of area 9 sq. ft.; the side of a square of area 12 sq. ft.

Express the statement in each of Problems 13 to 16 as a formula.

13. The lateral surface L of a cylinder is equal to twice the product of π, the radius r, and the length l.

14. The volume V of a pyramid with a square base is equal to one-third of the product of the square of one side s of the base, and the height h.

15. The mass M of a rectangular block of metal is the product of the length l, the width w, the height h, and the density d.

16. The distance s that a freely falling body travels if it starts from rest is equal to one-half of the product of the acceleration due to gravity g and the square of the time t.

In each of Problems 17 to 20, draw a figure similar to Fig. 1, locate on the line the points indicated in the problem, and then find the indicated distance.

17. $A = 10$, $B = 16$, $C = 20$. Find AB, BC, AC, CA, and CB.

18. $A = -6$, $B = -12$, $C = -15$. Find CB, CA, AB, AC.

19. $A = -10, B = -4, C = 12, D = 20.$ Find $AC, BA, CD, DA.$

20. $A = -16, B = -9, C = -5, D = 18.$ Find $AB + CD, CD - BC, AD - CB, BA + BC.$

21. In order to obtain the approximate normal weight of a person over 4 ft. in height, we subtract 60 from his height h in inches, multiply this result by 5.5, and then add 110. Express this statement as a formula and then find the normal weight of a person 6 ft. tall.

22. The total number of hours h of sleep needed by a child is equal to the sum of 8 and $\frac{1}{2}$ of the excess of 18 over the age a of the child. Express this as a formula and find the number of hours of sleep needed by a child 10 years of age.

23. The blood pressure p of a person should be the sum of $\frac{1}{2}$ of the age a of the person in years and 110. Express this as a formula and find the normal blood pressure of a person 56 years of age.

24. The average mileage m expected of an automobile tire is the diameter d of the wheel expressed in feet multiplied by 6545. Express this as a formula and find the average mileage expected of a tire 20 in. in diameter.

25. The speed S in feet per minute of a rope passing over a pulley d in. in diameter and revolving r times per minute is $\frac{1}{12}$ of the product of π, d, and r. Express this statement as a formula and then find the speed of a rope passing over a pulley 12 in. in diameter revolving at the rate of 4 revolutions per minute.

26. If two loads L_1 and L_2 are balanced on a lever at distances of d_1 and d_2, respectively, from the fulcrum, then the two products obtained by multiplying each weight by its distance from the fulcrum are equal. Express this statement as a formula, and then find what weight placed 11 ft. from the fulcrum will balance another weight of 100 lb. placed 16 ft. from the fulcrum.

27. The number of bushels of corn C that can be stored in a rectangular bin of dimensions l, w, and h is equal to the volume in cubic feet divided by 2.5. Express this statement as a formula and find the capacity in bushels of a bin 12 ft. long, 8 ft. wide, and 6 ft. high.

28. The horsepower H generated by a stream of water flowing between two points at the rate of c cu. ft. per min. is equal to the product of c and the head h divided by 528. The head is the vertical distance from the surface of the water at one point to the surface at another point. Express this statement as a formula; then find the horsepower generated by a stream flowing at the rate of 1000 cu. ft. per min. with a fall of 4 ft.

3. *Algebraic combinations; rules of signs.* The four fundamental operations of algebra are addition, subtraction, multiplication and division. They are indicated by the symbols

$+$, $-$, $\times$, and $\div$, respectively. The use of the fundamental operations in algebra has an aspect not found in arithmetic. This is due to the fact that in algebra we deal with numbers that are both positive and negative, while in arithmetic the numbers are usually positive. In this article we shall present methods for finding the sum, the product, and the quotient of two "signed" numbers and for ascertaining the sign to give the result. We shall also discuss briefly the notation and terminology to be used.

In algebra we use letters of the alphabet to represent numbers whose values are unknown or are temporarily undetermined. If numbers are expressed in this way, the result obtained by combining two or more of them by means of the fundamental operations can be expressed only symbolically. For example, the sum, the product, and the quotient of a and b are expressed as $a + b$, ab, and $\dfrac{a}{b}$, respectively. If $b = a$, we have $a + a = 2a$, $a \times a = a^2$, and $a \div a = \dfrac{a}{a} = 1$.

We frequently employ parentheses ( ) to avoid confusion when negative numbers enter into algebraic combinations. For example, the statement "a minus $-b$" is expressed $a - (-b)$, and "a times $-b$" is written $a(-b)$. The parentheses are also placed around a combination of numbers and letters to indicate that the combination is to be regarded as a single number.

We may obtain a geometrical representation of addition and subtraction by use of Fig. 1. For example, if we regard the numbers in the sum $5 + 3 = 8$ as points on the line, we may reach the sum 8 by starting at 5 and counting 3 units to the right. Likewise, in order to subtract 3 from 8, we start at 8 and count 3 units in the direction *opposite* the sign of 3. That is, $8 - 3 = 5$, and $8 - (-3) = 8 + 3 = 11$. If we express these results in terms of letters, we have $a + (-b) = a - b$ and $a - (-b) = a + b$.

In the rules that follow, we shall refer to the *numerical* or *absolute* value of a number. This means that we disregard the sign, or the directional aspect, of the number and consider it just as we did in arithmetic. Thus, the numerical value of -3 and of 3 is, in each case, 3. In connection with the "point-on-a-line" representation of a number, the numerical value is the distance between zero and the point representing the number, without reference to the direction of this distance.

RULE OF SIGNS FOR ADDITION.   *In order to find the sum of two numbers with like signs, we add the numerical values and prefix the common sign of the two.   If the two numbers are unlike in sign, we subtract the smaller numerical value from the larger and prefix the sign of the numerically larger number.*

EXAMPLES

$$(-3) + (-2) = -5.$$
$$2 + (-8) = -6.$$
$$10 + (-3) = 7.$$
$$6a + 2a - 3a = 8a - 3a = 5a.$$
$$5x - 2x - 7x = 5x - 9x = -4x.$$

RULE OF SIGNS FOR MULTIPLICATION.   *In order to find the product of two numbers, we multiply their numerical values and prefix a positive or negative sign according as the two numbers are like or unlike in sign.*

RULE OF SIGNS FOR DIVISION.   *In order to find the quotient of two numbers, we divide their numerical values and prefix a positive or negative sign according as the two numbers are like or unlike in sign.*

EXAMPLES

$$-6a \times -3a = 18a^2.$$
$$-4x \times 2x = -8x^2.$$
$$12 \div -3 = -4.$$
$$-18 \div -6 = 3.$$

We shall next define some of the results obtained by use of the fundamental operations.

DEFINITION I.   *If two or more numbers at least one of which is a letter are combined by one or more of the fundamental operations of algebra, the result is called an algebraic* **expression.**

DEFINITION II.   *Any combination of numbers in an expression, together with the sign that precedes it, that is separated from the remainder of the expression by a plus or minus sign is called a* **term.**

Four examples of expressions are $a + b$, $(6a - 2b)(4a^2 - b)$, $3x + \dfrac{2y + z}{4x - 2y}$, and $4xyz$. The last expression contains only one term and we can, with propriety, refer to it by the latter name. According to definition II, the only operations which may appear in a term are multiplication and division. If a term involves multiplication only, each of the numbers or letters appearing in it is a *factor* of the term. Furthermore, if one letter is selected, the remainder of the term is called the *coefficient* of that letter. These ideas are expressed more specifically in the following two definitions:

DEFINITION III. *Any one of the numbers entering into a product is called a **factor** of that product.*

DEFINITION IV. *If any single letter or group of letters in a term is specified, the product of the other numbers in the term is called the **coefficient** of that letter or group of letters.*

Thus, in $3x$, 3 is the coefficient of x, while in $3abc$, $3ab$ is the coefficient of c, $3c$ is the coefficient of ab, and 3 is the coefficient of abc.

Earlier in this article, we stated that $a \times a = a^2$ or that the product of two a's is written a^2. We call this number a-*square*. Similarly, we write the product of three a's as a^3 and call the result a-*cube*. In general, we write the product of n a's as a^n, which we call the *nth power of a* or, more briefly, *a to the nth*. We shall describe this notation more fully below.

DEFINITION V. *A number of the type a^n, where n is a positive integer, is called the **nth** power of **a**. The symbol **a** is the **base**. The symbol **n** is called the **exponent**, and it indicates the number of times **a** appears as a factor of a^n.*

NOTE: When the exponent is one, as in a^1, it is usually omitted. Furthermore, when no exponent appears on a letter, the exponent is understood to be one.

EXERCISE 2

Find the sums indicated in each of Problems 1 to 16.

1. 46	2. 187	3. 146	4. 139	5. -172
94	49	-98	-128	121

6. 381	7. -189	8. -256	9. 58	10. 75
-562	-236	-139	65	-98
			72	87

11. -48	**12.** 100	**13.** -49	**14.** 78	**15.** -39
-80	-86	-65	-65	85
96	-45	-72	14	-27

16. -180
-211
-146

Perform the addition indicated in Problems 17 to 32.

17. $36 + 47 + 28 + 16.$ **18.** $42 + 18 + 25 - 53.$

19. $65 + 18 - 42 - 81.$ **20.** $90 - 25 - 32 - 16.$

21. $73 - 27 + 16 - 63.$ **22.** $36 - 24 - 42 + 30.$

23. $-83 + 29 + 31 - 17.$ **24.** $-26 + 87 - 86 + 27.$

25. $48 + (-16).$ **26.** $68 - (+32).$

27. $-58 + (-27).$ **28.** $-75 + (-25).$

29. $67 - (-32).$ **30.** $-39 - (-87).$

31. $38 + (-25) - (-28).$ **32.** $-(-72) - (+67) + (-36).$

Combine similar terms in Problems 33 to 48.

33. $2a + 3a + b + 5b.$ **34.** $7x + 2x + 3x + 2y.$

35. $2m + 3n + 8m + 5n.$ **36.** $5q + 3r + 2s + 2r + 5s + 7q.$

37. $6a - 3b - 4a + 5b.$ **38.** $10h + 6k - 4k - 3h.$

39. $12x - 4y - 7x - 3y.$ **40.** $4p + 6q - 9p - 8q.$

41. $-8x + 3y - 2z + 4y - 3x + 5z.$

42. $6a - 4c + 2b + 4c - 2a + 5b.$

43. $12e - 4g - 6f + 8g - 2f - 7e.$

44. $10p - 12q - 4p - 16r - 8q - 11r.$

45. $24r - (-12s) + (-9t) - (-10s).$

46. $16x + (-12y) - 10z - (-4x) - (-6y) + 3z.$

47. $-(-15a) + (-13b) - (-8c) - 9a - (-5b) + 2c.$

48. $11v + (-4w) - (-6v) + 8x - (-7w) - 2x.$

Find the product in each of Problems 49 to 68.

49. $6(-12).$ **50.** $(-8)(9).$ **51.** $(-7)(-8).$

52. $(-9)(-8).$ **53.** $(-4)(-2\frac{1}{2}).$ **54.** $(6)(-1\frac{1}{3}).$

55. $(-12)(8\frac{1}{3}).$ **56.** $(-15)(-6\frac{1}{5}).$ **57.** $(6a)(a).$

58. $(8b)(-2b).$ **59.** $(-9c)(-7c).$ **60.** $(15x)(-10x).$

61. $(-6\frac{2}{3})(3).$ **62.** $(-8)(12\frac{1}{2}).$ **63.** $(-4)(-18\frac{3}{4}).$

64. $(-12)(-8\frac{1}{3}).$ **65.** $(-a)(-2a)(3b).$ **66.** $(5x)(-6y)(2y).$

67. $(-4r)(-6s)(-8r).$ **68.** $(-7u)(-9v)(3u).$

Find the quotient in each of Problems 69 to 80.

69. $(-128) \div (-32).$ **70.** $(63) \div (-21).$

71. $(-96) \div 12$.

72. $(-144) \div (-36)$.

73. $(121a) \div (11a)$.

74. $(-125b) \div (-25b)$.

75. $(225x) \div (-25x)$.

76. $(-324y) \div (18y)$.

77. $(76a^2) \div (-4a)$.

78. $(-124b^2) \div (-31b)$.

79. $(-147x) \div 7$.

80. $(-315w) \div (-5)$.

Perform the operations indicated in Problems 81 to 100. Combine the numbers in the parentheses first.

81. $8 + (5 - 2)$.

82. $10 - (6 + 2)$. 5

83. $7 - (9 - 2)$.

84. $5 - (4 + 3)$.

85. $(3 - 5) + 7$.

86. $(12 - 9) - 5$.

87. $(4 - 12) - 3$.

88. $(16 - 13) - 3$.

89. $(6a \times 2a) - 8a^2$.

90. $8y^2 - (2y \times 9y)$.

91. $(-4b \times 3c) + 6bc$.

92. $(-5h \times 4k) - 12hk$.

93. $(4 \times 3) \div (-6)$.

94. $(18 \div 2) \times (-4)$.

95. $144 \div (3 \times 4)$.

96. $-128 \div (4 \times 2)$.

97. $(6a + 9a) \div (-5a)$.

98. $-160b \div (12b + 8b)$.

99. $(5x - 17x) \div (4x - 2x)$.

100. $(8y - 20y) \div (4y - 7y)$.

4. *The equation.*   In Art. 1, we stated that a formula was an algebraic statement of a rule and that the use of formulas greatly simplifies the task of solving problems.   Frequently the method of solving a problem for which no specific rule is given can be seen easily if the problem is restated in algebraic language.   For example, consider this problem: "Tom had twice as much money as Bill when they went to the county fair.   Tom lost a dollar bill out of his pocket, Bill won a two-dollar prize on his bantam hen, and then the two boys had equal amounts of money.   How much did each have at first?"   In order to state this problem in symbols, we can let x stand for Bill's money, and then $2x$ represents Tom's.   After he had lost a dollar, Tom had $2x - 1$ dollars left, and Bill had $x + 2$ dollars after he had pocketed his prize. Hence, since they then had the same amount, we know that

$$(1) \qquad\qquad 2x - 1 = x + 2.$$

Now all that remains is to determine x so that (1) is a true statement.   In the following article, we shall present a method which will reduce the finding of x in a relation of this type to a matter of routine.   At present, we can only guess.   After trying a few small values of x, we may eventually come to 3, which does satisfy the condition since $2(3) - 1 = 3 + 2$.

The statement (1) is an illustration of one of the most powerful and useful tools of algebra, which we define as follows:

DEFINITION.   *An equation is a statement that two expressions are equal.*

5. Solution of linear equations in one unknown.   DEFINITION. *A linear equation in one unknown is an equation that contains only one unknown letter, and this letter appears to the first power but to no higher power.*

Such equations are also called *simple equations*.   For the present, we shall discuss only simple equations that involve no fractions except possibly as coefficients.

A value of the unknown which makes the equation a true statement is called a *solution*, or a *root*, of the equation and is said to *satisfy* it.

Before discussing the method for solving simple equations, we shall present three axioms upon which the method is based.

AXIOM I.   *If equals are added to equals, the sums are equal.*

AXIOM II.   *If equals are multiplied by equals, the products are equal.*

AXIOM III.   *If equals are divided by nonzero[1] equals, the quotients are equal.*

By use of Axiom I, we can derive a process that is very useful for solving equations.   For example, consider the equation

(1) $$ax - b = cx + d.$$

If this equation is satisfied by a given value of x, then, by Axiom I, the equation obtained from (1) by adding first b and then $-cx$, or $b - cx$, to each member will be satisfied by the same value of x. Performing this operation, we get

(2) $$ax - b + b - cx = cx + d + b - cx$$

or

(3) $$ax - cx = d + b.$$

Now we can see that the same result is obtained if we move cx and b in (1) from one side of the equality to the other and change

---

[1] We shall explain in Art. 14 why the divisor in Axiom III must not be zero.

the sign of each term that is moved in the process. We call this procedure *transposition*. By use of it, we may transpose a term from one member of an equation to the other provided that we change the sign of the term that is moved.

EXAMPLE 1

Solve the equation

(4) $$2x - 3 = x + 1.$$

Solution

Transposing -3 to the right and x to the left, we get

(5) $$2x - x = 1 + 3,$$

and then combining terms, we have

$$x = 4,$$

which is the value sought. We may check this solution by substituting 4 for x in (4), obtaining $2(4) - 3 = 8 - 3 = 5$ for the left member and $4 + 1 = 5$ for the right member. Hence, since the two members are equal, the solution checks.

By properly transposing and combining terms, we may reduce any simple equation to the form

(6) $$ax = b.$$

Now we use Axiom III and divide both members of (6) by a and obtain the solution

$$x = \frac{b}{a}.$$

EXAMPLE 2

Solve the equation

(7) $$4x - 6 = 4 - x.$$

Solution

Transposing terms, we get

$$4x + x = 4 + 6$$

or

$$5x = 10.$$

Now we may obtain the solution by dividing each member by 5, getting

$$x = 2.$$

As a check, we substitute 2 for x in (7), obtaining $4(2) - 6 = 8 - 6 = 2$ as the value of the left member and $4 - 2 = 2$ as the value of the right. Hence, since the two members are equal when $x = 2$, the solution checks.

If a is a fraction $\dfrac{c}{d}$, Eq. (6) becomes

(8)
$$\frac{c}{d} x = b.$$

By Axiom II, we may multiply each member of (8) by d and get

$$cx = bd,$$

which is the same form as (6).
Hence,

$$x = \frac{bd}{c}.$$

EXAMPLE 3

Solve

(9)
$$\tfrac{3}{4}x - 2 = \tfrac{1}{4}x + 6.$$

Solution

If we transpose -2 and $\tfrac{1}{4}x$, we get

$$\tfrac{3}{4}x - \tfrac{1}{4}x = 6 + 2$$

or

$$\tfrac{2}{4}x = 8.$$

Now we multiply each member by 4 and then divide by 2 and get

$$2x = 32,$$
$$x = 16.$$

We check this solution by finding the value of each member of (9) when $x = 16$. Thus, we get $\tfrac{3}{4}(16) - 2 = 12 - 2 = 10$ for the value of the left member and $\tfrac{1}{4}(16) + 6 = 4 + 6 = 10$ for the right member. Hence, the solution checks.

EXAMPLE 4

Using formula (1) of Art. 1, find the time required for $250 to amount to $285 at 4 per cent simple interest.

Solution

If we substitute \$285, \$250, and .04 for A, P, and r, respectively, in (1), Art. 1, we get

$$\$285 = \$250 + (\$250)(.04)t$$

or

$$285 = 250 + 10t.$$

Hence,

$$-10t = 250 - 285,$$
$$-10t = -35,$$
$$t = 3\tfrac{1}{2} \text{ years.}$$

EXERCISE 3

Solve the equations in Problems 1 to 60 and check the answers.

1. $3x = 12.$
2. $5x = -20.$
3. $-7x = -14.$
4. $-4x = 36.$
5. $\frac{1}{2}x = 4.$
6. $\frac{1}{4}x = 9.$
7. $\frac{2}{3}x = 4.$
8. $\frac{3}{4}x = -3.$
9. $2x + 4 = 0.$
10. $5x - 15 = 0.$
11. $12 - 4x = 0.$
12. $16 - 4x = 0.$
13. $7x - 2 = 12.$
14. $8x + 4 = 20.$
15. $5 - 2x = 3.$
16. $7 - 3x = 10.$
17. $3x - 2 = 2x + 3.$
18. $3 - 4x = 4 - 3x.$
19. $5x + 3 = 4 + 6x.$
20. $7x - 8 = 2 - 3x.$
21. $10x - 6 = -8 + 6x.$
22. $12 - 4x = 10 - 8x.$
23. $7 - 4x = 16 + 5x.$
24. $9 - 3x = 4x - 12.$
25. $3x + 1 = 7x - 15.$
26. $9x - 2 = 7 + 6x.$
27. $11x + 35 = 2x - 1.$
28. $15x - 25 = 13 - 4x.$
29. $18 - 10x = 4x - 10.$
30. $36 - 12x = 8x + 56.$
31. $27x - 9 = 12x + 21.$
32. $16x + 24 = 7x - 3.$
33. $2x - 4 - 5x = 5 - 6x.$
34. $3x - 7 = 4x + 3 - 2x.$
35. $3 - 4x + 5 = 2 - 2x.$
36. $11x - 3 = 4x + 7 + 9x.$
37. $3x - 5 - x + 3 = 4x - 7.$
38. $8 - 2x - 4 + x = 3x - 12.$
39. $9 - 8x = 2x - 6 - 5x + 5.$
40. $4 + 11x - 3 = 6x + 5 + x.$
41. $\frac{2}{3}x - 4 = 2 - \frac{1}{3}x.$
42. $\frac{3}{4}x - 8 = 4 - \frac{1}{4}x.$
43. $\frac{3}{2}x + \frac{2}{3} = \frac{1}{2}x - \frac{4}{3}.$
44. $\frac{2}{5}x - \frac{1}{4} = \frac{3}{4} - \frac{3}{5}x.$
45. $\frac{1}{2}x - 3 = \frac{1}{2} + x.$
46. $\frac{2}{3}x - 5 = \frac{1}{3}x + 3.$
47. $\frac{3}{4}x - \frac{1}{2} = \frac{1}{4}x + \frac{3}{2}.$
48. $\frac{5}{8}x + \frac{3}{5} = \frac{8}{5} + \frac{3}{8}x.$
49. $\frac{2}{7}x - \frac{3}{4} = \frac{1}{7}x + \frac{1}{4}.$
50. $\frac{4}{9}x - \frac{5}{3} = \frac{4}{3} + \frac{1}{3}x.$
51. $\frac{5}{12}x - \frac{4}{5} = \frac{7}{12}x + \frac{6}{5}.$
52. $\frac{3}{10} + \frac{4}{3}x = x - \frac{7}{10}.$
53. $\frac{7}{8} - \frac{3}{5}x = \frac{1}{8} - \frac{4}{5}x.$
54. $\frac{5}{4} + \frac{2}{7}x = \frac{3}{7}x - \frac{3}{4}.$
55. $\frac{7}{3} + \frac{5}{4}x = \frac{3}{4}x - \frac{5}{3}.$
56. $\frac{7}{15}x - \frac{5}{9} = \frac{2}{15}x + \frac{4}{9}.$

57. $\frac{4}{5}x - \frac{3}{2} + 2x = \frac{1}{2} - \frac{1}{5}x + 4$.   **58.** $\frac{5}{4}x - \frac{1}{2} + 3x = \frac{3}{2} + \frac{1}{4}x - 2$.

59. $\frac{1}{6}x - \frac{1}{4} - 3x = \frac{3}{4} - \frac{5}{6}x + 3$.   **60.** $\frac{5}{12}x - 4 + x = \frac{3}{2} - \frac{1}{12}x + \frac{1}{2}$.

61. The process of division involves the dividend D, the divisor d, the quotient q, and the remainder r. These quantities are connected by the relation $D = qd + r$. By use of this formula, find d if the dividend is 67, the quotient is 9, and the remainder is 4.

62. The relation between the cost c, the selling price s, and the rate of gain r is given by the formula $s = c + rc$. Find the rate of gain on a house that cost $10,000 and sold for $15,000.

63. By use of formula (1) of Art. 1, find the time required for $4000 to amount to $5440 at 6 per cent.

64. The distance traversed by a body that moves for t sec. subject to the uniform acceleration a and that starts with the velocity of v ft. per sec. is given by the formula $s = vt + \frac{1}{2}at^2$. Find a if a body starts with a velocity of 10 ft. per sec. and moves 6600 ft. in 20 sec.

65. The total surface area s of a right circular cylinder is given by the formula $s = 2\pi r(r + h)$, where r is the radius and h is the height. Find the height of a right circular cylinder of radius 7 in. if the surface area is 836 sq. in. (Use $3\frac{1}{7}$ for π.)

66. The sum of the terms in the sequence 2, 4, 6, 8, $\cdots$ and so on to n terms is given by the formula $s = \frac{1}{2}n(a + l)$, where a is the first term and l is the last. Find the last term if $s = 110$ and $n = 10$.

67. The area A of a trapezoid is given by the formula $A = \frac{1}{2}h(b_1 + b_2)$, where b_1 and b_2 are the lengths of the parallel sides and h is the altitude. Find the altitude of a trapezoid if the area is 88 sq. in. and the lengths of the parallel sides are 10 and 12 in., respectively.

68. The average A of three numbers a, b, and c is given by the formula $A = \frac{1}{3}(a + b + c)$. If the average is 67 and two of the numbers are 76 and 81, find the third number.

6. Solving problems by means of equations. In order to solve a problem by means of an equation, we select an unknown quantity in the problem, represent it by a letter, and express the other unknowns in terms of this letter. Finally, we form an equation that will yield the solution. The first step is to read the problem until the situation is thoroughly understood. The next step is to select the unknown that is to be represented by x. Then we find two quantities that are equal, and that are such that one or both of them can be expressed in terms of x. When we find these two quantities, express them in terms of x, and equate them, we have the equation. After we solve this equation, we have the value of one unknown, and we can find the others.

In each case, the values of the unknown should be checked to see if they satisfy the conditions of the problem.

The process of solving a problem by means of an equation is not easy, but skill comes with practice.   One must be sure that he fully understands the situation described in the problem.   If the problem asks us to find only one quantity, this quantity is the one we usually represent by x.   If it asks for more than one quantity, the equation can often be found if one of these is represented by x and the others are expressed in terms of x.   If neither of these approaches yields an equation, the proper quantity to be represented by x may be found after some experimentation.

The solutions of the following problems illustrate the processes described above.   The reader is urged to study them carefully before attempting to solve the problems in the next exercise.

EXAMPLE 1

After Mr. Smith received $75 as a payment on a debt from Mr. Brown, he had twice as much money as Mr. Brown had left.   If Mr. Smith had $175 before the payment, how much did Mr. Brown have?

Solution

Here the answer called for is the amount of money Mr. Brown had before the payment.   Hence, we shall make a trial start by letting x represent this amount.   Then the steps in obtaining the equation are:

(1) Let

$$x = \text{the amount of money Mr. Brown had}$$
$$\text{before the payment.}$$

(2) Then

$$x - 75 = \text{the amount he had after the payment,}$$

(3) and

$$175 + 75 = 250 = \text{the amount Mr. Smith had after}$$
$$\text{the payment.}$$

(4) Since Mr. Smith then had twice as much as Mr. Brown,

$$2(x - 75) = 250$$

(5) or

$$2x - 150 = 250.$$

This is the desired equation, and we can find x by transposing -150 and then dividing by 2.   Thus,

$$2x = 250 + 150,$$
$$2x = 400,$$
$$x = 200.$$

This amount $200 satisfies the problem since after payment Mr. Brown had $200 − $75 = $125, and Mr. Smith had $175 + $75 = $250.

If a problem is long and complicated or if its equation is not readily found, it frequently helps to follow the procedure suggested below.

1. List in a column every quantity mentioned in the problem, and every quantity that might be needed in solving it.

2. List the relations between the quantities listed in Step 1 that are mentioned in the problem or that common sense suggests.

3. At the right of each quantity listed in Step 1, enter its value, if the value is given.

4. Now study the quantities in Step 1 whose values are not given, and see how they are connected by the relations in Step 2.   Then select one of these unknowns, label it x, and use the relations in Step 2 to express the other unknowns in terms of x.

Usually the desired equation can be found by the time Step 4 is completed, provided the work in performing the three previous steps has been carefully and completely done.

We shall illustrate the above procedure in solving the following examples:

EXAMPLE 2

A cowboy rode a horse at 8 miles per hr. from a line camp to the ranch headquarters.   He then went to town in a car at the rate of 40 miles per hr.   If he spent twice as much time in the car as on the horse, and if the distance from the camp to town by way of the headquarters is 44 miles, find the time spent in the car, the time on horseback, the distance from camp to headquarters, and the distance from headquarters to town.

Solution

We shall first show the list obtained by following the directions given in Steps 1 to 4 and then explain how we applied the directions.

Quantities

   (*a*) Speed of horse   8 miles per hr.

   (*b*) Speed of car   40 miles per hr.

(c) Time on horseback x hr.
(d) Time in car $2x$ hr.
(e) Distance from camp to headquarters $8x$ miles
(f) Distance from headquarters to town $(40)(2x) = 80x$ miles
(g) Distance from camp to town   44 miles
(h) Distance on horseback $8x$ miles
(i) Distance in car $80x$ miles

Relations

(j) Quantity (d) = twice quantity (c).
(k) Quantity (e) = quantity (a) times quantity (c).
(l) Quantity (f) = quantity (b) times quantity (d).
(m) Quantity (h) = quantity (e).
(n) Quantity (i) = quantity (f).
(o) Quantity (g) = quantity (e) + quantity (f).

Step 1.   The quantities mentioned in the problem are those from (a) to (g) in the column at the left above.   Quantities (h) and (i) are not specifically mentioned but are needed in the solution.

Step 2.   The relations in the list above are either mentioned or implied in the problem.

Step 3.   The values of (a), (b), and (g) are given in the problem, and these are listed in the proper places in the column at the right.

Step 4.   Relation (j) is the key to the remainder of the work, for if we let (c) = x, then (d) = $2x$, and the values of the other unknowns in terms of x can be found at once.   When these are determined and listed properly on the right, we can see that relation (o) gives us the equation

$$44 = 8x + 80x.$$

Transposing and combining terms, we have

$$88x = 44,$$
$$x = \tfrac{1}{2} \text{ hr.}   \text{(time on horseback)}.$$

Then

$$2x = 1 \text{ hr.}   \text{(time in car)},$$
$$8x = 4 \text{ miles}   \text{(distance from camp to headquarters)},$$
$$80x = 40 \text{ miles}   \text{(distance from headquarters to town)}.$$

EXAMPLE 3

If Sam is $\tfrac{3}{2}$ as old as James and 10 years ago he was twice as old, find the present age of each.

Solution

The quantities and relations mentioned in this problem are:

Quantities

    (a) Sam's age now
    (b) James' age now
    (c) Sam's age 10 years ago
    (d) James' age 10 years ago

Relations

    (e) Quantity (a) = $\frac{3}{2}$ quantity (b).
    (f) Quantity (c) = two times quantity (d).

The problem does not tell us the value of any of the quantities listed above. However, if we let quantity (b) be x years, then relation (e) tells us that quantity (a) will be $\frac{3}{2}x$ years. Then the values shown below are easily obtained.

    (a) Sam's age now $\frac{3}{2}x$ years
    (b) James' age now x years
    (c) Sam's age 10 years ago $\frac{3}{2}x - 10$ years
    (d) James' age 10 years ago $x - 10$ years

Hence, by relation (f), we have the equation

$$\tfrac{3}{2}x - 10 = 2(x - 10)$$

or

$$\tfrac{3}{2}x - 10 = 2x - 20.$$

Transposing, we have

$$\tfrac{3}{2}x - 2x = -20 + 10$$

or

$$-\tfrac{1}{2}x = -10.$$

Hence, if we multiply each member above by -2, we get

$$x = 20 \quad \text{(James' present age)},$$

and hence,

$$\tfrac{3}{2}x = 30 \quad \text{(Sam's present age)}.$$

EXERCISE 4

1. Find two numbers such that one is twice the other and their sum is 36.

2. Find two numbers such that one is 5 greater than the other and their sum is 27.

3. Find two numbers such that one is three times the other and their difference is 30.

4. One number is twice another. If the larger number is decreased by 12 and the smaller is increased by 8, the results will be equal. Find the numbers.

5. The sum of three times one number and twice another is 28. Find the numbers if their sum is 12.

6. If a number is increased by one-half of itself, the result is 51. Find the number.

7. The difference between two-thirds of a number and one-half of it is 11. Find the number.

8. Five times a number minus 3 is equal to three times the number plus 9. Find the number.

9. A student bought a slide rule and a brief case for $40. Find the cost of each if the price of the brief case was $4 more than that of the slide rule.

10. A merchant made a trip to a wholesale center and returned by another route that was 25 miles longer; he found that he had traveled 655 miles. Find the distance traveled on each part of the trip.

11. A man in a clothing store was shown two suits of clothes priced at figures that were respectively $5 more and $10 less than the amount of money in his pocket book. If the combined cost of the two suits was $135, find the amount of money that he had and the price of the two suits.

12. Two brothers earned a total of $200 during a summer vacation. If one of the boys' earnings were $85 less than twice the other's, find the amount earned by each.

13. A football team scored 41 points in three games. Find the score in each if the scores in the second and third games were 7 points and 16 points, respectively, greater than that of the first game.

14. The largest of three college clubs has twice as many members as the smallest and 10 more than the third. Find the membership of each club if there are 115 members in all.

15. On a fishing trip John caught three times as many fish as Tom and 12 less than Harry. If the total catch was 96 fish, how many were caught by each?

16. The perimeter of a triangle is 33 in. Find the length of each side if the first is twice as long as the second and the length of the third side is 3 in. less than the sum of the first two.

17. Bill paid Jack $5 for a fielder's glove, and then the two boys had the same amount of money. If, before the transaction, Bill had three times as much money as Jack, how much was possessed by each?

18. At the end of a game, Charles had twice as many marbles as James.

After he traded James 10 glass marbles for 2 agates, the two boys had the same number. How many did each have before the trade?

19. In a contest for cash prizes Bob won $5 more than Dick. Later, after Bob had earned $9 more and Dick had paid a debt of $3, the former had twice as much money as the latter. Find the amount of each prize.

20. A used-car dealer who operated two lots had three times as many cars on the first lot as on the second. After he had sold 30 cars from the first lot, he transferred 20 cars from the first to the second. Then the number of cars on the two lots was the same. How many cars were on each lot originally?

21. If a boy is three times as old as his younger brother and in 5 years he will be twice as old, find the age of each.

22. When Ann is twice her present age, she will be one-half as old as Jane. How old is Ann if Jane is 12 years of age?

23. In 3 years Alice will be four times as old as she was 9 years ago. Find her present age.

24. At present, Joe's age is three times Mary's. In 4 years he will be five times as old as Mary was 4 years ago. Find Joe's age.

HINT FOR PROBLEMS 25 TO 28: If a, b, and c are the hundreds digit, the tens digit, and the units digit, respectively, in a number, then the number is $100a + 10b + c$.

25. The units digit in a number is three times the tens digit. If 18 is added to the number, the digits are reversed. Find the number.

26. Find the two-digit number with the units digit 6 that is equal to four times the sum of its digits.

27. Find the number with digits that are two consecutive integers that is equal to five times the sum of its digits.

28. Each digit, after the first, in a three-digit number is twice the preceding. If 297 is added to the number, the units and hundreds digit are interchanged. Find the number.

29. A man drove his car 500 miles in 8 hr. If he averaged 65 miles per hr. over a portion of his trip and 55 miles per hr. over the remainder, find the distance traveled at each speed.

30. A man left town A in a car on a trip to town B 345 miles away. At the same time a man left B in a truck and traveled toward A at a speed that averaged 5 miles per hr. less than the car. If they met after 3 hr., find the average speed of each.

31. A pilot flew from his home field to another at the rate of 180 miles per hr. and returned at the rate of 150 miles per hr. If the outward trip required 1 hr. less time than the return trip, find the distance between the fields.

32. Two ships passed in mid-ocean and traveled in opposite directions.

After 7 hr. they were 280 nautical miles apart. Find the speed of each if they differed by 4 knots. NOTE: A knot is the speed of 1 nautical mile per hr.

33. A man fenced a rectangular lot with a 60-ft. front and a 400-ft. perimeter at a cost of $372. If the cost of the front fence was 20 cents more per foot than that of the other three sides, find the price per foot of each type of fencing.

34. The total annual income from rent on two houses was $1800. Find the monthly rental on each if they differ by $15 and the more expensive house was vacant for 2 months.

35. Mr. Jones, Mr. Smith, and Mr. Brown purchased a store for $25,000. Jones and Smith contributed $17,000, and Brown's share in the purchase was $1000 more than Smith's. Find the amount of money advanced by each.

36. A portion of $7000 was invested at 3 per cent and the remainder at 4 per cent. If the total income was $240, how much was invested at each rate?

37. On Jan. 1, Mr. Smith invested in a type of stock that paid an annual dividend of 4 per cent. At the beginning of the second year he sold $3000 worth of his stock and reinvested the proceeds in a business that paid 5 per cent per year. If the total income from these investments for 2 years was $430, what was the amount of the original investment?

38. A Sunday-school collection made up of nickels, dimes, and quarters amounted to $6. There were twice as many dimes as quarters in the collection, and as many nickels as there were dimes and quarters combined. How many coins of each denomination were in the collection?

39. A rectangular lot that has a perimeter of 420 ft. is enclosed with a fence that cost $1.20 per foot across the front and $1 per foot around the other three sides. Find the dimensions if the total cost of the front fence was one-fifth of the cost of the remainder.

40. A man invested a sum of money at 5 per cent and a second sum that was $1500 more than the first at 4 per cent. Find the amount invested at each rate if the total annual income was $330.

41. A grocer combined two grades of coffee worth 80 cents and $1 per pound, respectively, in order to obtain 100 lb. of a mixture that sold for 95 cents per pound. How many pounds of each grade were used?

42. How many pounds of coffee at 75 cents per pound must be combined with 30 lb. that sells for 95 cents per pound in order to obtain a mixture that sells for 90 cents per pound?

43. A tobacco wholesaler combined two grades of tobacco worth $3 and $5 per pound, respectively, in order to obtain 60 lb. of a mixture to sell for $3.75 per pound. How much of each grade was used?

44. A tobacco dealer sold a portion of a 50-lb. shipment of tobacco worth $3.50 per pound and combined the remainder with 30 lb. of a grade worth $2.50 per pound. He sold the mixture at $2.75 per pound. If he lost nothing in the transaction, how many pounds did he sell before mixing the two grades?

45. Two men left the same hotel at the same time and traveled in the same direction on the same highway. After 5 hr. their cars were 50 miles apart. Find the speed of each if one car traveled $\frac{5}{6}$ as fast as the other.

46. Two cars filled with tourists left the same hotel on a scenic loop and traveled in opposite directions around the loop. Their speeds were 50 and 40 miles per hour, respectively. Find the distance around the loop if the faster car completed the round trip 54 min. ahead of the other.

47. A car left Baton Rouge for Houston at 1 P.M., and another left Houston for Baton Rouge at 2 P.M. on the same day. They met at 4 P.M. The speed of the second car was 10 miles per hr. less than the first, and the two cities are 245 miles apart. Find the speed of each.

48. Five minutes after an accident caused by a hit-and-run driver, a highway patrol car reached the scene of the accident. One of the patrolmen started immediately in pursuit of the offender and overtook him in 1 hr. and 10 min. Find the speed of each car if the speed of the patrol car was 5 miles per hr. greater than that of the other car.

CHAPTER 2

THE FOUR FUNDAMENTAL OPERATIONS

7. Addition. We have used the fact that the sum of two monomials containing different letters can be expressed only by writing the two monomials with a plus sign between them. We follow the same practice if three or more monomials are involved, or if they contain different powers of the same letter. Thus, the sum of $3a$, $2b$, and $-4b^2$ is written $3a + 2b + (-4b^2)$. If each of the monomials to be added contains the same letters and the same powers thereof, the sum is expressed as a monomial containing the same letters as the addends and with a coefficient which is the sum of the coefficients in the addends. For example, $5ab + 3ab - 2ab = 6ab$.

At this point, we shall define three terms that will be employed frequently in the remainder of this book.

DEFINITION. *An expression which contains more than one term is called a* **polynomial.** *If the expression contains two terms, it is called a* **binomial.** *If it contains three terms, it is called a* **trinomial.**

The addition of two or more polynomials is based on an axiom known as the commutative law of addition, and it permits us to combine the numbers in a sum in any order we please. In arithmetic, it is readily verified that the sum of two or more numbers is the same regardless of the order in which they are added. We shall assume that this fact is always true and thus we have the following axiom:

AXIOM. *Addition is* **commutative,** *that is,* $a + b = b + a.$

The use of this axiom in finding the sum of two or more polynomials is illustrated in the following example.

EXAMPLE 1

Find the sum of $3x^2 - 2xy + y^2$, $2xy - 3y^2 - 2x^2$, and $4y^2 - 5x^2 + 4xy$.

Solution

This problem requires us to find the value of

$$3x^2 - 2xy + y^2 + 2xy - 3y^2 - 2x^2 + 4y^2 - 5x^2 + 4xy.$$

By the commutative axiom, we may rearrange the terms so that those containing the same letter or combination of letters are together and obtain

$$3x^2 - 2x^2 - 5x^2 - 2xy + 2xy + 4xy + y^2 - 3y^2 + 4y^2.$$

Now, by combining like terms, we get $-4x^2 + 4xy + 2y^2$.

This process justifies the following shorter procedure, which is the one ordinarily used. Rewrite the expressions so that each one after the first is below the preceding, and at the same time rearrange terms so that those containing the same letters and powers thereof form vertical columns. Finally, draw a horizontal line below the last expression. Then we combine like terms and write the result below the line. When this is done, we have

$$
\begin{array}{r}
3x^2 - 2xy + y^2 \\
-2x^2 + 2xy - 3y^2 \\
-5x^2 + 4xy + 4y^2 \\
\hline
-4x^2 + 4xy + 2y^2.
\end{array}
$$

EXAMPLE 2

Find the sum of $3a^2 - 2a - 2b^2$, $2ab - 3b - 2a^2$, and $3b^2 - 4a + 4a^2 - 2b$.

Solution

We proceed in this problem as we did in Example 1. However, since the first expression contains neither a b-term nor an ab-term and the second contains neither an a-term nor a b^2-term, when we write the second below the first, we leave the spaces under $-2a$ and $-2b^2$ blank and write $-3b$ and $2ab$ at the right. Thus, we have

$$
\begin{array}{l}
3a^2 - 2a - 2b^2 \\
-2a^2 - 3b + 2ab \\
4a^2 - 4a + 3b^2 - 2b \\
\hline
5a^2 - 6a + b^2 - 5b + 2ab.
\end{array}
$$

8. Subtraction. In elementary arithmetic, the *difference* between two numbers is defined as the result obtained by taking one number from another. The process is called *subtraction*, and the number subtracted is called the *subtrahend* and the other is the *minuend*. Since no negative numbers are employed in introductory arithmetic, subtraction is possible there only if the minuend is larger than the subtrahend. We shall replace this conception of subtraction by the one used in algebra. It can be applied to both positive and negative numbers and includes the arithmetical method as a special case.

A graphical interpretation of arithmetical addition and subtraction will assist us to understand the algebraic rule that is to be given presently. The sum of 8 and 5 is 13, and this number is represented by the point in Fig. 1 that is 5 units to the right of the one represented by 8. On the other hand, the sum of 8 and -5 is carried out graphically by starting at 8, counting 5 units to the left, and arriving at the point represented by 3. The same result is also obtained by subtracting 5 from 8. Hence, we see that subtraction can be thought of graphically as a process in which we change the sign of the subtrahend and then proceed as in addition. This is the algebraic interpretation of subtraction which we shall state formally below.

RULE FOR SUBTRACTION. *In order to subtract one number (or one polynomial) from another, we change the sign (or the signs) of the subtrahend and then proceed as in addition.*

EXAMPLE 1

Subtract $8a^2$ from $6a^2$.

Solution

In accordance with the above rule, the solution is

$$6a^2 + (-8a^2) = 6a^2 - 8a^2 = -2a^2.$$

EXAMPLE 2

Subtract $-4xy$ from $-8xy$.

Solution

If we change the sign of the subtrahend and add, we have

$$-8xy + (+4xy) = -8xy + 4xy = -4xy.$$

EXAMPLE 3

Subtract $3a^2 - 2a + 4ab + 3b^2$ from $4a^2 - 2ab - b^2 + 2b$.

Solution

We first write the minuend and then place the subtrahend below it so that like terms in the two expressions are together, thus

$$
\begin{array}{ll}
4a^2 - 2ab - \ \ b^2 + 2b & \text{(minuend)} \\
\underline{3a^2 + 4ab + 3b^2 \qquad\quad - 2a} & \text{(subtrahend)} \\
& \text{(difference).}
\end{array}
$$

Now *mentally* we change the sign of each term in the subtrahend, add it to the like term in the minuend, and write the result in the difference. The completed problem thus appears

$$
\begin{array}{l}
4a^2 - 2ab - \ \ b^2 + 2b \\
\underline{3a^2 + 4ab + 3b^2 \qquad\quad - 2a} \\
a^2 - 6ab - 4b^2 + 2b + 2a.
\end{array}
$$

EXERCISE 5

Find the sum of the expressions in each of Problems 1 to 16.

1. $2x^2 + 3x - 2, \ 4x^2 - 5x + 6$.
2. $5a^2 - 7a - 8, \ -2a^2 + 3a + 12$.
3. $2x^3 + 3x^2 - 5x, \ -x^3 + 4x + 7$.
4. $6c^3 - 7c^2 + 3c - 2, \ c^3 + 3c^2 - 9c$.
5. $2a^2 - 3ab - b^2, \ -3a^2 + 4ab + b^2$.
6. $-3z^2 + 8zw - 4w^2, \ 2z^2 - 7zw + 6w^2$.
7. $5c^3d - 3c^2d^2 + 2cd^3 - d^4, \ -3c^3d + 3c^2d^2 + 4cd^3 + 2d^4$.
8. $-7r^3s + 2r^2s^2 - 3rs^3 + 6s^4, \ 4r^3s - 3r^2s^2 + 4rs^3 - 8s^4$.
9. $3a^3 - 2a^2b + ab^2 + b^3, \ a^3 + a^2b - ab^2 - 2b^3,$
$-2a^3 + a^2b - 2ab^2 + b^3$.
10. $4x^4 + 3x^2 - 3, \ 3x^3 + 2x + 1, \ 2x^4 - 5x^2 - 3x$.
11. $6b^5 - 3b^4 + 4b^3 - 3, \ 4b^4 - 3b^2 - 5b, \ -4b^5 - b^4 + 2b^2 + 3b + 2$.
12. $7x^4 - 6x^3y + 2x^2y^2 - 5xy^3 - 2y^4, \ 4x^3y - x^2y^2 + 2xy^3,$
$-6x^4 + x^2y^2 + 3xy^3 + 2y^4$.
13. $6w^5 + 4w^4 - 3w^3 - 2w^2 - 3, \ -2w^4 + 3w^2 + 4w, \ -5w^5 + 2w^3 + 5,$
$3w^3 + w^2 - 2w$.
14. $3x^3 - 2x^2y + y^3, \ 3x^2y + 4xy^2, \ -2x^3 - x^2y - 3y^3,$
$2x^2y - 3xy^2 + 2y^3$.
15. $5a^4b + 3a^2b^3 - 3ab^4, \ 2a^3b^2 + 3ab^4, \ -8a^4b - 7a^2b^3 + 2ab^4,$
$-4a^3b^2 + 4a^2b^3 - 2ab^4$.
16. $7c^4d^2 - 6c^3d^3 + 5cd^5 - 3d^6, \ 4c^3d^3 - 3c^2d^4 - 3cd^5 + 2d^6,$
$-5c^4d^2 - 3c^3d^3 + 2cd^3 - d^6, \ 2c^2d^4 - cd^3 + 2d^6$.

In each of Problems 17 to 24, subtract the first expression from the second.

17. $3x^2 + 2x - 1$, $5x^2 + 6x + 3$.

18. $2w^2 - 6w - 4$, $3w^2 + 2w - 3$.

19. $4z^3 + 2z^2 - 3z + 1$, $5z^2 - 7z + 4$.

20. $-3u^3 + 8u^2 - 3u + 5$, $4u^3 - 6u^2 - 2u + 5$.

21. $5a^2 - 7ab - b^2$, $-2a^2 + 3ab + 2b^2$.

22. $7w^2 + 2wz + 3z^2$, $8w^2 - 3wz - z^2$.

23. $2c^3d + 3c^2d^2 - 2cd^3 + 4d^4$, $3c^3d + 4c^2d^2 - cd^3 + d^4$.

24. $-5x^3y + 2x^2y - 3xy^2 - y^5$, $2x^3y - 3x^2y + 2xy^2 + 2y^5$.

25. Subtract $x^2 + 2x + 3$ from the sum of $3x^2 + x - 1$ and $2x^2 - 3x + 2$.

26. Subtract $2a^3 + 5a^2 - 7$ from the sum of $4a^3 - 5a^2 + 3a - 1$ and $-2a^3 + 6a^2 + 3a - 4$.

27. Subtract $2c^2 + 3cd + 4d^2$ from the sum of $6c^2 - 2cd + 4d^2$ and $-3c^2 + 2cd - d^2$.

28. Subtract $4w^3z + 2w^2z^2 - wz^3 + z^4$ from the sum of $5w^3z + 4w^2z^2 - 2wz^3 - z^4$ and $-2w^3z - 2w^2z^2 + 5wz^3 + 3z^4$.

29. Subtract the sum of $2r^2 + 5r - 7$ and $3r^2 + 2r + 1$ from $6r^2 + 7r - 2$.

30. Subtract the sum of $7m^3 + 3m^2 - 4m + 1$ and $2m^3 - 4m^2 + m - 5$ from $6m^3 - 3m^2 + 4m - 2$.

31. Subtract the sum of $p^2 - 5pq + 4q^2$ and $p^2 + 2pq + q^2$ from $6p^2 - 3pq + 5q^2$.

32. Subtract the sum of $8x^3y + 2x^2y^2 - 3xy^3 + 5y^4$ and $3x^3y - 5x^2y^2 + 2y^4$ from $11x^3y - 3x^2y^2 - 8xy^3 + 3y^4$.

33. Subtract the sum of $2a^2 - 3a + 1$ and $3a^2 - 2a - 3$ from the sum of $4a^2 - 5a + 3$ and $3a^2 + 5a - 1$.

34. Subtract the sum of $2b^3 + 3b^2 - 5b + 2$ and $-3b^3 + 2b^2 + 5b - 1$ from the sum of $4b^3 - 5b^2 + 2b - 1$ and $2b^3 - 3b + 4$.

35. Subtract the sum of $5c^2 - cd - d^2$ and $2c^2 + cd - d^2$ from the sum of $3c^2 + 2cd - 3d^2$ and $c^2 - cd + 2d^2$.

36. Subtract the sum of $x^3y + 2x^2y^2 - xy^3$ and $2x^3y + 3x^2y^2 + 4y^4$ from the sum of $3x^3y + 4x^2y^2 + 2xy^3 + 3y^4$ and $5x^3y + x^2y^2 - 3xy^3 + y^4$.

In the following problems, arrange the terms in each expression according to the descending powers of the variable, and then find the sum.

37. $1 - x^3 + 2x^5 - 3x + 2x^2$, $5x^2 - 3x^4 - 2x + 3x^3 - x^5$, $4x - 2x^2 - 3x^4 + 2x^3 - 3$.

38. $-3a + 4a^3 - 6a^6 + 4a^4$, $5a^2 - 7a^4 + 2a + 7a^6$, $4 - 4a + 5a^6 - 2a^3 + 4a^5 - 4a^2$.

39. $3w - 2w^2 + 4w^5$, $2 - 4w^3 + 5w^2$, $-4w + 3w^4 - 3$, $6w^4 - 3w - 4w^2$.

40. $3b^2 - 4b^3 - 5b$, $7 - 2b^4 + 3b^3$, $2b^2 + 5b^5 - 6b - b^6$, $4b^4 - 3b^6 - 2 + 3b - 4b^3$.

9. *Multiplication of monomials.* DEFINITION. *If one number is multiplied by another, the result is the **product**. The number multiplied is the **multiplicand**, and the number it is multiplied by is the **multiplier**. The multiplicand and the multiplier are called the **factors** of the product.*

In Art. 3, we stated that the product of a and b was written ab. In other words, when two or more numbers are written adjacent to each other with no sign between them, the group stands for the product of the numbers involved. We also stated that if all factors in a product are the same, we can write the product in a shorter form using an exponent. For example, $aaa = a^3$.

In arithmetic, we took for granted the fact that the order of the factors in multiplication was immaterial or, in other words, that we could combine numbers in multiplication in any order we desired. Certainly this can be verified for any set of numbers we choose. We shall assume that this aspect of multiplication is true for numbers in algebra and state this assumption as an axiom.

AXIOM. *Multiplication is commutative, that is, **ab = ba**.*

We may use this axiom and the definition of exponents to find a short form for the product of several groups of monomials in which some of the letters occur in more than one of the monomials. For example, $ab \times ab \times ab = a \times a \times a \times b \times b \times b = a^3b^3$. Similarly,

$$3xy \times 2x \times 4y = 3 \times 2 \times 4 \times x \times x \times y \times y = 24x^2y^2.$$

If the numbers to be multiplied contain powers of the same letter, we can find the shortest form for the product by further use of the definition of exponents (definition V, Art. 3) and of the above axiom. For example, consider first the product of a^3 and a^2. Here we have the product of three a's by two more a's, and this gives us the product of five a's, or a^5. In short,

$$a^3 \times a^2 = a^5.$$

Likewise, in general,

(1) $$a^n \times a^m = a^{m+n}.$$

If the coefficients in the monomials to be multiplied are different from 1, as in $3a^4 \times 2a^3$, we change the order and obtain

$$3 \times 2 \times a^4 \times a^3 = 6a^7.$$

Again, in general, we have

(2) $$ba^n \times ca^m = bca^{m+n}.$$

We may summarize this discussion in the following rule:

RULE. *The coefficient in the product of two monomials involving the same letter is equal to the product of the two coefficients. The exponent of the letter in the product is the sum of the two exponents.*

10. Symbols of grouping. We stated in Art. 3 that the sum of two different letters such as a and b can be expressed only as $a + b$. Frequently it is desirable and advantageous to consider such a sum as a single number. If this is to be done, we place parentheses ( ) around the expression to indicate the intention. We also use parentheses to indicate the order in which certain operations are to be performed. For example, consider $15 - 4 \times 2$. If there were no rule to tell us how to proceed, we would not know whether to first subtract 4 from 15 and then multiply the result by 2, obtaining 22, or to first multiply 4 by 2 and then subtract the product from 15, getting 7. We can use the parentheses here to indicate clearly what is to be done first; thus,

$$15 - (4 \times 2) = 15 - 8 = 7,$$

and $(15 - 4) \times 2 = 11 \times 2 = 22$.

Other symbols of grouping frequently used are the brackets [ ] and the braces { }. If an expression already containing parentheses is to be enclosed in another pair of grouping symbols, we use the brackets, and if the expression to be enclosed contains both brackets and parentheses, we use the braces.

Frequently it is desirable to remove the symbols of grouping from an expression, and it is the purpose of the remainder of this article to show how this can be done without changing the value of the expression. We shall first consider the case $c(a + b)$, which means that a and b are first added and then the sum is multiplied by c. If we try the same situation with numbers instead of letters, we see that it makes no difference whether we

first add and then multiply, or multiply and then add the products.
Thus,

$$4(3 + 5) = 4(8) = 32,$$

and $4(3 + 5) = 4(3) + 4(5) = 12 + 20 = 32$.   Hence, it is rea-
sonable to assume that $c(a + b) = ca + cb$ for any values that
may be assigned to a, b, and c.   This is used as an axiom, is known
as the distributive law of multiplication with respect to addition,
and is stated more formally thus:

AXIOM.   *Multiplication is distributive with respect to addition,
that is,* $c(a + b) = ca + cb$.

The axiom can be extended to include cases in which the parentheses contain any number of terms and the terms may be either
positive or negative.   For example, $v(x + y - z) = vx + vy - vz$.
    If a pair of parentheses enclosing an expression is preceded
by a minus sign, it is understood that the expression is to be multiplied by -1.   Thus, $-(-a + b - c) = -1(-a + b - c)$, and
this, by the above axiom, is equal to

$$(-1)(-a) + (-1)(b) + (-1)(-c) = a - b + c.$$

In other words, $-(-a + b - c) = a - b + c$.   The same statement could be made if the parentheses were replaced by any
other pair of grouping symbols.   Hence, *if a pair of grouping
symbols which enclose an expression is preceded by a minus sign,
the sign of every term in the expression must be changed when the
grouping symbols are removed.*
    If the grouping symbols are preceded by a plus sign only, every
term within them is to be multiplied by $+1$; hence, the symbols
can be removed without changes in the enclosed expression.
    When removing the grouping symbols from an expression in
which one pair of symbols is enclosed within another pair, it is
customary to remove the innermost pair first.

EXAMPLE 1

Remove the parentheses from the following expression and collect like
terms:

$$a - b + 2(3a - 4b) - (-3a + 8b).$$

Solution

We multiply the terms in the first parentheses by 2 and change all signs in the last and obtain

$$a - b + 2(3a - 4b) - (-3a + 8b) = a - b + 6a - 8b + 3a - 8b$$
$$= a + 6a + 3a - b - 8b - 8b$$
$$= 10a - 17b.$$

EXAMPLE 2

Remove the symbols of grouping from

$$3x - \{4x - 2y - 3[4x - 3y + z - (2x - 4y + 3z) - 2x] + 4z\} - 3y.$$

Solution

Since the parentheses are the innermost symbols, we shall remove them first. Next we remove the brackets, and finally the braces. Thus, we obtain

$$3x - \{4x - 2y - 3[4x - 3y + z - (2x - 4y + 3z) - 2x] + 4z\} - 3y$$
$$= 3x - \{4x - 2y - 3[4x - 3y + z - 2x + 4y - 3z - 2x] + 4z\} - 3y$$
$$= 3x - \{4x - 2y - 12x + 9y - 3z + 6x - 12y + 9z + 6x + 4z\} - 3y$$
$$= 3x - 4x + 2y + 12x - 9y + 3z - 6x + 12y - 9z - 6x - 4z - 3y$$
$$= 3x - 4x + 12x - 6x - 6x + 2y - 9y + 12y - 3y + 3z - 9z - 4z$$
$$= -x + 2y - 10z.$$

NOTE: The work in problems similar to the above can frequently be shortened if, after removing the first pair of symbols, we collect the terms enclosed by the remaining innermost pair before proceeding further. Thus, in the above example, if, after removing the parentheses, we collect the terms in the brackets, we have

$$3x - \{4x - 2y - 3[y - 2z] + 4z\} - 3y$$
$$= 3x - \{4x - 2y - 3y + 6z + 4z\} - 3y \qquad \text{(removing brackets)}$$
$$= 3x - \{4x - 5y + 10z\} - 3y \qquad \text{(collecting terms in braces)}$$
$$= 3x - 4x + 5y - 10z - 3y \qquad \text{(removing braces)}$$
$$= -x + 2y - 10z.$$

EXAMPLE 3

Remove the signs of grouping from

$$2a[a - b^2 - 3b(-4a + 2b) - 10ab + 5b^2].$$

Solution

$2a[a - b^2 - 3b(-4a + 2b) - 10ab + 5b^2]$

$= 2a[a - b^2 + 12ab - 6b^2 - 10ab + 5b^2]$ (removing parentheses)

$= 2a[a - 2b^2 + 2ab]$ (collecting terms in brackets)

$= 2a^2 - 4ab^2 + 4a^2b.$ (removing brackets)

EXERCISE 6

Remove the symbols of grouping and combine like terms.

1. $(2x + 1) + (4x - 2).$ **2.** $(5x - 3) + (2x + 4).$

3. $(7x + y) + (3x - 2y).$ **4.** $(-2x + 5) + (3x + 2).$

5. $(3x + 4) - (2x - 1).$ **6.** $-(6x + 5) + (3x + 2).$

7. $(5x - 3) - (-3x + 2).$ **8.** $-(2x + 3) - (4x + 7).$

9. $(a + 2b - 3) + (2a - b + 2).$

10. $(3a - 4b + 5) + (2a - 3b - 1).$

11. $(a - x + 4) - (2a + 3x - 2).$

12. $(4a - y - 2) - (-2a + 2y - 3).$

13. $2(2x - 3y) + 3(x + 2y).$ **14.** $3(a - b) + 5(2a + b).$

15. $4(3a - 2x) - 7(a - x).$ **16.** $7(2a - 3b) - 4(3a - 5b).$

17. $6(2a + b) - 5(a - 2b).$ **18.** $4(x - 2a) - 3(2x - 3a).$

19. $9(2x - 3b) - 4(4x - 7b).$ **20.** $8(5x + 3y) - 7(6x - 4y).$

21. $2(3a - b + 2c) + 3(2a + b - c) - (4a - 5b + 2c).$

22. $4(2a - x - y) - 2(3a + 2x - 3y) - 3(2a - 3x - 2y).$

23. $5(x^2 - 3x + 2) - 2(2x^2 - 4x + 3) - 3(x^2 - 2x + 1).$

24. $6(2x^2 + 5x - 3) - 7(x^2 + 3x - 4) - 2(2x^2 + 4x - 3).$

25. $a + [2a - (b - a) + 2b].$ **26.** $3a + [a - (2a - b) - 3b].$

27. $2x - [4y - (x + 3y) - x].$ **28.** $4x - [3y - (4x - 3y) - 4x].$

29. $5a - 2[3a - 3(a - 2b) - 4b].$

30. $3x - 4[y - 2(2x + 3y) + 3x].$

31. $2y - 5[2y + 3(2x - 3y) - 5x].$

32. $7a - 3[a - 2(-3a + 2b) + 3b].$

33. $2\{3x - 5[2x - 3(x + 2) + 5] + 2x\}.$

34. $5\{2x - 3[4x - 2(3x - 4) - 7] - 7x\}.$

35. $3\{3x - 2[5x - 7(x - 1) - 5] - 6x\}.$

36. $4\{5x + 3[2x - 5(x + 2) + 9] + 3x\}.$

37. $6\{3a - 2[3a - 2(3a - 2) + 3a] + 2\}.$

38. $-2\{34a + 3[5a - 4(6a - 2) + 8a] - 19\}.$

39. $-1\{12x - 3[34x - 5(6x + 2) - 8x] - 9\}.$

40. $-3\{2x - 2[x + 3(2x - 3) - 6x] - 16\}.$

41. $x(x^2 - 2) - 2x^2(x - 1).$ **42.** $-x(2x^2 - 3) + 3x^2(x + 2).$

43. $2x(x^2 - 3x) + 3x^2(x + 2).$ **44.** $3x^2(2x - 3) - 2x(5x^2 - 4).$

45. $2a[a - 2a(2a - 3) - 4a].$ **46.** $3a[12a - 4a(a + 2) + 3a^2].$

47. $-3x[2 - 5x(2 - 3x) - 13x^2]$.

48. $-2x^2[3 - x(3 - 2x) - x^2 + 2x]$.

49. $2y\{3 - 4y[2 - y(4 + y) + y^2 - 3] - 4y\}$.

50. $5a\{a^2 - 3a[2a - 4(3a - 2) + 8a - 7] + 2\}$.

51. $-2a\{a^2 - a[3a - 2(a + 2) + 3] + a^2\}$.

52. $-4y\{2y^2 - y[4y - 3y(2y - 5) - 18y] + 3y^2\}$.

53. $2b - \{5b + 3[2b + 2(3b + 2c) - (b - c) - 5(b + c) + 4c]$
$- (9b + 8c)\} + 3c$.

54. $3y - 2\{2y - 3[2(2y - 3) - (4y - 3) + y - 2] - 10\} + 5$.

55. $x - \{6x + [2(x + 1) - (x + 2) - 4] - 3[5 - (2x + 7)$
$+ 4(x + 2)] + 10\} - 12$.

56. $a - 2\{5a + [a + 2(a - 2) - (3a + 1)] - 3[(a - 3) - (2 - a)]$
$-8\} + 4$.

57. $c^2 + d\{2ec - [2dc + e(c + 3d) - d(4c + 3e) + c(2d - 2e)$
$+ 3ec] - 3d\} + 2d^2$.

58. $m^2 - \{-mn + [4mp + p(2m - 3n) - n(m + 2p) - 2m(p - n)$
$+ 5pn] - 3mp\} + n^2$.

59. $x^3 - \{x^2y + y[yz - x(2y - z) - z(2x + y) - xz] + 2xy^2\} + y^3$.

60. $3ab + \{ac - b[4a + a(a - 2b + c) - (a^2 - 2ab - 3c) - 4c]$
$- abc\} - 2ac$.

11. *Multiplication involving polynomials.* The product of two polynomials is defined as the sum of the products obtained by multiplying each term of the multiplicand by each term of the multiplier.

The commutative law of addition and the distributive law of multiplication with respect to addition permit us to condense multiplication to the form usually employed. This can best be explained by means of an example.

EXAMPLE

Multiply $3x^3 - 4y^3 - 6x^2y + 2xy^2$ by $2xy - 5x^2 + 3y^2$.

Solution

The detailed work for obtaining the product is shown below, and we shall explain how each step in the process is carried out.

We first rearrange the terms in each polynomial so that the exponents of one of the letters are in numerical order. In this case, our arrangement is based on the exponents of x and the rearranged multiplicand and multiplier are written on lines (1) and (2), respectively, below. Next we multiply each term in line (1) by the first term, $-5x^2$, in line (2) and write the products in line (3). We repeat this process for each of the other terms in the multiplier and obtain lines (4) and (5). In each case, we take care to place the product underneath a like term in the previous line, if there is one. Terms that differ from any of those in the previous lines are written at the extreme right. As a final step, we add lines (3), (4), and (5) and write the result in line (6).

$$
\begin{aligned}
(1) \quad & 3x^3 - 6x^2y + 2xy^2 - 4y^3 \quad \text{(multiplicand)} \\
(2) \quad & - 5x^2 + 2xy + 3y^2 \quad \text{(multiplier)} \\
\hline
(3) \quad & -15x^5 + 30x^4y - 10x^3y^2 + 20x^2y^3 \\
(4) \quad & + 6x^4y - 12x^3y^2 + 4x^2y^3 - 8xy^4 \\
(5) \quad & + 9x^3y^2 - 18x^2y^3 + 6xy^4 - 12y^5 \\
\hline
(6) \quad & -15x^5 + 36x^4y - 13x^3y^2 + 6x^2y^3 - 2xy^4 - 12y^5 \quad \text{(product).}
\end{aligned}
$$

12. Zero in multiplication. We shall first consider a product in which either the multiplier or the multiplicand is zero. Since zero can be written as the difference of two equal numbers, we may replace zero in the product $n \times 0$ by $c - c$ and obtain $n \times 0 = n(c - c) = nc - nc = 0$. Hence, since $n \times 0 = 0 \times n$, we have

$$
(1) \qquad\qquad n \times 0 = 0 \times n = 0.
$$

In words, we may state that *the product of any number whatsoever and zero is zero.*

We shall next prove that *if the product of two numbers is zero, at least one of the numbers is zero.* Suppose that

$$
(2) \qquad\qquad nk = 0
$$

and that n is not zero; then by Axiom I of Art. 5, we have

$$
(3) \qquad\qquad nk + n = n
$$

or

$$
(4) \qquad\qquad n(k + 1) = n.
$$

Now, by Axiom III of Art. 5, we have

$$
k + 1 = 1
$$

and, by transposing the 1 from the left member to the right, we get

$$
k = 0.
$$

13. Division of monomials. DEFINITION. *The quotient obtained* *by dividing* **a** *by* **b** *is defined to be the number* **x** *such that*

(1)
$$bx = a.$$

The number a is called the *dividend*, and b is the *divisor*.

The process is indicated either by $a \div b = x$ or by $\dfrac{a}{b} = x$.

If the rule of signs for multiplication is applied to the left member of (1), we see that x must have the sign indicated in each of the cases listed below.

(a) a positive, b positive, x positive;
(b) a negative, b negative, x positive;
(c) a positive, b negative, x negative;
(d) a negative, b positive, x negative.

These conclusions justify the law of signs for division stated in Art. 3. We shall restate the law here for the convenience of the reader.

RULE OF SIGNS FOR DIVISION. *The quotient of two numbers with like signs is positive. The quotient of two numbers with unlike signs is negative.*

If in (1), $a = z^m$ and $b = z^n$, with $m > n$, then $x = z^{m-n}$, since $z^{(m-n)} = z^{m-n+n} = z^m$. Hence,

(2)
$$\frac{a^m}{a^n} = a^{m-n}, \qquad m > n.$$

Hence, we have the following rule:

RULE OF EXPONENTS IN DIVISION. *The quotient of two powers of the same letter is another power of that letter in which the exponent is the exponent of the dividend minus that of the divisor.*

For the present, we shall limit the application of this rule to cases in which the exponent of the dividend is greater than that of the divisor. This restriction will be removed later.

EXAMPLE 1

$$x^6 \div x^2 = x^{6-2} = x^4.$$

By the rules of multiplication, we have

$$qy^n \left(\frac{p}{q}\right) y^{m-n} = q \left(\frac{p}{q}\right) y^{n+m-n} = py^m.$$

Hence, if in (1), $b = qy^n$ and $a = py^m$, then $x = \left(\dfrac{p}{q}\right)y^{m-n}$. In other words,

(3) $$\frac{py^m}{qy^n} = \frac{p}{q}\,y^{m-n}, \qquad m > n.$$

EXAMPLE 2

$$15x^8 \div 3x^2 = \tfrac{15}{3}x^{8-2} = 5x^6.$$

14. Zero in the division process. In ancient times, division was regarded as a process of repeated subtraction. The quotient of two numbers was found by subtracting the divisor from the dividend, then by again subtracting the divisor from the remainder just obtained, and so on, until a final remainder was reached which was either zero or less than the divisor. The number of subtractions required was the quotient. The present method of division is in reality a condensed form of this process. When division is thought of in this way, we see that *division by zero is meaningless*, since an ultimate remainder of zero would never be obtained regardless of the number of times the subtraction process is repeated. Hence, we conclude that in any division process, *if the divisor is zero, the quotient does not exist.*

If in (1) of Art. 13, $a = 0$ and b is not zero, we have $bx = 0$. Then by the last italicized statement of Art. 12, $x = 0$. Hence, *if the dividend is zero and the divisor is not zero, the quotient is zero.*

If we apply the rule of exponents for division to the quotient $\dfrac{a^n}{a^n}$, we obtain $\dfrac{a^n}{a^n} = a^{n-n} = a^0$. This is an expression that our definition of exponents does not cover. However, since $\dfrac{a^n}{a^n} = 1$, we shall, for the sake of consistency, make the following definition:

DEFINITION. *The value of **a**⁰, where **a** is not equal to zero, is defined to be **one**.*

In symbols this definition becomes

(1) $$a^0 = 1.$$

15. Division involving polynomials. If the dividend is the sum of two or more numbers such as $p + q - r$ and the divisor is a single number b, the quotient, by (1) of Art. 13, is the value of x such that

(1) $$bx = p + q - r.$$

If we multiply each side of (1) by $\dfrac{1}{b}$, we obtain

$$x = \frac{1}{b}(p + q - r) = \frac{p}{b} + \frac{q}{b} - \frac{r}{b}.$$

Hence, *if the dividend is a polynomial and the divisor is a monomial, the quotient is the algebraic sum of the quotients obtained by dividing each term in the dividend by the divisor.*

EXAMPLE 1

$$\frac{6x^4 + 4x^3y^3 - 3x^2y^2 - 2x^2}{3x^2} = \frac{6x^4}{3x^2} + \frac{4x^3y^3}{3x^2} - \frac{3x^2y^2}{3x^2} - \frac{2x^2}{3x^2}$$
$$= 2x^2 + \tfrac{4}{3}xy^3 - x^0y^2 - \tfrac{2}{3}x^0$$
$$= 2x^2 + \tfrac{4}{3}xy^3 - y^2 - \tfrac{2}{3}.$$

If both the dividend and the divisor are polynomials, we must resort to the process of long division. We can best explain this by means of an example.

EXAMPLE 2

Divide $6x^4 - 6x^2y^2 - 3y^4 + 5xy^3 - x^3y$ by $-2y^2 + 2x^2 + xy$.

Solution

We shall indicate the successive steps in the solution. The numbers refer to the lines in the actual computation which follows the explanation.

1. First arrange the terms in the dividend and divisor according to descending powers of one of the letters (in this case, x) and write the rearranged expressions in line (2).

2. Divide the first term of the dividend by the first term of the divisor and obtain $3x^2$ and write it as the first term of the quotient in line (1).

3. Multiply the divisor by $3x^2$ and write the product in line (3), taking care to place each term beneath a like term in the dividend.

4. Subtract this product from the dividend, place the difference on line (4), and bring down $5xy^3$ from the dividend.

5. Treat the expression in line (4) as a new dividend and repeat the above process.

6. Continue this process until a remainder is obtained in which the exponent of x is less than the largest exponent of x in the divisor.

$$
\begin{array}{llll}
(1) & & 3x^2 - 2xy + y^2 \quad \text{(quotient)} \\
(2) & 2x^2 + xy - 2y^2 \,\big|\, 6x^4 - \ \ x^3y - 6x^2y^2 + 5xy^3 - 3y^4 \\
(3) & & \underline{6x^4 + 3x^3y - 6x^2y^2} \\
(4) & & \quad -4x^3y \qquad\qquad + 5xy^3 \\
(5) & & \quad \underline{-4x^3y - 2x^2y^2 + 4xy^3} \\
(6) & & \qquad\qquad 2x^2y^2 + \ xy^3 - 3y^4 \\
(7) & & \qquad\qquad \underline{2x^2y^2 + \ xy^3 - 2y^4} \\
(8) & & \qquad\qquad\qquad\qquad - y^4 \quad \text{(remainder).}
\end{array}
$$

EXERCISE 7

Perform the indicated multiplications in Problems 1 to 36.

1. $(x - 2)(x + 3)$.
2. $(a + 4)(a - 1)$.
3. $(b - 1)(b - 2)$.
4. $(c + 2)(c + 4)$.
5. $(2z - 1)(3z + 2)$.
6. $(5a - 2)(2a - 3)$.
7. $(3w - 4)(5w + 3)$.
8. $(4b + 3)(7b - 2)$.
9. $(ax + 2)(cx - 3)$.
10. $(ax - 1)(2x - b)$.
11. $(bx + c)(3x + 2)$.
12. $(2x + a)(bx + 3)$.
13. $(3x - 2y)(2x + 3y)$.
14. $(5a - 7b)(2a - b)$.
15. $(2c + 5d)(3c - 4d)$.
16. $(7w - 6d)(2w + 5d)$.
17. $(ax + 2y)(bx - 3y)$.
18. $(2p - cq)(dp + 3q)$.
19. $(ax + by)(5x - 2y)$.
20. $(ax + by)(cx + dy)$.
21. $(2x - 1)(x^2 - 3x + 1)$.
22. $(3x + 2)(2x^2 - 3x - 1)$.
23. $(5a - 3)(a^2 - 2a + 2)$.
24. $(3c + 4)(c^2 - 3c + 4)$.
25. $(ax + b)(x^2 + 2x + 3)$.
26. $(cx - d)(2x^2 - x + 3)$.
27. $(2y - 3)(ay^2 + by + c)$.
28. $(3z + 5)(az^2 + bz + c)$.
29. $(w^2 - 2w + 3)(2w^2 - w + 3)$.
30. $(2a^2 + 3a - 4)(3a^2 + 4a - 2)$.
31. $(7y^2 + 4y - 1)(y^2 + 7y - 4)$.
32. $(3b^2 - 5b - 4)(4b^2 + 3b - 5)$.
33. $(x^2 - xy + 2y^2)(2x^2 + xy - y^2)$.
34. $(b^2 - 2bc + 3c^2)(2b^2 + 3bc - c^2)$.
35. $(4w^2 - 3wz + z^2)(3w^2 - 2wz + 4z^2)$.
36. $(2x^2 - 5xy - 2y^2)(3x^2 + xy + 2y^2)$.

Perform the indicated divisions in Problems 37 to 72.

37. $\dfrac{a^2 - 5a + 6}{a - 2}$.

38. $\dfrac{x^2 - 3x - 10}{x + 2}$.

39. $\dfrac{2y^2 - 7y + 6}{2y - 3}$.

40. $\dfrac{3z^2 + 13z + 12}{3z + 4}$.

41. $\dfrac{6x^2 + x - 2}{2x - 1}.$

42. $\dfrac{6b^2 + 11b + 3}{3b + 1}.$

43. $\dfrac{15c^2 - 11c + 2}{5c - 2}.$

44. $\dfrac{8x^2 - 14x - 15}{4x + 3}.$

45. $(3d^2 - 5de - 2e^2) \div (d - 2e).$

46. $(6a^2 + ab - 2b^2) \div (2a - b).$

47. $(12w^2 + 17wz - 5z^2) \div (4w - z).$

48. $(10c^2 - 11cd - 6d^2) \div (5c + 2d).$

49. $[abx^2 + (2a + 3b)x + 6] \div (ax + 3).$

50. $[cdy^2 + (c^2 - d^2)y - cd] \div (cy - d).$

51. $[2az^2 + (ab - 6)z - 3b] \div (2z + b).$

52. $[3aw^2 + (3b - 4a)w - 4b] \div (aw + b).$

53. $(2x^3 - 3x^2 + 7x - 3) \div (2x - 1).$

54. $(3a^3 + 8a^2 - 5a - 6) \div (3a + 2).$

55. $(4b^3 + 12b^2 + 15b + 25) \div (2b + 5).$

56. $(4z^3 + 5z^2 + 6z - 9) \div (4z - 3).$

57. $(2x^3 + 3x^2 - x - 12) \div (x^2 + 3x + 4).$

58. $(6w^3 - 7w^2 - 17w + 4) \div (2w^2 - 5w + 1).$

59. $(6u^3 - 13u^2 - 7u + 5) \div (3u^2 + u - 1).$

60. $(12r^3 + r^2 - 7r - 2) \div (4r^2 - r - 2).$

61. $[2ay^3 + (4 - 3a)y^2 + (a - 6)y + 2] \div (ay + 2).$

62. $[3z^3 + (b - 15)z^2 - (5b + 6)z - 2b] \div (3z + b).$

63. $[3ax^3 + (2a - 9)x^2 + (a - 6)x - 3] \div (ax - 3).$

64. $[2aw^3 + (2 - 4a)w^2 - (a + 4)w - 1] \div (aw + 1).$

65. $(2a^4 - 5a^3 + 11a^2 - 9a + 9) \div (a^2 - 2a + 3).$

66. $(3b^4 + 11b^3 + 19b^2 + 11b + 4) \div (b^2 + 3b + 4).$

67. $(2c^4 - 3c^3 + 6c^2 - 2c - 3) \div (2c^2 - c - 1).$

68. $(3y^4 + 8y^3 + 14y^2 + 8y + 3) \div (3y^2 + 2y + 1).$

69. $(2x^4 - x^3y + 2xy^3 - y^4) \div (x^2 - xy + y^2).$

70. $(3z^4 - 5z^3w - 6z^2w^2 + zw^3 + w^4) \div (3z^2 + zw - w^2).$

71. $(10x^4 - 3x^3y - 28x^2y^2 - 4xy^3 + 5y^4) \div (2x^2 - xy - 5y^2).$

72. $(6x^4 - 5x^3y + 6x^2y^2 - 5xy^3 + 6y^4) \div (3x^2 + 2xy + 3y^2).$

REVIEW EXERCISE FOR CHAPTERS 1 AND 2

Perform the indicated operations in Problems 1 to 34.

1. $a + 3a - 2a.$

2. $2x - x + 5x.$

3. $3a + 2a - 6a.$

4. $5b - 2b - 6b.$

5. $x^2 + 2xy + 3x^2 - 5xy.$

6. $3b^2 - 2bc + b^2 + 6bc.$

7. $2x^2 - 3xy^2 + x^2y - x^2.$

8. $3c^2d + 4cd + 2cd^2 - 5dc.$

9. $3(x + 3) - 4(5x - 2).$

10. $2(x - 2) + 3(-2x + 1).$

11. $-2(-x + 3) - 3(2x - 1).$

12. $6(3x - 4) - 5(2x + 3).$

13. $3(x^2 - 5x + 7) - 2(-3x^2 + 6x - 5) + 4(-x^2 + 2x - 3)$.

14. $2(x^2 - 5x - 3) + 4(-2x^2 + x - 5) - (3x^2 - 2x + 8)$.

15. $2[x - 2(x - 2)]$.   **16.** $3[x - 3(x - 3)]$.

17. $2[x^2 - 3x + 2 - 2(3x^2 + 3x + 4)]$.

18. $5[x^2 - 6x + 3 - 2(-x^2 + 2x + 4)]$.

19. $2\{3x^2 + 5x - 3 - 4[x^2 + 6x - 7 + 3(2x^2 - 3x + 4)]\}$.

20. $3\{2x^2 - 6x + 1 - [-2x^2 + 3x + 4 - 2(x^2 - 5x + 3)]\}$.

21. $a(a^2 - 5a + 7) - 2a(a^2 - 6a + 5)$.

22. $a(3a^2 + 2a - 9) - 3a(a^2 - a + 2)$.

23. $2a[a^2 + 6a - 2 - 3a(-a + 7)]$.

24. $3a[4a^2 - 5a + 2 - 5a(a + 3)]$.

25. $a\{a^3 - 5a^2 + 6a + 3 + 2a[-a^2 + 3a - 2 - a(3a - 4)]\}$.

26. $2a\{3a^3 + 8a^2 - 5a + 7 - 3a[a^2 + 4a - 2 - 5(a - 1)]\}$.

27. $(3x^2 + 2x - 5)(-2x^2 - 3x + 4)$.

28. $(4x^2 - x + 2)(-x^2 + 3x + 5)$.

29. $(3x^2 + 2xy - y^2)(2x^2 - 3xy + y^2)$.

30. $(2x^2 - xy + 5y^2)(3x^2 + 4xy - y^2)$.

31. $\dfrac{6x^3 + 5x^2 - 3x - 2}{3x - 2}$.   **32.** $\dfrac{6x^3 - 3x^2 - 7x - 3}{2x - 3}$.

33. $\dfrac{10x^4 - 13x^3 + 17x^2 - 8x + 4}{2x^2 - x + 1}$.

34. $\dfrac{3x^4 - 11x^3 + 11x^2 - 3x - 4}{x^2 - 2x - 1}$.

35. If John has J books and Tom has 5 more than twice as many as John, find an expression for the number Tom has.

36. If Lillian is L years of age, find an expression for Janet's age if she is 7 years less than twice Lillian's age.

37. How many days are in 3 weeks and d days?

38. How many minutes are in 5 hr. and m min.?

39. How many days are in w weeks and d days?

40. How many weeks are in w weeks and d days?

41. Find three consecutive integers whose sum is 96.

42. Mr. Jones and Mr. Smith own farms that together contain 537 acres. If Mr. Smith's farm lacks 21 acres of being twice the size of Mr. Jones's, find the number of acres in each.

43. A boy walked for 2 hr. at a certain rate and then rode in a wagon at 3 times that rate for 4 hr. and 20 min. Find his rate of walking if the total distance traveled was 60 miles.

44. A boy started from A to B on a bicycle, and 2 hr. later a man in a car started over the same route and overtook the boy after 30 min. Find the boy's rate if the man traveled 32 miles per hr. faster than the boy.

45. John is now $\frac{3}{2}$ as old as Mary.   In 8 years, he will be $\frac{4}{3}$ as old as she will be at that time.   How old is Mary now?

46. Jane is 3 years younger than Tom.   In 6 years, she will be $\frac{8}{9}$ as old as he is at that time.   How old is Tom now?

47. How much pure silver must be mixed with 60 oz. of a 40 per cent alloy in order to produce a 50 per cent alloy?

48. How much milk that contains 8 per cent butterfat must be mixed with 400 lb. of milk that contains 3 per cent butterfat in order to produce a mixture with 3.6 per cent butterfat?

CHAPTER 3

SPECIAL PRODUCTS AND FACTORING

16. *Introduction*. In this chapter, we shall present methods which contribute to speed and accuracy in computation. First, we shall discuss certain products in which the computation can be performed mentally. We shall also present methods for factoring certain types of expressions. The process of factoring is necessary for handling fractions, is useful in solving equations, and is often helpful in simplifying complicated expressions.

17. *The product of two binomials*. The product of the two binomials $4x + 3y$ and $2x - 5y$ obtained by the method of Art. 11 is shown below.

$$
\begin{array}{r}
4x + 3y \\
2x - 5y \\
\hline
8x^2 + 6xy \\
- 20xy - 15y^2 \\
\hline
8x^2 - 14xy - 15y^2.
\end{array}
$$

Now, if we study the following diagram, we see that (1) the first and last terms of the above product may be obtained by multiplying the two members of the pair of numbers connected by

$$
\begin{array}{c}
8x^2 \qquad - 15y^2 \\
(4x + 3y)(2x - 5y) = 8x^2 - 14xy - 15y^2. \\
6xy \\
-20xy
\end{array}
$$

each of the arrows above the line; (2) the middle term of the product is the algebraic sum of the products of the quantities connected by each of the arrows below the line. Since this procedure can be applied to any two binomials, we have Rule I, which follows.

RULE I.   *The three terms in the product of two binomials are* (1) *the product of the two first terms in the binomials;* (2) *the algebraic sum of the products of the first term in one by the second term of the other;* (3) *the product of the two second terms of the binomials.*

If we state this rule as a formula, we have

(1) $(ax + by)(cx + dy) = acx^2 + (ad + bc)xy + bdy^2.$

$by cx$

EXAMPLE

Find the product $(3x + 2y)(2x - 3y)$ by use of Rule I.

Solution

If we perform the steps in Rule I mentally, we obtain

(1) The product of the two first terms: $(3x)(2x) = 6x^2$;

(2) The algebraic sum of the products of the first term in one binomial by the second term in the other:

$$(3x)(-3y) + (2x)(2y) = -9xy + 4xy = -5xy;$$

(3) The product of the two second terms: $(2y)(-3y) = -6y^2$. Hence, we have $(3x + 2y)(2x - 3y) = 6x^2 - 5xy - 6y^2$.

The Square of a Binomial.   The application of formula (1) to the product $(ax + b)(ax + b) = (ax + b)^2$ yields

(2) $(ax + b)^2 = (ax)^2 + (ab + ab)x + b^2$
                 $= a^2x^2 + 2abx + b^2.$

Hence, we have

RULE II.   *The square of a binomial is equal to the square of the first term plus twice the product of the first by the second plus the square of the last.*

NOTE: Since the square of any number is positive, the first and last terms in the square of a binomial are positive.   The middle term is positive if the two terms in the binomial are like in sign, but it is negative if the two terms are unlike in sign.

EXAMPLES

1. $(3x + 4y)^2 = (3x)^2 + 2(3x)(4y) + (4y)^2$
           $= 9x^2 + 24xy + 16y^2.$
2. $(2a - 5b)^2 = (2a)^2 + 2(2a)(-5b) + (-5b)^2$
           $= 4a^2 - 20ab + 25b^2.$

The Product of the Sum and Difference of Two Numbers. The product of the sum and difference of two numbers can be expressed symbolically as $(a + b)(a - b)$. If we apply formula (1) to this product, we have

$$(3) \qquad (a + b)(a - b) = (a)(a) + (-ab + ab) + (b)(-b)$$
$$= a^2 - b^2.$$

Hence, we have

Rule III. *The product of the sum and difference of two numbers is equal to the difference of their squares.*

EXAMPLE

$$(2x + 3y)(2x - 3y) = (2x)^2 - (3y)^2$$
$$= 4x^2 - 9y^2.$$

18. *The square of a polynomial.* Much time and effort is saved if one can write the square of a polynomial without resorting to the method of Art. 11. The proof of the rule stated below is beyond the scope of this book, but its usefulness justifies its inclusion here.

Rule. *The square of a polynomial is equal to the sum of the squares of the separate terms increased by the algebraic sum of twice the product of each term by every term that follows it.*

EXAMPLE

$$(2x + 3y - 4z - 2w)^2 = (2x)^2 + (3y)^2 + (-4z)^2 + (-2w)^2$$
$$+ 2(2x)(3y) + 2(2x)(-4z)$$
$$+ 2(2x)(-2w) + 2(3y)(-4z)$$
$$+ 2(3y)(-2w) + 2(-4z)(-2w)$$
$$= 4x^2 + 9y^2 + 16z^2 + 4w^2 + 12xy - 16xz$$
$$- 8xw - 24yz - 12yw + 16zw.$$

EXERCISE 8

Find the products in the following problems by the methods of Art. 17.

1. $(3x + 1)(x + 5)$.
2. $(6x + 3)(x + 1)$.
3. $(2x + 4)(x + 2)$.
4. $(x + 3)(4x + 5)$.
5. $(5x + 1)(x + 6)$.
6. $(2x + 2)(x + 4)$.
7. $(x + 7)(3x + 3)$.
8. $(2x + 4y)(x + 2y)$.
9. $(c - 2d)(2c - 3d)$.
10. $(a - 3b)(3a - 2b)$.
11. $(u - 5w)(4u - 7w)$.
12. $(f - 4g)(5f - 6g)$.

13. $(x - 8y)(2x - 4y)$.

14. $(r - s)(6r - 3s)$.

15. $(x - 6y)(8x - 5y)$.

16. $(9a - 3b)(a - 2b)$.

17. $(3x + 2y)(x - y)$.

18. $(4r - 3s)(r + s)$.

19. $(f - 2g)(5f + 6g)$.

20. $(u + 4w)(6u - 3w)$.

21. $(7x - 3y)(x + 4y)$.

22. $(c - 9d)(2c + 8d)$.

23. $(3y - 7z)(y + 2z)$.

24. $(6x + 4y)(x - 8y)$.

25. $(2a + 3b)(3a - 4b)$.

26. $(4x + 4y)(5x - 2y)$.

27. $(3r - 8s)(4r - 2s)$.

28. $(5c - 6d)(2c - 3d)$.

29. $(8x + 2y)(3x + 9y)$.

30. $(7u + 3w)(3u + 4w)$.

31. $(3a - 5b)(4a + 3b)$.

32. $(6z + 7w)(3z - 4w)$.

33. $(2x + 3y)^2$.

34. $(5c - 2d)^2$.

35. $(3a - 7)^2$.

36. $(8r + 3)^2$.

37. $(6m + 3n)^2$.

38. $(4x + 6)^2$.

39. $(7x - 1)^2$.

40. $(3a - 9b)^2$.

41. $(9p - 7q)^2$.

42. $(6x - 4y)^2$.

43. $(5r + 3s)^2$.

44. $(7u + 2v)^2$.

45. $(x + 4)(x - 4)$.

46. $(x + 7)(x - 7)$.

47. $(x - y)(x + y)$.

48. $(x - 8)(x + 8)$.

49. $(3x + 4)(3x - 4)$.

50. $(6r - 2s)(6r + 2s)$.

51. $(2m + 3n)(2m - 3n)$.

52. $(4x + 5y)(4x - 5y)$.

53. $(5u - 4w)(5u + 4w)$.

54. $(3c + 6d)(3c - 6d)$.

55. $(8x - 3y)(2x + 5y)$.

56. $(7a - 6b)(3a + 2b)$.

57. $(2a^2 - b)(3a^2 + 2b)$.

58. $(x - 3y^2)(2x + 4y^2)$.

59. $(2f - 4g^2)(3f + 5g^2)$.

60. $(5x^2 + 2y^2)(4x^2 - y^2)$.

61. $\left(\dfrac{x}{3} + \dfrac{y}{2}\right)\left(\dfrac{3x}{2} - \dfrac{2y}{3}\right)$.

62. $\left(x - \dfrac{5y}{4}\right)\left(x + \dfrac{4y}{5}\right)$.

63. $(3a^2 - b)^2$.

64. $(4x + 2y^2)^2$.

65. $(5r^2 + 3y)^2$.

66. $(2c - 3d^2)^2$.

67. $(3g^3 - 4h)^2$.

68. $(4r^2 + 7y^2)^2$.

69. $(6x^2 + 2)(6x^2 - 2)$.

70. $(4a - 2b^2)(4a + 2b^2)$.

71. $(2m^2 + 4n)(2m^2 - 4n)$.

72. $(3c^2 - 5d^2)(3c^2 + 5d^2)$.

73. $(x + y + z)^2$.

74. $(a - b + c)^2$.

75. $(u - v - w)^2$.

76. $(x + 2y - 2z)^2$.

77. $(2a + 3b - 5c)^2$.

78. $(4m - 2n - 3d)^2$.

79. $(3r - 5s + 7t)^2$.

80. $(5x - 6y - 4z)^2$.

81. $[a + (b - c)][3a + (b - c)]$.

82. $[2(a + b) - 2c][3(a + b) - 3c]$.

83. $[(3a + b) - c][(3a + b) + 4c]$.

84. $[4(a + 2b) - 3c][3(a + 2b) - 4c]$.

85. $[2a - 3(b + c)][4a - 4(b + c)]$.

86. $[3a - 4(b + c)][3a + 4(b + c)]$.

87. $[6(x + y) - 4z][6(x + y) + 4z]$.

88. $[3(c - 2d) + 4e][3(c - 2d) - 4e]$.

19. *Factors of a trinomial.* A polynomial is factored if it is expressed as the product of two or more expressions.

If a trinomial is equal to the product of two binomials, then by Rule I of Art. 17, the following requirements must be satisfied:

(*a*) The product of the two first terms of the binomial factors must be the first term of the trinomial;

(*b*) The product of the two last terms in the binomial factors must be the last term of the trinomial;

(*c*) The algebraic sum of the products of the first term in each factor by the second term in the other must be the second term of the trinomial.

Hence, the problem of factoring a trinomial consists of finding two binomials that satisfy (*a*), (*b*), and (*c*). It is easy to select the binomials so that (*a*) and (*b*) are satisfied, and this can usually be done in several ways. From these possibilities, we select the one that satisfies (*c*).

EXAMPLE 1

Find the two binomial factors of $x^2 - 2x - 8$.

Solution

By (*a*), the first term in each of the two factors is x, since their product must be x^2. For the present, we shall let u and v represent the second terms in the factors. Then we have

$$x^2 - 2x - 8 = (x + u)(x + v).$$

Hence, by (*b*),

$$uv = -8.$$

Furthermore, by (*c*),

$$ux + vx = (u + v)x = -2x.$$

Hence,

$$u + v = -2.$$

Obviously, both of these conditions are satisfied if $u = -4$, and $v = 2$. Hence,

$$x^2 - 2x - 8 = (x - 4)(x + 2).$$

EXAMPLE 2

Factor $5x^2 + 29x - 6$.

Solution

Using the method of the above example, we have x and $5x$ for the first terms of the factors, and if we again use u and v for the second terms, we have

$$5x^2 + 29x - 6 = (5x + u)(x + v).$$

Hence, by (*b*),

$$uv = -6$$

and, by (*c*),

$$5v + u = 29.$$

The following pairs of values of u and v satisfy the first condition: $u = 3$, $v = -2$; $u = -3$, $v = 2$; $u = 2$, $v = -3$; $u = -2$, $v = 3$; $u = 6$, $v = -1$; $u = -6$, $v = 1$; $u = 1$, $v = -6$; $u = -1$, $v = 6$. We must next select the pair of these values that satisfies the second condition. By trial, we see that the last pair, and only the last, satisfies $5v + u = 29$. Hence,

$$5x^2 + 29x - 6 = (5x - 1)(x + 6).$$

EXAMPLE 3

Factor $8x^2 - 29x - 12$.

Solution

In this problem, we have two choices for the first terms of the factors, either $4x$ and $2x$ or $8x$ and x. We shall start with the first pair and let u and v be the second terms. Then we have

$$8x^2 - 29x - 12 = (4x + u)(2x + v).$$

From this, we see that

$$uv = -12$$

and

$$2u + 4v = -29.$$

The values of u and v which satisfy the first condition are $u = 4$, $v = -3$; $u = -4$, $v = 3$; $u = 3$, $v = -4$; $u = -3$, $v = 4$; $u = 6$, $v = -2$; $u = -6$, $v = 2$; $u = 2$, $v = -6$; $u = -2$, $v = 6$; $u = 12$, $v = -1$; $u = -12$, $v = 1$; $u = 1$, $v = -12$; $u = -1$, $v = 12$. However, by trial, we can see that no one of these pairs satisfies the second condition, $2u + 4v = -29$. Hence, we must try the second choice, $8x$ and x, for first terms and have

$$8x^2 - 29x - 12 = (8x + u)(x + v).$$

Hence,

$$uv = -12$$

and

$$8v + u = -29.$$

Since each of the above pairs of values of u and v satisfies the first of these conditions, we must select by trial the pair which satisfies the second. Such a trial reveals that $u = 3$, $v = -4$ meets this requirement. Hence,

$$8x^2 - 29x - 12 = (8x + 3)(x - 4).$$

After sufficient practice, one can perform most of the steps illustrated in the above examples mentally and can usually arrive at the proper combination quickly.

20. Trinomials that are perfect squares. If a trinomial is the square of a binomial, we know by Rule II, Art. 17, that two of its terms are perfect squares, and hence are positive, and the third term is twice the product of the square roots of these two. Furthermore, such a trinomial is the square of a binomial composed of the square roots of the two perfect-square terms of the trinomial connected by the sign of the other term.

EXAMPLE 1

Factor $4x^2 - 12xy + 9y^2$.

Solution

Since $4x^2 = (2x)^2$, $9y^2 = (3y)^2$, and $12xy = 2(2x)(3y)$, we have

$$4x^2 - 12xy + 9y^2 = (2x - 3y)(2x - 3y) = (2x - 3y)^2.$$

EXAMPLE 2

$$9a^2 + 24ab + 16b^2 = (3a + 4b)^2.$$

EXAMPLE 3

$$(2a - 3b)^2 - 8(2a - 3b) + 16 = [(2a - 3b) - 4]^2$$
$$= (2a - 3b - 4)^2.$$

NOTE: A trinomial that is a perfect square can be factored by the method of Art. 19. However, if a trinomial is recognized as a perfect square, it can be factored more quickly by the above method.

EXERCISE 9

Factor each of the following expressions.

1. $x^2 + x - 12$.
2. $x^2 - x - 12$.
3. $a^2 - a - 20$.
4. $a^2 + a - 20$.
5. $x^2 - 6xy + 5y^2$.
6. $x^2 - 6xy + 8y^2$.
7. $x^2 - 9xy + 8y^2$.
8. $a^2 - 6ab + 5b^2$.
9. $c^2 + 8cd + 7d^2$.
10. $p^2 + 7pq + 10q^2$.
11. $z^2 - zw - 6w^2$.
12. $c^2 + 2cd - 15d^2$.
13. $3m^2 + 4mn + n^2$.
14. $2a^2 + 4ab + 2b^2$.
15. $2x^2 + 5xy + 3y^2$.
16. $3r^2 + 8rs + 5s^2$.
17. $3h^2 - 10hk + 3k^2$.
18. $2a^2 - 3ab + b^2$.
19. $3x^2 - 6xy + 3y^2$.
20. $2m^2 - 5mn + 3n^2$.

21. $2a^2 + 3ab - 2b^2$.

22. $3x^2 - xy - 2y^2$.

23. $2h^2 - hk - 3k^2$.

24. $5m^2 + 9mn - 2n^2$.

25. $x^2 - 10x + 25$.

26. $x^2 - 8x + 16$.

27. $a^2 + 6a + 9$.

28. $m^2 + 4m + 4$.

29. $4x^2 + 16xy + 16y^2$.

30. $9x^2 - 6xy + y^2$.

31. $9a^2 - 18ab + 9b^2$.

32. $16m^2 + 16mn + 4n^2$.

33. $4c^2 + 8cd + 4d^2$.

34. $25r^2 + 30rs + 9s^2$.

35. $9a^2 - 30ab + 25b^2$.

36. $16z^2 - 56zw + 49w^2$.

37. $25e^2 + 80ef + 64f^2$.

38. $16x^2 + 72xy + 81y^2$.

39. $25h^2 - 70hk + 49k^2$.

40. $36c^2 + 132cd + 121d^2$.

41. $3x^2 + 11xy + 6y^2$.

42. $2a^2 - 2ab - 4b^2$.

43. $6m^2 + 8mn + 2n^2$.

44. $5r^2 - 12rs + 4s^2$.

45. $4c^2 - 16cd + 7d^2$.

46. $3x^2 + 3xy - 6y^2$.

47. $6a^2 + 7ab - 5b^2$.

48. $7x^2 - 12xy - 4y^2$.

49. $6c^2 + 2cd - 8d^2$.

50. $6c^2 - 4cd - 10d^2$.

51. $6c^2 + 6cd - 12d^2$.

52. $8a^2 + 18ab + 10b^2$.

53. $6x^2 + 10xy - 4y^2$.

54. $6r^2 - 10rs - 16s^2$.

55. $6m^2 - 26mn - 20n^2$.

56. $6m^2 - 2mn - 20n^2$.

57. $8x^2 + 2x - 21$.

58. $10x^2 + 7x - 12$.

59. $10a^2 - ab - 21b^2$.

60. $12z^2 - 52zw - 9w^2$.

61. $12h^2 - hk - 6k^2$.

62. $24x^2 + 23xy - 12y^2$.

63. $36c^2 + 24cd - 5d^2$.

64. $36m^2 + 65mn - 36n^2$.

65. $(2x - y)^2 + (2x - y) - 6$.

66. $4(a - b)^2 - 16(a - b) + 15$.

67. $12(2u + 3v)^2 - 19(2u + 3v) + 4$.

68. $8(c + 2d)^2 + 2(c + 2d) - 15$.

69. $2a^2 + a(b - 3c) - 6(b - 3c)^2$.

70. $6x^2 + 5x(2y - 3z) - 4(2y - 3z)^2$.

71. $8p^2 + 18p(4q - 3r) - 5(4q - 3r)^2$.

72. $2r^2 + 7r(3s - 4t) + 6(3s - 4t)^2$.

21. *Factors of a binomial. The Difference of Two Squares.*
If we state Rule III, Art. 17, in another way, we have the following
rule for factoring the difference of two squares:

RULE I. *The difference of the squares of two numbers is equal to
the product of the sum and the difference of the two numbers.*

Stated in symbols, this rule becomes

(1) $$a^2 - b^2 = (a + b)(a - b).$$

EXAMPLE 1

$$49a^2 - 16b^2 = (7a + 4b)(7a - 4b).$$

EXAMPLE 2

$$(a + 3b)^2 - 4 = [(a + 3b) + 2][(a + 3b) - 2].$$

EXAMPLE 3

$$x^2 - (y + z)^2 = [x + (y + z)][x - (y + z)]$$
$$= (x + y + z)(x - y - z).$$

The Sum and Difference of Two Cubes. The sum and difference of two cubes can be expressed as $x^3 + y^3$ and $x^3 - y^3$, respectively. If we divide $x^3 + y^3$ by $x + y$ by the method of Art. 15, we get $x^2 - xy + y^2$ as a quotient. Hence,

(2) $$x^3 + y^3 = (x + y)(x^2 - xy + y^2).$$

Similarly,

(3) $$x^3 - y^3 = (x - y)(x^2 + xy + y^2).$$

Hence, we have the following two rules:

RULE II. *If a binomial is expressed as the sum of the cubes of two numbers, one factor is the sum of the two numbers. The other factor is the square of the first number minus the product of the two numbers plus the square of the second number.*

RULE III. *If a binomial is expressed as the difference of the cubes of two numbers, one factor is the difference of the two numbers. The other factor is the square of the first number plus the product of the two numbers plus the square of the second number.*

EXAMPLE 4

$$8x^3 + 27y^3 = (2x)^3 + (3y)^3 = (2x + 3y)[(2x)^2 - (2x)(3y) + (3y)^2]$$
$$= (2x + 3y)(4x^2 - 6xy + 9y^2).$$

EXAMPLE 5

$$27a^3 - 64b^3 = (3a)^3 - (4b)^3 = (3a - 4b)[(3a)^2 + (3a)(4b) + (4b)^2]$$
$$= (3a - 4b)(9a^2 + 12ab + 16b^2).$$

NOTE 1: In the case of the sum of two cubes, the sign between the two terms of the first factor is plus, and the sign of the middle term of the second factor is minus.

NOTE 2: In the case of the difference of two cubes, the sign between the two terms of the first factor is minus, and the sign of the middle term of the second factor is plus.

NOTE 3: In each case, the middle term of the second factor is the product of the two terms of the first factor (not twice the product).

Frequently the factors obtained by use of Rules I, II, or III may be further factored by a repeated application of one or more of these rules.

EXAMPLE 5

$$x^6 - y^6 = (x^3 - y^3)(x^3 + y^3) \qquad \text{(by Rule I)}$$
$$= (x - y)(x^2 + xy + y^2)(x + y)(x^2 - xy + y^2) \qquad \text{(by Rules II and III)}$$

EXERCISE 10

By use of Rule I, Art. 21, find the factors of the expression in each of Problems 1 to 20.

1. $x^2 - 1$.
2. $x^2 - 16$.
3. $x^2 - 9y^2$.
4. $x^2 - 16y^2$.
5. $9x^2 - 4y^2$.
6. $16a^2 - 4b^2$.
7. $9m^2 - 16n^2$.
8. $9c^2 - 36d^2$.
9. $36x^2 - 4y^2$.
10. $16x^2 - 25y^2$.
11. $a^4 - 4b^2$.
12. $9x^6 - 4y^2$.
13. $16x^4 - 9y^6$.
14. $36a^6 - 4b^4$.
15. $25c^6 - 16a^2$.
16. $9x^6 - 25y^4$.
17. $36p^4 - q^2$.
18. $16r^6 - 9s^4$.
19. $25a^8 - 4b^4$.
20. $144x^6 - 49y^8$.

Find the factors of the expression in each of Problems 21 to 40 by use of Rules II and III of Art. 21.

21. $x^3 - 1$.
22. $x^3 + 1$.
23. $a^3 + 8$.
24. $z^3 - 27$.
25. $x^3 - 27y^3$.
26. $27a^3 + b^3$.
27. $8x^3 - y^3$.
28. $8c^3 + 27d^3$.
29. $64x^3 + 8y^3$.
30. $125a^3 + 27b^3$.
31. $27m^3 - 64n^3$.
32. $8x^3 - 125y^3$.
33. $27a^3 - 125b^3$.
34. $64c^3 + 125d^3$.
35. $x^6 + y^6$.
36. $27a^3 - y^6$.
37. $m^9 - 8n^3$.
38. $27c^6 + 8d^9$.
39. $z^{12} - 8y^3$.
40. $8a^9 + 125b^6$.

Factor the expressions in Problems 41 to 52.

41. $(x + 3y)^2 - z^2$.
42. $(2a - b)^2 - c^2$.
43. $(c + 4d)^2 - f^2$.
44. $(3m + 2n)^2 - 9m^2n^2$.
45. $r^2 - (3s + 2t)^2$.
46. $4x^2 - (2y - 4z)^2$.
47. $16a^2 - (5b + 3c)^2$.
48. $9x^2 - (3y - 2z)^2$.
49. $(x + y)^3 - z^3$.
50. $(x + 3y)^3 + 27$.
51. $z^3 + (x + y)^3$.
52. $a^3 - (b + 3c)^3$.

Factor the following expressions by repeated applications of Rules I, II, or III.

53. $a^4 - 1$.
54. $x^8 - 16$.
55. $a^8 - b^4$.

56. $c^8 - 1$. **57.** $x^6 - y^6$. **58.** $u^{12} - v^8$.
59. $c^9 + d^9$. **60.** $a^{12} - b^{12}$.

22. *Common factors.* Each term of a polynomial may be divisible by a common factor. Such a polynomial can be factored by expressing it as the product of the common factor and the sum of the quotients obtained by dividing each term in the polynomial by the common factor. The common factor may contain one or more terms.

EXAMPLES

1. $ax + ay - az = a(x + y - z)$.
2. $u(y + z) - 2v(y + z) + 3w(y + z) = (y + z)(u - 2v + 3w)$.
3. $(a + b)(2c + d) - (a + b)(a + d) + (a + b)(2b - c)$
$$= (a + b)[(2c + d) - (a + d) + (2b - c)]$$
$$= (a + b)(2c + d - a - d + 2b - c)$$
$$= (a + b)(c - a + 2b).$$
4. $a^3 - 2a^2b + ab^2 = a(a^2 - 2ab + b^2)$
$$= a(a - b)^2.$$

23. *Factoring by grouping.* Polynomials that contain four or more terms may often be reduced to a factorable type by suitably grouping the terms, and then by factoring each group.

EXAMPLE 1

Factor $ax + bx - ay - by$.

Solution

If we enclose the first two terms and the last two terms, respectively, in parentheses, we get
$$(ax + bx) - (ay + by).$$
Next, if we factor each of these groups, we have
$$x(a + b) - y(a + b).$$
Now we see that each group has the common factor $a + b$, and by using the method of Art. 22, we get
$$(a + b)(x - y),$$
which are the required factors. The condensed form of the solution follows.
$$ax + bx - ay - by = (ax + bx) - (ay + by)$$
$$= x(a + b) - y(a + b)$$
$$= (a + b)(x - y).$$

EXAMPLE 2

Factor $a^2 + ab - 2b^2 + 2a - 2b$.

Solution

We first divide the expressions into the two groups shown below

$$(a^2 + ab - 2b^2) + (2a - 2b).$$

Factoring the two groups, we have

$$(a + 2b)(a - b) + 2(a - b).$$

Now, since each group has the common factor, $a - b$, we may use the method of Art. 22 and obtain

$$(a - b)(a + 2b + 2).$$

The condensed form follows.

$$
\begin{aligned}
a^2 + ab - 2b^2 + 2a - 2b &= (a^2 + ab - 2b^2) + (2a - 2b) \\
&= (a + 2b)(a - b) + 2(a - b) \\
&= (a - b)(a + 2b + 2).
\end{aligned}
$$

EXAMPLE 3

Factor $4c^2 - a^2 + 2ab - b^2$.

Solution

If we enclose the last three terms of this expression in parentheses, we have

$$
\begin{aligned}
4c^2 - a^2 + 2ab - b^2 &= 4c^2 - (a^2 - 2ab + b^2) \\
&= (2c)^2 - (a - b)^2 \\
&= [2c + (a - b)][2c - (a - b)] \\
&= (2c + a - b)(2c - a + b).
\end{aligned}
$$

24. Trinomials reducible to the difference of two squares. Frequently it is possible to convert a trinomial into the difference of two squares by adding and subtracting a monomial that is a perfect square. For example, if we add $4a^2b^2$ to $a^4 + 2a^2b^2 + 9b^4$ and then subtract $4a^2b^2$, we have

$$
\begin{aligned}
a^4 + 2a^2b^2 + 9b^4 &= a^4 + 2a^2b^2 + 9b^4 + 4a^2b^2 - 4a^2b^2 \\
&= a^4 + 6a^2b^2 + 9b^4 - 4a^2b^2 \\
&= (a^2 + 3b^2)^2 - (2ab)^2.
\end{aligned}
$$

The above process is possible only when the trinomial becomes a perfect square when a perfect-square monomial is *added* to it.

After a trinomial has been converted into the difference of two squares, it can be factored by use of Rule I, Art. 21.

EXAMPLE

Factor $4x^4 - 21x^2y^2 + 9y^4$.

Solution

In this trinomial, $4x^4$ and $9y^4$ are perfect squares, and twice the product of their square roots is $2(2x^2)(3y^2) = 12x^2y^2$. Hence, the trinomial becomes a perfect square if we add $9x^2y^2$ to it. Then we must also subtract $9x^2y^2$ and have

$$\begin{aligned}
4x^4 - 21x^2y^2 + 9y^4 &= 4x^4 - 21x^2y^2 + 9y^4 + 9x^2y^2 - 9x^2y^2 \\
&= 4x^4 - 12x^2y^2 + 9y^4 - 9x^2y^2 \\
&= (2x^2 - 3y^2)^2 - (3xy)^2 \\
&= [(2x^2 - 3y^2) + 3xy][(2x^2 - 3y^2) - 3xy] \\
&\qquad\qquad\qquad\qquad \text{(by Rule I, Art. 21)} \\
&= (2x^2 + 3xy - 3y^2)(2x^2 - 3xy - 3y^2).
\end{aligned}$$

EXERCISE 11

Factor the expression in each of Problems 1 to 12 by the method explained in Art. 22.

1. $2x + 6$.
2. $3a - 6$.
3. $2c + 8$.
4. $4m - 12$.
5. $y^2 + 4y$.
6. $b^2 - 5b$.
7. $2d^2 + 3d$.
8. $4n^2 - 16n$.
9. $2x^2 + 12x + 16$.
10. $3a^2 + 3a - 18$.
11. $2r^2 + 12r + 10$.
12. $2d^2 - 8d + 6$.

Factor the expression in each of Problems 13 to 48 by the methods suggested in Art. 23.

13. $ax - ay + bx - by$.
14. $3a - ab - 3c + cb$.
15. $xy + 3xz + 2y + 6z$.
16. $3bc - 6bd + 2c - 4d$.
17. $rs - 2t + 2s - rt$.
18. $6ac - bd + 2ad - 3bc$.
19. $4xz + 3y - 4yz - 3x$.
20. $2ax - 3by + 3ay - 2bx$.
21. $3x^2 - x + 6xy - 2y$.
22. $2a^2 - 3ac + 4ab - 6bc$.
23. $9wx^2 - 15x^2z - 6wy + 10yz$.
24. $8r^2 + 2rt - 12rs^2 - 3s^2t$.
25. $a^3 + 4a^2 - 4a - 16$.
26. $x^3 - 3x^2 - x + 3$.
27. $2b^3 + 5b^2 - 18b - 45$.
28. $3m^3 + m^2 - 12m - 4$.
29. $6y^3 - 2y^2 - 4y$.
30. $6a^3 - 15a^2 - 36a$.
31. $12c^3 - 10c^2 - 12c$.
32. $9d^3 + 24d^2 - 9d$.
33. $2x^3 - 12x^2 + 18x$.
34. $12b^3 + 12b^2 + 3b$.
35. $5m^3 - 20m^2 + 20m$.
36. $16a^3 + 48a^2 + 36a$.
37. $4x^2 + 4xy + y^2 - 4$.
38. $a^2 + 6ab + 9b^2 - 9$.
39. $4b^2 + 9c^2 - 4d^2 + 12bc$.
40. $9r^2 + 4s^2 - 9t^2 + 12rs$.

41. $4p^2 - m^2 - n^2 + 2mn$.
42. $4a^2 - 4b^2 - c^2 - 4bc$.
43. $x^2 - y^2 - 9z^2 - 6yz$.
44. $9b^2 - 4c^2 - 25d^2 + 20cd$.
45. $a^4 - b^4 - a^2 + b^2$.
46. $x^4 - y^4 - x^2 + 2xy - y^2$.
47. $c^3 - d^3 - c^2 + d^2$.
48. $w^4 - z^4 - w^6 + z^6$.

Factor the expressions in Problems 49 to 60 by the method of Art. 24.

49. $x^4 - 7x^2 + 1$.
50. $a^4 - 8a^2 + 4$.
51. $y^4 + 2y^2 + 9$.
52. $c^4 + 4d^2$.
53. $a^4 - 12a^2b^2 + 16b^4$.
54. $m^4 - 3m^2n^2 + 9n^4$.
55. $x^4 - 13x^2y^2 + 4y^4$.
56. $4a^4 + 8a^2b^2 + 9b^4$.
57. $9c^4 + 15c^2d^2 + 16d^4$.
58. $25x^4 - 34x^2y^2 + 9y^4$.
59. $16m^4 - 33m^2n^2 + 9n^4$.
60. $x^4 - 6x^2 + 1$.

REVIEW EXERCISE FOR CHAPTER 3

Find the products indicated in Problems 1 to 32 by the methods of Arts. 17 and 18.

1. $(4x + 3y)(x - 2y)$.
2. $(7r - 2s)(r + 4s)$.
3. $(m - 3n)(5m + n)$.
4. $(3a + 2b)(4a - 3b)$.
5. $(6p + 5q)(4p - 3q)$.
6. $(4c - d)(2c + 6d)$.
7. $(10x - 5y)(5x + 8y)$.
8. $(8x - 2y)(2x - 4y)$.
9. $(2x + 7y)^2$.
10. $(5a - 3b)^2$.
11. $(4c + d)^2$.
12. $(6r - 2s)^2$.
13. $(8m + 2n)^2$.
14. $(3p - 6q)^2$.
15. $(-2r - 4s)^2$.
16. $(-5c - 2d)^2$.
17. $(3a - 3b)(3a + 3b)$.
18. $(8c - 4d)(8c + 4d)$.
19. $(4m - 2n)(4m + 2n)$.
20. $(10x - 5y)(10x + 5y)$.
21. $(12r - 2s)(12r + 2s)$.
22. $(7a + 3b)(7a - 3b)$.
23. $(5x + 6y)(5x - 6y)$.
24. $(6c - 3d)(6c + 3d)$.
25. $(a + b - 3)(a + b + 3)$.
26. $(3x + y - 2z)(3x + y + 2z)$.
27. $(c - 3d + e)(c - 3d - e)$.
28. $(3a - 2b + c)(3a + 2b + c)$.
29. $(2r - 3s + t)^2$.
30. $(4x + 2y - 3z)^2$.
31. $(5a + 2b - 2c)^2$.
32. $(3x - 3y - 2z)^2$.

Factor the expressions in Problems 33 to 80.

33. $2x^2 - 7x + 3$.
34. $3x^2 + x - 2$.
35. $3a^2 - 4a - 4$.
36. $4c^2 + 4cd - 3d^2$.
37. $2x^2 + 7xy + 6y^2$.
38. $5m^2 - 7mn - 6n^2$.
39. $8x^2 - 10xy - 18y^2$.
40. $6x^2 + 3xy - 18y^2$.
41. $r^2 + 12rs + 36s^2$.
42. $4a^2 + 12ab + 9b^2$.
43. $16x^2 + 24xy + 9y^2$.
44. $81m^2 - 72mn + 16n^2$.
45. $25x^2 - 9y^2$.
46. $16a^2 - 81b^2$.
47. $64c^2 - 100$.
48. $36r^2 - 49s^2$.
49. $x^2 - (3y + z)^2$.
50. $16a^2 - (4b - 2c)^2$.

51. $(2x + y)^2 - 25x^2$.

52. $(3r - 2t)^2 - 49s^2$.

53. $2ax + ay + 2bx + by$.

54. $4wy + 2wz - 2xy - xz$.

55. $3ac - ad + 6bc - 2bd$.

56. $6pq - 4pt + 15qs - 10st$.

57. $x^2 - xy - 2y^2 - 2x + 4y$.

58. $a^2 - 4b^2 + 3a + 6b$.

59. $m^2 - 9n^2 + 4m - 12n$.

60. $2c^2 + 7cd + 3d^2 + 3c + 9d$.

61. $8x^3 - 64y^3$.

62. $27a^3 + 125b^3$.

63. $125r^3 - 64s^3$.

64. $64c^3 + 27d^3$.

65. $(x - y)^3 - z^3$.

66. $a^3 + (b - c)^3$.

67. $2x^4y - 16xy^4$.

68. $a - 16a^5$.

69. $16x^4 - y^4$.

70. $a^6 - b^6$.

71. $m^8 - n^8$.

72. $d^4 - 81$.

73. $16r^2 - 4s^2 + 4st - t^2$.

74. $9t^2 - 16m^2 - 16mn - 4n^2$.

75. $25a^2 - b^2 - 6bc - 9c^2$.

76. $16x^2 - 9y^2 + 30yz - 25z^2$.

77. $s^4 + 4s^2t^2 + 16t^4$.

78. $a^4 - 15a^2b^2 + 9b^4$.

79. $x^4 + 6x^2y^2 + 25y^4$.

80. $x^4 - 19x^2y^2 + 25y^4$.

CHAPTER 4

FRACTIONS AND FRACTIONAL EQUATIONS

25. *Introduction.* There are two ways of thinking about a fraction. One of these, and historically the first, is that a fraction represents a certain number of equal parts of a unit. Thus, the fraction $\frac{5}{7}$ means that the unit is divided into seven equal parts and that we are considering five of them. The other, and the one used almost exclusively in algebra, is that *a fraction is the indicated quotient of two numbers.* A fraction is written as one number above another with the two numbers separated by a horizontal line,[1] thus, $\frac{a}{b}$. The number above the line is called the *numerator*, and the one below the line is called the *denominator*. We shall frequently speak of the numerator and denominator as the members of the fraction.

There are three signs associated with a fraction; namely, the sign of the numerator, the sign of the denominator, and the sign preceding the fraction. The latter is called the sign of the fraction.

26. *Reduction of fractions.* *The product of two fractions is defined as a fraction whose numerator is the product of the two numerators, and whose denominator is the product of the denominators.* Hence,

$$\frac{a}{b} \times \frac{c}{d} = \frac{ac}{bd}.$$

In accordance with the above definition, we have

(1) $$\frac{a}{b} \times \frac{c}{c} = \frac{ac}{bc}.$$

[1] A fraction is also written with the two parts on the same line with the dividend first and the two parts separated by a solidus. thus a/b.

However, since $\dfrac{c}{c} = 1$, we also have

(2) $$\frac{a}{b} \times \frac{c}{c} = \frac{a}{b} \times 1 = \frac{a}{b}.$$

Thus, since the left members of (1) and (2) are equal, the right members are also equal and we have

(3) $$\frac{a}{b} = \frac{ac}{bc}.$$

Now, if we read relation (3) from left to right and also from right to left, we see that *if the numerator and the denominator of a fraction are multiplied or divided by the same nonzero number, the value of the fraction is not changed.*

This fact enables us to simplify a fraction by dividing the numerator and the denominator by any common factor that they may have. This process is called *reducing a fraction to lower terms.*

It is good practice to *factor both the numerator and denominator of a fraction before reducing it to lowest terms,* and we shall do that in the following examples.

EXAMPLES

1. $\dfrac{12}{20} = \dfrac{4 \times 3}{4 \times 5} = \dfrac{3}{5}.$

2. $\dfrac{(x + y)(x - 3y)}{(x + y)(x + 2y)} = \dfrac{x - 3y}{x + 2y}.$

3. $\dfrac{a^2 - 4b^2}{3a^2 - 2ab - 8b^2} = \dfrac{(a - 2b)(a + 2b)}{(a - 2b)(3a + 4b)} = \dfrac{a + 2b}{3a + 4b}.$

4. $\dfrac{x - y}{a - b} = \dfrac{(x - y)(-1)}{(a - b)(-1)} = \dfrac{-x + y}{-a + b} = \dfrac{y - x}{b - a}.$

In Example 4 above, we see that the last fraction on the right is the original fraction with every sign in it changed. Since such a process is always equivalent to multiplying the numerator and the denominator by -1, we conclude that

If every sign in both the numerator and denominator of a fraction is changed, the value of the fraction is not altered.

On the other hand, changing the sign of only one member is equivalent to multiplying the fraction by

$$\frac{-1}{1} = -1 \qquad \text{or by} \qquad \frac{1}{-1} = -1.$$

In either case, this process is equivalent to multiplying the fraction by -1, and hence it changes the sign before the fraction. Hence,

If every sign in either the numerator or the denominator is changed, the sign of the fraction is changed.

EXAMPLES

1. $\dfrac{a^2 - ab - b^2}{a^2 - b^2} = \dfrac{-a^2 + ab + b^2}{-a^2 + b^2}.$

2. $\dfrac{x^2 - y^2}{x - 2y} = -\dfrac{y^2 - x^2}{x - 2y} = -\dfrac{x^2 - y^2}{2y - x}.$

EXERCISE 12

Change the fraction in each of Problems 1 to 16 to an equivalent fraction that has the expression at the right as a numerator.

1. $\dfrac{x^3 y^4}{x^2 y^5},\ x.$

2. $\dfrac{4a^3 b^3 c^2}{10 a^2 b^4 c^3},\ 2ab.$

3. $\dfrac{15 r^3 s^2 t}{20 r s t^3},\ 3r^2 s.$

4. $\dfrac{24 x^6 y^8 z^3}{42 x^5 y^{10} z^8},\ 4x.$

5. $\dfrac{a(a - b)}{a^3(a + b)},\ a - b.$

6. $\dfrac{x^3(x + y)^2}{x^4(x + y)(x - y)},\ x + y.$

7. $\dfrac{c^2 d(c - d)}{c d^3(c - d)},\ c.$

8. $\dfrac{m(m - n)^2}{mn(m - n)},\ m - n.$

9. $\dfrac{-x^3 y^6}{-x^4 y^3 z^2},\ y^3.$

10. $\dfrac{-r^3 s^2 t}{r^2 s t^5},\ rs.$

11. $\dfrac{x(x - y)}{y(y - x)},\ x.$

12. $\dfrac{a^5(a - b)}{-a^4 b(b - a)},\ a.$

13. $\dfrac{2 x^2 y}{3 x^3 y^4},\ 4.$

14. $\dfrac{3 x y^3}{7 y^5},\ 6 x^3.$

15. $\dfrac{a - b}{c},\ a^2 - b^2.$

16. $\dfrac{c + d}{c - d},\ c^2 - d^2.$

Change the fraction in each of Problems 17 to 32 to an equivalent fraction that has the expression at the right as the denominator.

17. $\dfrac{-cd}{d - c},\ c - d.$

18. $\dfrac{x - y}{y - x},\ x - y.$

19. $\dfrac{2r - s - 3t}{r - 2s - t}$, $t + 2s - r$.

20. $\dfrac{n^3(m + n)}{n^2(n - m)}$, $m - n$.

21. $\dfrac{x(x + y)}{x^2 - y^2}$, $x - y$.

22. $\dfrac{2a + 4b}{a^2 + 4ab + 4b^2}$, $a + 2b$.

23. $\dfrac{m^2 - n^2}{m^2 + 2mn + n^2}$, $m + n$.

24. $\dfrac{c^3 + d^3}{c^2 - d^2}$, $c - d$.

25. $\dfrac{r + s}{3r}$, $6r^2$.

26. $\dfrac{2a - b}{5b}$, $-10b^3$.

27. $\dfrac{x + y}{x^2 + xy + y^2}$, $x^3 - y^3$.

28. $\dfrac{2m - 5n}{n - 2m}$, $4m^2 - n^2$.

29. $\dfrac{c^2 - 2c}{c^2 - c - 2}$, $c + 1$.

30. $\dfrac{a^3 - b^3}{3a^2 - ab - 2b^2}$, $3a + 2b$.

31. $\dfrac{4r^2 + 4rs - 3s^2}{6r^2 + 13rs + 6s^2}$, $3r + 2s$.

32. $\dfrac{4h^2 - 2hk - 6k^2}{2h^2 - 5hk + 3k^2}$, $h - k$.

Reduce the following fractions to lowest terms.

33. $\dfrac{x^2 + 2x - 8}{x^2 + 6x + 8}.$

34. $\dfrac{a^2 - ab - 12b^2}{a^2 - 3ab - 4b^2}.$

35. $\dfrac{2p^2 - pq - 3q^2}{3p^2 + 5pq + 2q^2}.$

36. $\dfrac{3m^2 - 7mn + 2n^2}{3m^2 + 5mn - 2n^2}.$

37. $\dfrac{(c - d)(2c^2 + 3cd + d^2)}{(2c + d)(c^2 + cd - 2d^2)}.$

38. $\dfrac{(r - 2s)(2r^2 + 9rs + 4s^2)}{(r + 4s)(r^2 - 5rs + 6s^2)}.$

39. $\dfrac{(x - y)(x^2 + 7xy + 10y^2)}{(x + 5y)(x^2 + 2xy - 3y^2)}.$

40. $\dfrac{(h + 2k)(h^2 - 3hk + 2k^2)}{(h - 2k)(h^2 + 3hk + 2k^2)}.$

41. $\dfrac{2ax + 2ay + bx + by}{2ay - 2ax + by - bx}.$

42. $\dfrac{3wy - 6wz - xy + 2xz}{6wy - 2xy + 3wz - xz}.$

43. $\dfrac{3ac - 2bd - 3ad + 2bc}{6ac - 6bd - 9ad + 4bc}.$

44. $\dfrac{rt - 3su + 3st - ru}{rt - 3st - ru + 3su}.$

45. $\dfrac{x^2 - y^2}{x^3 - y^3}.$

46. $\dfrac{m^2 - n^2}{m^3 + n^3}.$

47. $\dfrac{a^4 - b^4}{a^6 - b^6}.$

48. $\dfrac{c^9 + d^9}{c^6 - d^6}.$

49. $\dfrac{x^4 + x^2y^2 + y^4}{x^3 + y^3}.$

50. $\dfrac{a^4 + a^2b^2 + b^4}{a^6 - b^6}.$

51. $\dfrac{m^4 + 4m^2 + 16}{m^3 + 8}.$

52. $\dfrac{c^4 + c^2d^2 + d^4}{c^3 - d^3}$

53. $\dfrac{x-2}{(3x-5)x-2}.$

54. $\dfrac{y+4}{(2y+9)y+4}.$

55. $\dfrac{m-3}{(3m-8)m-3}.$

56. $\dfrac{a-1}{(2a-1)a-1}.$

57. $\dfrac{x+2}{(x+1)(x+2)+3x+6}.$

58. $\dfrac{b-2}{b(2b-4)+(b-4)+2}.$

59. $\dfrac{(c+2)(c-3)}{-3(c+2)+(c+2)c}.$

60. $\dfrac{(2r+1)(r-3)}{4(r-3)-(2r+1)+14}.$

27. Multiplication of fractions. The definition of multiplication of fractions in the previous article may be extended to include the product of two or more fractions and may be stated as follows:

The product of two or more fractions is a fraction whose numerator is the product of the numerators, and whose denominator is the product of the denominators.

EXAMPLE 1

$$\frac{a}{b} \times \frac{c}{d} \times \frac{x-y}{x+y} = \frac{ac(x-y)}{bd(x+y)}.$$

Frequently the numerator and denominator of a product have a common factor. In such cases, the fraction should be reduced to lowest terms by dividing both members by the common factor. It is simpler if the common factor that is to appear in the product is determined in advance and then neglected when the product is written. The following procedure is suggested:

1. *Factor both members of each fraction that appears in the product.*
2. *Cancel any pair of equal factors if one appears in the numerator and the other in the denominator.*
3. *Write the product of the factors that remain in the numerator as a new numerator, and the product of those that remain in the denominator as a new denominator.*

EXAMPLE 2

$$\frac{2}{3} \times \frac{6}{7} \times \frac{21}{8} = \frac{\cancel{2}}{\cancel{3}} \times \frac{(\cancel{3})(\cancel{2})}{\cancel{7}} \times \frac{(3)(\cancel{7})}{(\cancel{2})(\cancel{2})(2)} = \frac{3}{2}.$$

EXAMPLE 3

Find the following product:

$$\frac{a^2-4b^2}{2a^2-7ab+3b^2} \times \frac{6a-3b}{2a+4b} \times \frac{a^2-4ab+3b^2}{a^2-ab-2b^2}.$$

Solution

After the members of each of the above fractions are factored, the problem appears as

$$\frac{(a - 2b)(a + 2b)}{(2a - b)(a - 3b)} \times \frac{3(2a - b)}{2(a + 2b)} \times \frac{(a - b)(a - 3b)}{(a + b)(a - 2b)}.$$

We may now see that $a - 2b$ appears as a factor of a numerator and of a denominator. The same may be said of $a + 2b$, $a - 3b$, and $2a - b$. If these common factors are canceled and the remaining factors multiplied together, the problem appears as

$$\frac{\cancel{(a - 2b)}\cancel{(a + 2b)}}{\cancel{(2a - b)}\cancel{(a - 3b)}} \times \frac{3\cancel{(2a - b)}}{2\cancel{(a + 2b)}} \times \frac{(a - b)\cancel{(a - 3b)}}{(a + b)\cancel{(a - 2b)}} = \frac{3(a - b)}{2(a + b)}.$$

28. Division of fractions. In arithmetic, when we were required to divide a number by a fraction, we learned to perform this operation by inverting the terms of the divisor and then multiplying. The reason for this procedure was usually not given. The following justification of the method is suggested. Since we may express the quotient of a and b as a fraction $\dfrac{a}{b}$, and since $\dfrac{a}{b} = \dfrac{an}{bn}$, we have $a \div b = an \div bn$, or, in words, if the dividend and divisor are multiplied by the same number, the quotient is not changed. Hence,

$$\frac{x}{y} \div \frac{u}{v} = \left(\frac{x}{y}\right)\left(\frac{v}{u}\right) \div \left(\frac{u}{v}\right)\left(\frac{v}{u}\right) = \left(\frac{x}{y}\right)\left(\frac{v}{u}\right) \div 1 = \frac{xv}{yu}.$$

Therefore, *in order to obtain the quotient of two fractions we multiply the dividend by the divisor inverted.*

EXAMPLE 1

$$\frac{a^2 - b^2}{a^2 - ab - 2b^2} \div \frac{a^2 - 2ab + b^2}{a^2 - 2ab} = \frac{a^2 - b^2}{a^2 - ab - 2b^2} \times \frac{a^2 - 2ab}{a^2 - 2ab + b^2}$$

$$= \frac{(a - b)(a + b)}{(a - 2b)(a + b)} \times \frac{a(a - 2b)}{(a - b)(a - b)}$$

$$= \frac{a}{a - b}.$$

EXAMPLE 2

$$\frac{3x - 3y}{2x^2 - xy} \times \frac{2x^2 + xy - y^2}{x^2 - 2xy + y^2} \div \frac{3xy + 3y^2}{2x^2 - 2xy}$$

$$= \frac{3(x - y)}{x(2x - y)} \times \frac{(2x - y)(x + y)}{(x - y)(x - y)} \times \frac{2x(x - y)}{3y(x + y)} = \frac{2}{y}.$$

EXERCISE 13

Perform the operations indicated in each of the following problems.

1. $\frac{2}{3} \times \frac{3}{7} \times \frac{21}{4}$.

2. $\frac{3}{5} \times \frac{35}{11} \times \frac{44}{21}$.

3. $\frac{5}{13} \times \frac{26}{15} \times \frac{6}{7}$.

4. $\frac{2}{7} \times \frac{21}{10} \times \frac{20}{3}$.

5. $\frac{3}{13} \times \frac{39}{5} \div \frac{27}{25}$.

6. $\frac{12}{5} \times \frac{25}{36} \times \frac{2}{3} \div \frac{10}{9}$.

7. $\frac{16}{3} \times \frac{9}{64} \times \frac{12}{5} \div \frac{6}{5}$.

8. $\frac{8}{7} \times \frac{15}{16} \times \frac{56}{25} \div \frac{12}{35}$.

9. $\frac{2a^2}{3b^2} \times \frac{6ab}{7} \times \frac{14b^3}{5a^3}$.

10. $\frac{6x^2}{5y^2} \times \frac{15y}{8x} \times \frac{10y^3}{9x}$.

11. $\frac{3c^4}{4d^4} \times \frac{12d^2}{5c^3} \times \frac{10d^3}{9c^2}$.

12. $\frac{5r^5}{14s^3} \times \frac{21s^7}{25r^3} \times \frac{20r^4}{9s^2}$.

13. $\frac{x^3z}{y^2w} \times \frac{x^2w^4}{yz^3} \times \frac{y^4z^2}{x^4w^2}$.

14. $\frac{a^2d^6}{b^5c^4} \times \frac{a^3b^2}{cd^4} \times \frac{b^3c^5}{a^4d^3}$.

15. $\frac{2a^2b^3}{3cd^2} \times \frac{3a^3c^2}{4bd^2} \times \frac{4cd^5}{3a^4b}$.

16. $\frac{14a^3b}{5c^2d^4} \times \frac{15ab^2}{16cd^3} \times \frac{6c^3d^6}{7a^4b^4}$.

17. $\frac{a^3b^2}{c^2d} \times \frac{ac^3}{bd^2} \div \frac{a^3c}{b^2d}$.

18. $\frac{w^4x^3}{y^2z^2} \times \frac{w^2y}{xz^3} \div \frac{w^5x^2}{y^2z^4}$.

19. $\frac{18a^2b^2}{5c^2} \times \frac{25bc^3}{6a^3} \div \frac{15b^3}{7ac}$.

20. $\frac{25x^2y^2}{3y^4} \times \frac{4x^3z^3}{39z^2} \div \frac{15x^4}{26y^2z^2}$.

21. $\frac{5a - 5b}{a + 2b} \times \frac{2a + 4b}{a - b}$.

22. $\frac{x(x + y)}{x - y} \times \frac{2x - 2y}{x^2 - y^2}$.

23. $\frac{a(a - b)^3}{b(a^2 - b^2)} \times \frac{b(a + b)}{a^2(a - b)^2}$.

24. $\frac{8h + 20k}{h^2 - 3hk} \times \frac{hk - 3k^2}{12h + 30k}$.

25. $\frac{4x - 2y}{5x + 10y} \div \frac{2xy - y^2}{x^2 + 2xy}$.

26. $\frac{3wz - 7z^2}{w^2 + 5wz} \div \frac{12w - 28z}{3w + 15z}$.

27. $\frac{x(x + 2y)^2}{x - 3y} \div \frac{x^2 + 2xy}{x - 3y}$.

28. $\frac{a - 5b}{(a + b)^3} \div \frac{(a - 5b)^2}{(a + b)^4}$.

29. $\frac{x^2}{x - y} \times \frac{x^2 - y^2}{x^3} \times \frac{x}{x + y}$.

30. $\frac{a^3}{a + 2b} \times \frac{a^2 - 4b^2}{b^3} \times \frac{b^4}{a - 2b}$.

31. $\frac{p^2 - q^2}{pq^2} \times \frac{p^2}{pq + q^2} \times \frac{q^4}{p^2 - pq}$.

32. $\frac{3c^2d}{c^2 - d^2} \times \frac{c(c + d)}{2d^2} \times \frac{2d(c - d)}{3c^3}$.

33. $\dfrac{2x^2 + x - 1}{x^2 - 4} \div \dfrac{2x - 1}{x + 2}.$

34. $\dfrac{a^2 - 4b^2}{a^2 - b^2} \div \dfrac{a + 2b}{a - b}.$

35. $\dfrac{2c^2 + cd - 3d^2}{c^2 - cd - 2d^2} \div \dfrac{c - d}{c + d}.$

36. $\dfrac{2u^2 - uv - 6v^2}{u^2 + 3uv + 2v^2} \div \dfrac{2u + 3v}{u + 2v}.$

37. $\dfrac{a^2}{(a - 2b)^2} \times \dfrac{a + 2b}{3a} \times \dfrac{(a - 2b)^3}{(a + 2b)^2}.$

38. $\dfrac{x(x - 3y)}{x + 2y} \times \dfrac{x - 2y}{(x - 3y)^2} \times \dfrac{(x + 2y)^2}{x - 2y}.$

39. $\dfrac{3(c + 2d)}{c^2 - d^2} \times \dfrac{c(c + d)}{(c + 2d)^2} \times \dfrac{c - d}{3c}.$

40. $\dfrac{wz}{(w - z)^2} \times \dfrac{w - z}{w(w + z)} \times \dfrac{w^2 - z^2}{z^2}.$

41. $\dfrac{a^2 + ab - 2b^2}{a^2 - 3ab + 2b^2} \div \dfrac{a^2 + 5ab + 6b^2}{a^2 - ab - 2b^2}.$

42. $\dfrac{4m^2 - 4mn - 3n^2}{m^2 - 2mn - 3n^2} \div \dfrac{4m^2 - 9n^2}{2m^2 + 5mn + 3n^2}.$

43. $\dfrac{4x^2 - 15xy - 4y^2}{3x^2 - xy - 4y^2} \div \dfrac{4x^2 - 3xy - y^2}{3x^2 - 7xy + 4y^2}.$

44. $\dfrac{15s^2 + 2st - 8t^2}{3s^2 + st - 2t^2} \div \dfrac{5s^2 - st - 4t^2}{2s^2 + st - t^2}.$

45. $\dfrac{2x^2 - x}{2x^2 - x - 1} \times \dfrac{10x^2 + 3x - 1}{6x^2 + x - 2} \div \dfrac{5x^2 - x}{3x + 2}.$

46. $\dfrac{3a^2 + 2a - 5}{2a^2 + a - 6} \times \dfrac{2a^2 + 3a - 2}{a^2 + 2a - 3} \div \dfrac{3a + 5}{2a - 3}.$

47. $\dfrac{4y^2 + 5y - 6}{5y^2 + 2y - 3} \times \dfrac{5y - 3}{y + 2} \div \dfrac{4y^2 + 9y - 9}{y^2 - 1}.$

48. $\dfrac{4b - 3}{b + 2} \times \dfrac{2b^2 + 2b - 12}{b^2 + b - 12} \div \dfrac{4b^2 + 9b - 9}{b^2 + 6b + 8}.$

49. $\dfrac{x^3 - y^3}{x^2 - xy + y^2} \times \dfrac{x^3 + y^3}{x^2 + xy + y^2} \div \dfrac{x^2 - y^2}{x^2 + y^2}.$

50. $\dfrac{a^2 + ab - 2b^2}{a - ab + b - b^2} \times \dfrac{a^2 - ab - 2b^2}{a^2 + a - ab - b} \div \dfrac{a^2 - 4b^2}{a^2 - 1}.$

51. $\dfrac{b^3 - 1}{2b^2 + b - 1} \times \dfrac{b^3 + 1}{b^4 + b^2 + 1} \div \dfrac{2b^2 - b - 1}{2b^2 + b - 1}.$

52. $\dfrac{w^6 - 1}{w^4 - 1} \times \dfrac{w^4 + 2w^2 + 1}{w^8 - 1} \div \dfrac{w^4 + w^2 + 1}{w^4 + 1}.$

53. $\dfrac{(x-y)^2}{x+y} \times \dfrac{x+(x+y)}{x-y} \times \dfrac{2x-(x-y)}{2x+y}.$

54. $\dfrac{a+(a-2b)}{a+2b} \times \dfrac{2a-(a-2b)}{a-2b} \times \dfrac{2a-(a+2b)}{a-b}.$

55. $\dfrac{(x-3)x+2}{(x-1)x-2} \times \dfrac{x-1}{x+2} \div \dfrac{x-1}{x+1}.$

56. $\dfrac{(a-2)a-3}{(a-3)a-4} \times \dfrac{a+2}{a-3} \div \dfrac{a-2}{a-4}.$

57. $\dfrac{(z-1)z-2}{z^2-4} \times \dfrac{z(z-3)+2(z-3)}{(z+1)(z-1)} \div \dfrac{z-3}{z+1}.$

58. $\dfrac{(2c-3)c-2}{(2c-3)(c+1)} \times \dfrac{2c(c+1)+(c+1)}{2(c+1)(c-1)-3c} \div \dfrac{2c+1}{(2c+1)-4}.$

59. $\dfrac{b^2-1}{b^2-b(b+1)} \times \dfrac{b^2-3b}{(b-1)b+(b-1)2} \div \dfrac{(b^2-3b)-4}{b+2}.$

60. $\dfrac{(x-2)x-3}{x^2-9} \times \dfrac{x(x-2)+3(x-2)}{(x-2)(x-3)} \div \dfrac{x+1}{x-3}.$

29. The lowest common multiple. *The lowest common multiple* (**LCM**) *of a set of polynomials is the polynomial of lowest degree[1] with the least integral coefficients which is exactly divisible by each polynomial of the set.*

EXAMPLES

1. The LCM of $3x$, $4x^2y$, $8x^5y^2$, and $36x^4$ is $72x^5y^2$.
2. The LCM of $2(x-y)$, $3(x+y)$, and $(x-y)^2$ is $6(x-y)^2(x+y)$.

If the given polynomials are in factored form, then from the definition we see that the factored form of the LCM must satisfy the following requirements:

1. Every factor of each polynomial must appear as a factor of the LCM. Furthermore, each factor in the LCM must be raised to a power *equal* to the largest power that this factor has in any one of the given factored polynomials.

2. The LCM can have no factor that does not appear in one of the factored polynomials.

---

[1] The degree of a polynomial is the largest of the numbers obtained by adding the exponents of the letters appearing in the separate terms. For example, the degree of $2x^3-3x^2+4x$ is 3, and the degree of $3x^2y^2-2xy+3y^2$ is 4.

Hence, we have the following method for obtaining the **LCM** of a set of polynomials:

1. *Factor each of the polynomials.*
2. *Write in the LCM each of the **different** prime[1] factors of the polynomials and then raise each factor to the highest power that it has in any one of the factored polynomials.*

EXAMPLE 3

Find the LCM of $x^2 - 2xy + y^2$, $x^2 + 2xy + y^2$, $x^2 - y^2$, $x^2 - 3xy + 2y^2$, and $2x^2 + 3xy + y^2$.

Solution

We first write each of these polynomials in the factored form shown below.

$$x^2 - 2xy + y^2 = (x - y)^2.$$
$$x^2 + 2xy + y^2 = (x + y)^2.$$
$$x^2 - y^2 = (x - y)(x + y).$$
$$x^2 - 3xy + 2y^2 = (x - 2y)(x - y).$$
$$2x^2 + 3xy + y^2 = (2x + y)(x + y).$$

The prime factors which appear above are $(x - y)$, $(x + y)$, $(x - 2y)$, and $(2x + y)$. However, $(x - y)$ and $(x + y)$ have exponents 2 in the first and second polynomials, respectively. Hence, the LCM is $(x - y)^2(x + y)^2(x - 2y)(2x + y)$.

30. Addition of fractions. *The sum of two or more fractions with the same denominator is a fraction whose numerator is the sum of the numerators, and whose denominator is the denominator common to all the fractions.*

EXAMPLES

1. $\dfrac{2}{9} + \dfrac{4}{9} + \dfrac{5}{9} = \dfrac{2 + 4 + 5}{9} = \dfrac{11}{9}.$

2. $\dfrac{1}{3a} + \dfrac{2}{3a} + \dfrac{4}{3a} = \dfrac{7}{3a}.$

3. $\dfrac{a}{d} + \dfrac{b}{d} + \dfrac{c}{d} = \dfrac{a + b + c}{d}.$

If the denominators of the fractions to be added are not the same, we change them, by a method to be explained later, to fractions in which the denominators are the same and then apply

[1] A prime number is a number that has no factors except itself and one.

the above method of addition. For the sake of simplicity, the denominator of the changed fractions should be the least common multiple of the denominators involved.

EXAMPLE 4

Find the sum of $\dfrac{a}{2} + \dfrac{2a}{3} - \dfrac{3a}{8}$.

Solution

The LCM of the denominators is 24. Hence, we multiply both the numerators and the denominators of the given fractions by 12, 8, and 3, respectively,[1] and get

$$\frac{a}{2} + \frac{2a}{3} - \frac{3a}{8} = \frac{12\,(a)}{12\,(2)} + \frac{8\,(2a)}{8\,(3)} - \frac{3\,(3a)}{3\,(8)}$$

$$= \frac{12a}{24} + \frac{16a}{24} - \frac{9a}{24}$$

$$= \frac{12a + 16a - 9a}{24}$$

$$= \frac{19a}{24}.$$

EXAMPLE 5

Combine into a single fraction $\dfrac{3b + 2a}{4ab} - \dfrac{9b - 8a}{12ab} - \dfrac{a - 2b}{2ab}$.

Solution

In this problem, the least common multiple of the denominators is $12ab$. Hence, we multiply both members of the fractions by 3, 1, and 6, respectively, and obtain

$$\frac{3\,(3b + 2a)}{3\,(4ab)} - \frac{1\,(9b - 8a)}{1\,(12ab)} - \frac{6\,(a - 2b)}{6\,(2ab)}$$

$$= \frac{9b + 6a}{12ab} - \frac{9b - 8a}{12ab} - \frac{6a - 12b}{12ab}.$$

We now write the algebraic sum of the numerators above the common denominator and have

$$\frac{(9b + 6a) - (9b - 8a) - (6a - 12b)}{12ab}.$$

---

[1] These numbers were obtained by dividing the LCM by the denominators of the given fractions.

Finally, we remove the parentheses, combine, and reduce to lowest terms and get

$$\frac{9b + 6a - 9b + 8a - 6a + 12b}{12ab} = \frac{8a + 12b}{12ab} = \frac{4(2a + 3b)}{4(3ab)}$$

$$= \frac{2a + 3b}{3ab}.$$

If the explanation is omitted, the essential steps are

$$\frac{3b + 2a}{4ab} - \frac{9b - 8a}{12ab} - \frac{a - 2b}{2ab} = \frac{9b + 6a}{12ab} - \frac{9b - 8a}{12ab} - \frac{6a - 12b}{12ab}$$

$$= \frac{(9b + 6a) - (9b - 8a) - (6a - 12b)}{12ab}$$

$$= \frac{9b + 6a - 9b + 8a - 6a + 12b}{12ab}$$

$$= \frac{8a + 12b}{12ab} = \frac{4(2a + 3b)}{4(3ab)} = \frac{2a + 3b}{3ab}.$$

After one has had some practice in the addition of fractions, he can perform some of the above steps mentally and write the solution as

$$\frac{3b + 2a}{4ab} - \frac{9b - 8a}{12ab} - \frac{a - 2b}{2ab} = \frac{9b + 6a - 9b + 8a - 6a + 12b}{12ab}$$

$$= \frac{8a + 12b}{12ab} = \frac{2a + 3b}{3ab}.$$

When the shorter form is used, it must be remembered that *the sign of every term contributed to the sum by the fractions preceded by a minus sign must be changed.*

Since most of the work, after the common denominator is found, is in adding the numerators, a student may forget to write the denominator. This is a serious error, and care should be taken to avoid it.

EXAMPLE 6

Combine into a single fraction $\dfrac{3}{2x - y} + \dfrac{4}{x + y} - \dfrac{2}{x - 2y}.$

Solution

Since the denominators are not factorable and no two are alike, the **LCM** is their product $(2x - y)(x + y)(x - 2y)$. In order to reduce each of the fractions to fractions having this expression as a common denominator, we multiply[1] both members of the first by $(x + y)(x - 2y)$, of the second by $(2x - y)(x - 2y)$, and the third by $(2x - y)(x + y)$. When this is done and the algebraic sum is written over the common denominator, we obtain

$$\frac{3}{2x - y} + \frac{4}{x + y} - \frac{2}{x - 2y}$$

$$= \frac{3(x + y)(x - 2y)}{(2x - y)(x + y)(x - 2y)} + \frac{4(2x - y)(x - 2y)}{(2x - y)(x + y)(x - 2y)}$$

$$- \frac{2(2x - y)(x + y)}{(2x - y)(x + y)(x - 2y)}$$

$$= \frac{3(x^2 - xy - 2y^2) + 4(2x^2 - 5xy + 2y^2) - 2(2x^2 + xy - y^2)}{(2x - y)(x + y)(x - 2y)}$$

$$= \frac{3x^2 - 3xy - 6y^2 + 8x^2 - 20xy + 8y^2 - 4x^2 - 2xy + 2y^2}{(2x - y)(x + y)(x - 2y)}$$

$$= \frac{7x^2 - 25xy + 4y^2}{(2x - y)(x + y)(x - 2y)}.$$

EXAMPLE 7

Combine $\dfrac{3a}{a^2 - b^2} - \dfrac{1}{a + b} - \dfrac{2}{a - b}$ into a single fraction.

Solution

Using the method of Art. 29, we obtain $a^2 - b^2$ as the LCM of the denominators. Now, if we multiply both members of the fractions in our problem by[1] 1, $a - b$, and $a + b$, respectively, we get

$$\frac{3a}{a^2 - b^2} - \frac{1}{a + b} - \frac{2}{a - b} = \frac{3a}{a^2 - b^2} - \frac{a - b}{a - b}\frac{1}{a + b} - \frac{a + b}{a + b}\frac{2}{a - b}$$

$$= \frac{3a - (a - b) - 2(a + b)}{a^2 - b^2}$$

$$= \frac{3a - a + b - 2a - 2b}{a^2 - b^2}$$

$$= \frac{-b}{a^2 - b^2}.$$

[1] In order to change a given fraction into another having a specified denominator, we multiply both members of the given fraction by the quotient of the desired denominator and the denominator in the given fraction.

EXAMPLE 8

Combine $\dfrac{1}{x - 2y} + \dfrac{3x + y}{x^2 - y^2} - \dfrac{2x - y}{x^2 - xy - 2y^2}$ into a single fraction.

Solution

We first write the fractions with the denominators in factored form and have

$$\frac{1}{x - 2y} + \frac{3x + y}{(x - y)(x + y)} - \frac{2x - y}{(x + y)(x - 2y)}.$$

By the method of **Art. 29**, the **LCM** of the denominators is

$$(x - 2y)\,(x - y)(x + y).$$

Hence, we change the given fractions into fractions having this expression as a common denominator and get

$$\frac{1}{x - 2y} + \frac{3x + y}{(x - y)(x + y)} - \frac{2x - y}{(x + y)(x - 2y)}$$

$$= \frac{(x - y)(x + y)}{(x - y)(x + y)} \frac{1}{x - 2y} + \frac{x - 2y}{x - 2y} \frac{3x + y}{(x - y)(x + y)}$$

$$- \frac{x - y}{x - y} \frac{2x - y}{(x + y)(x - 2y)}$$

$$= \frac{x^2 - y^2 + (3x^2 - 5xy - 2y^2) - (2x^2 - 3xy + y^2)}{(x - 2y)(x - y)(x + y)}$$

$$= \frac{x^2 - y^2 + 3x^2 - 5xy - 2y^2 - 2x^2 + 3xy - y^2}{(x - 2y)(x - y)(x + y)}$$

$$= \frac{2x^2 - 2xy - 4y^2}{(x - 2y)(x - y)(x + y)}$$

$$= \frac{2(x^2 - xy - 2y^2)}{(x - 2y)(x - y)(x + y)}$$

$$= \frac{2\cancel{(x - 2y)}\cancel{(x + y)}}{\cancel{(x - 2y)}(x - y)\cancel{(x + y)}}$$

$$= \frac{2}{x - y}.$$

EXERCISE 14

Combine the fractions in the following problems into a single fraction.

1. $\frac{2}{3} - \frac{5}{8} + \frac{1}{12}$.
2. $\frac{1}{12} - \frac{4}{15} + \frac{1}{20}$.
3. $\frac{1}{4} + \frac{1}{12} + \frac{1}{6}$.
4. $\frac{9}{4} - \frac{1}{12} - \frac{3}{2}$.
5. $\frac{11}{24} + \frac{5}{4} + \frac{1}{6} - \frac{9}{8}$.
6. $\frac{1}{4} - \frac{5}{12} + \frac{7}{15} + \frac{1}{2}$.

7. $\frac{7}{18} - \frac{23}{24} - \frac{1}{6} + \frac{1}{9}.$

8. $\frac{2}{3} - \frac{3}{7} + \frac{5}{14} - \frac{1}{6}.$

9. $\frac{3x}{2y} - \frac{2y}{3z} + \frac{z}{4x}.$

10. $\frac{4a}{3bc} - \frac{2b}{9ac} - \frac{5c}{2ab}.$

11. $\frac{3c}{7de} + \frac{5d}{14ec} - \frac{e}{4cd}.$

12. $\frac{5p}{6qr} - \frac{3q}{10pr} + \frac{2r}{15pq}.$

13. $\frac{3x^2 - 2y}{xy} + \frac{2}{x} - \frac{12x}{5y}.$

14. $\frac{4a}{5b} - \frac{2b}{3a} + \frac{40b^2 + 27a^2}{60ab}.$

15. $\frac{d}{c} - \frac{17c^2 + 12d^2}{12cd} + \frac{3c}{4d}.$

16. $\frac{5u}{8v} + \frac{v}{4u} - \frac{11u^2 - 6v^2}{24uv}.$

17. $\frac{5x + 4y}{5xz} + \frac{2x + 3z}{3xy} - \frac{3y + 2z}{3yz}.$

18. $\frac{a + 5b}{-3a^2} + \frac{3a + 2b}{6ab} + \frac{5a - 2b}{4b^2}.$

19. $\frac{3e + 2d}{2d^3} - \frac{3e + d}{3d^2e} + \frac{2e + 3d}{6de^2}.$

20. $\frac{9x + 2y}{9x^3} + \frac{x - y}{x^2y} + \frac{x - 3y}{3xy^2} + \frac{5x - 4y}{12y^3}.$

21. $\frac{x + 3y}{2x + y} - \frac{x}{y}.$

22. $\frac{3p}{2q} - \frac{3p + 4q}{5p + 2q}.$

23. $\frac{6a + b}{3a - 9b} + \frac{2a}{3b}.$

24. $\frac{2v + 5w}{6v + 4w} - \frac{v}{2w}.$

25. $\frac{a^2 - 2ab - b^2}{b(a - b)} + \frac{a + b}{a - b}.$

26. $\frac{3x^2 - 2y^2}{4y(x - 2y)} - \frac{3x - y}{2x - 4y}.$

27. $\frac{15k^2 + 4h^2}{3k(2h - 3k)} - \frac{2h + 5k}{2h - 3k}.$

28. $\frac{d + c}{d - c} - \frac{d^2 + c^2}{d(d - c)}.$

29. $\frac{4y^2}{x^2 - y^2} + \frac{2x - 4y}{x - y}.$

30. $\frac{b^2}{4a^2 - b^2} + \frac{a + b}{2a + b}.$

31. $\frac{v^2}{u^2 - 3uv + 2v^2} - \frac{u - v}{u - 2v}.$

32. $\frac{3c + 8d}{c + 2d} + \frac{16d^2}{3c^2 + 4cd - 4d^2}.$

33. $\frac{3x}{y} - \frac{3x + 2y}{x + y} + \frac{2y}{x}.$

34. $\frac{5a}{b} - \frac{3b}{a} - \frac{5a - 3b}{a + b}.$

35. $\frac{2c}{3d} - \frac{2c + 3d}{3d - 4c} + \frac{3d}{4c}.$

36. $\frac{z}{2w} - \frac{z + 5w}{2w + 6z} + \frac{5w}{6z}.$

37. $\frac{1}{x^2} + \frac{2x}{x + 1} - \frac{2x^3 - x^2 + 1}{x^2(x + 1)}.$

38. $\frac{4a^2 + 5a + 2}{a^2(a + 1)} - \frac{1}{a + 1} - \frac{2}{a^2}.$

39. $\dfrac{1}{y^2 - 1} - \dfrac{1}{y^2} + \dfrac{4y^3 - 4y - 1}{y^2(y^2 - 1)}.$

40. $\dfrac{5z^2 + 3z + 2}{2z^2(z + 1)} - \dfrac{1}{z^2} - \dfrac{z - 1}{z(z + 1)}.$

41. $\dfrac{1}{x + 1} - \dfrac{1}{x(x - 1)} + \dfrac{2}{x^2 - 1}.$

42. $\dfrac{1}{a + b} - \dfrac{b}{a(a - b)} + \dfrac{2b}{a^2 - b^2}.$

43. $\dfrac{3}{2w - 3z} + \dfrac{w}{z(2w + 3z)} - \dfrac{9z}{4w^2 - 9z^2}$

44. $\dfrac{b}{c(2b - c)} - \dfrac{c}{4b^2 - c^2} - \dfrac{1}{2b + c}.$

45. $\dfrac{2}{x - 1} - \dfrac{1}{x + 1} - \dfrac{2}{x^2 - 1}.$ **46.** $\dfrac{2}{x - 3} + \dfrac{1}{x + 3} - \dfrac{12}{x^2 - 9}.$

47. $\dfrac{3}{2x - 1} - \dfrac{1}{x + 2} - \dfrac{5}{2x^2 + 3x - 2}.$

48. $\dfrac{2}{x - 3} - \dfrac{3}{3x + 2} - \dfrac{11}{3x^2 - 7x - 6}.$

49. $\dfrac{3}{a - b} - \dfrac{1}{a + b} - \dfrac{4}{2a - b}.$ **50.** $\dfrac{1}{u + v} - \dfrac{4}{2u - v} + \dfrac{1}{u - 2v}.$

51. $\dfrac{16}{x - 2} + \dfrac{9}{x + 3} - \dfrac{5}{x - 1}.$ **52.** $\dfrac{3}{3c - 2d} + \dfrac{7}{c + 2d} - \dfrac{2}{2c + d}.$

53. $\dfrac{2}{(u + 2v)(u + v)} + \dfrac{2}{(u - v)(u + v)} - \dfrac{3}{(u + 2v)(u - v)}.$

54. $\dfrac{3}{(2z - w)(z - 2w)} - \dfrac{2}{3(2z - w)(z - w)} - \dfrac{2}{3(z - w)(z - 2w)}.$

55. $\dfrac{5}{(x + 2y)(4x + 3y)} + \dfrac{3}{(2x + y)(4x + 3y)} - \dfrac{3}{(2x + y)(x + 2y)}.$

56. $\dfrac{15}{2(4a + b)(3a + 2b)} + \dfrac{4}{(4a + b)(2a + b)} - \dfrac{3}{2(3a + 2b)(2a + b)}.$

57. $\dfrac{2x + 4y}{(x + y)(x - 3y)} - \dfrac{x}{(x - y)(x + y)} - \dfrac{5y}{(x - 3y)(x - y)}.$

58. $\dfrac{9a + 10b}{(3a - 4b)(2a + b)} + \dfrac{5a + 5b}{(3a + 4b)(2a + b)} - \dfrac{11a + 25b}{(3a + 4b)(3a - 4b)}.$

59. $\dfrac{3(7z - 2w)}{(4z + w)(z - 2w)} + \dfrac{7(z - w)}{(4z + w)(z + 2w)} + \dfrac{5w}{(z - 2w)(z + 2w)}.$

60. $\dfrac{3c}{(c+d)(c-d)} - \dfrac{4c-d}{(2c+d)(c-d)} + \dfrac{d}{(2c+d)(c+d)}.$

31. Complex fractions. A *complex fraction* is a fraction whose numerator or denominator or both contain fractions. For example,

$$\frac{\frac{1}{2}+1}{3}, \qquad \frac{2a}{a+\frac{1}{a}}, \qquad \frac{\frac{2}{3}}{\frac{5}{8}}, \qquad \frac{2+\dfrac{x}{x-1}}{3-\dfrac{x}{x+1}}$$

are complex fractions.

There are two methods for reducing complex fractions to simple fractions. The first of these consists of multiplying the numerator and the denominator of the complex fraction by the LCM of the denominators in the fraction. This method is advisable when the denominators are single terms.

EXAMPLE 1

The LCM of the denominators in $\dfrac{\frac{1}{2}+1}{3}$ is 2, since it is understood that 1 and 3 are fractions with the denominator 1. If we multiply the numerator and denominator of our fraction by 2, we get

$$\frac{\frac{1}{2}+1}{3} = \frac{(2)(\frac{1}{2}+1)}{(2)(3)} = \frac{1+2}{6} = \frac{3}{6} = \frac{1}{2}.$$

EXAMPLE 2

Reduce $\dfrac{\dfrac{2}{3a}+\dfrac{1}{2a}}{\dfrac{3}{a}-\dfrac{5}{6a}}$ to a simple fraction.

Solution

In this problem, the LCM of the denominators is $6a$. Hence,

$$\frac{\dfrac{2}{3a}+\dfrac{1}{2a}}{\dfrac{3}{a}-\dfrac{5}{6a}} = \frac{6a\left(\dfrac{2}{3a}+\dfrac{1}{2a}\right)}{6a\left(\dfrac{3}{a}-\dfrac{5}{6a}\right)} = \frac{4+3}{18-5} = \frac{7}{13}.$$

If the expressions in the complex fraction are complicated, it is sometimes easier to reduce the numerator and denominator to simple fractions and then proceed as in division.

EXAMPLE 3

Reduce $\dfrac{\dfrac{1}{1+x} + \dfrac{1}{1-x}}{x + \dfrac{x^3}{1-x^2}}$ to a simple fraction.

Solution

The steps in the solution are, first, find the sum of the fractions in the numerator and the sum of those in the denominator; second, invert the terms of the denominator (or the divisor) and multiply. The solution follows.

$$\frac{\dfrac{1}{1+x} + \dfrac{1}{1-x}}{x + \dfrac{x^3}{1-x^2}} = \frac{\dfrac{1-x+1+x}{1-x^2}}{\dfrac{x-x^3+x^3}{1-x^2}} = \frac{\dfrac{2}{1-x^2}}{\dfrac{x}{1-x^2}}$$

$$= \frac{2}{1-x^2} \times \frac{1-x^2}{x} = \frac{2}{x}.$$

EXERCISE 15

Simplify the following complex fractions.

1. $\dfrac{1}{1+\frac{2}{3}}$.

2. $\dfrac{1}{1-\frac{3}{5}}$.

3. $\dfrac{2}{1+\frac{1}{3}}$.

4. $\dfrac{3}{2+\frac{1}{4}}$.

5. $\dfrac{1+\frac{1}{2}}{4+\frac{1}{2}}$.

6. $\dfrac{1+\frac{1}{3}}{2+\frac{2}{3}}$.

7. $\dfrac{2+\frac{1}{2}}{1+\frac{2}{3}}$.

8. $\dfrac{2+\frac{1}{4}}{1+\frac{1}{2}}$.

9. $\dfrac{\dfrac{2}{x} + \dfrac{1}{2x}}{x + \dfrac{x}{2}}$.

10. $\dfrac{\dfrac{1}{2} - \dfrac{1}{x}}{\dfrac{1}{6x} - \dfrac{1}{3x^2}}$.

11. $\dfrac{\dfrac{a}{3b} - \dfrac{2}{3}}{\dfrac{1}{12} - \dfrac{b}{6a}}$.

12. $\dfrac{\dfrac{1}{4} - \dfrac{1}{2x}}{\dfrac{1}{3y} - \dfrac{2}{3xy}}$.

13. $\dfrac{x-1}{1-\dfrac{2}{x+1}}.$

14. $\dfrac{a+3}{1+\dfrac{6}{a-3}}.$

15. $\dfrac{1-\dfrac{3v}{u+v}}{u-2v}.$

16. $\dfrac{2-\dfrac{w-z}{w-z}}{2w-3z}.$

17. $\dfrac{1-\dfrac{c}{b-c}}{1-\dfrac{3c}{b+c}}.$

18. $\dfrac{2-\dfrac{3q}{p+2q}}{2+\dfrac{5q}{p-2q}}.$

19. $\dfrac{1-\dfrac{3y}{3x+5y}}{1+\dfrac{6y}{3x-4y}}.$

20. $\dfrac{3-\dfrac{b}{a+b}}{\dfrac{3}{2}+\dfrac{13b}{2(2a-3b)}}.$

21. $\dfrac{1}{1-\dfrac{1}{1+\dfrac{1}{a}}}.$

22. $\dfrac{2}{1-\dfrac{1}{1+\dfrac{2}{x}}}.$

23. $\dfrac{4}{\dfrac{1}{1-\dfrac{4}{y}}-1}.$

24. $\dfrac{3}{\dfrac{1}{1-\dfrac{3}{b}}-1}.$

25. $\dfrac{x}{1-\dfrac{1}{1+\dfrac{x}{y}}}.$

26. $\dfrac{t}{\dfrac{1}{1-\dfrac{t}{3}}-1}.$

27. $\dfrac{2r}{1-\dfrac{1}{1+\dfrac{2r}{3s}}}.$

28. $\dfrac{5x}{1+\dfrac{1}{\dfrac{5x}{2y}-1}}.$

29. $\dfrac{x+1}{x-\dfrac{1}{1-\dfrac{4}{x+3}}}.$

30. $\dfrac{1-\dfrac{1}{a}}{1+\dfrac{1}{1+\dfrac{2}{a-2}}}.$

31. $\dfrac{ab}{ab+\dfrac{1}{\dfrac{1}{2a^2}-\dfrac{1}{2ab}}}.$

32. $\dfrac{x-y}{3x-\dfrac{y}{\dfrac{1}{4}+\dfrac{3y}{2(4x+2y)}}}.$

33. $\dfrac{1+\dfrac{1}{1-\dfrac{c}{d}}}{1-\dfrac{3}{1-\dfrac{c}{d}}}.$

34. $\dfrac{1-\dfrac{1}{2+\dfrac{u}{v}}}{1+\dfrac{3}{\dfrac{u}{v}-2}}.$

35. $\dfrac{2 - \dfrac{5}{1 - \dfrac{a}{b}}}{2 + \dfrac{1}{1 + \dfrac{a}{b}}}.$

36. $\dfrac{\dfrac{1}{2} - \dfrac{5}{2 + \dfrac{4w}{z}}}{\dfrac{1}{2} - \dfrac{3}{\dfrac{4w}{z} - 2}}.$

37. $\dfrac{1}{1 + \dfrac{1}{1 + \dfrac{1}{1 + \frac{1}{2}}}}.$

38. $\dfrac{1}{1 + \dfrac{1}{1 + \dfrac{1}{1 - \frac{1}{3}}}}.$

39. $\dfrac{1}{1 + \dfrac{1}{-1 + \dfrac{1}{1 - x}}}.$

40. $\dfrac{1}{1 + \dfrac{1}{1 + \dfrac{1}{1 + \dfrac{x}{y}}}}.$

32. Equations that involve fractions. If we multiply both members of an equation that involves fractions by the LCM of the denominators that occur, we obtain an equation that is free of fractions. We call this process *clearing the equation of fractions.* If the LCM is a constant, the cleared equation will have the same roots as the original. If the LCM involves the variable, the cleared equation may have solutions that are not roots of the original.

If only first powers of the unknown appear in the cleared equation, we can solve it by the method of Art. 5.

For the convenience of the reader, we shall list below the steps in the process of solving a fractional equation.

1. *Find the LCM of the denominators in the equation.*
2. *Multiply both members of the equation by this LCM.*
3. *Simplify the products thus obtained.*
4. *Transpose and collect terms.*
5. *Divide both members of the equation thus obtained by the coefficient of x, thus getting the solution.*
6. *Check by substituting this number for x in both members of the original equation and simplifying.*

EXAMPLE 1

Solve the equation $2x - \dfrac{5x}{6} - 1 = \dfrac{x}{2} + \dfrac{1}{3}.$

Solution

The numbers on the left below indicate the steps in the above process that we are using.

1. The LCM of the denominators is 6.
2. Multiplying through by the LCM, we obtain

$$6(2x) - 6\left(\frac{5x}{6}\right) - 6(1) = 6\left(\frac{x}{2}\right) + 6\left(\frac{1}{3}\right).$$

3. Simplifying by removing the parentheses, we have

$$12x - 5x - 6 = 3x + 2.$$

4. Transposing and collecting terms, we get

$$12x - 5x - 3x = 2 + 6,$$
$$4x = 8.$$

5. Dividing by the coefficient of x, we get

$$x = 2.$$

6. We check by substituting 2 for x in each member of the equation and obtain for the left member

$$2(2) - \left(\frac{5}{6}\right)(2) - 1 = 4 - \frac{5}{3} - 1 = \frac{12 - 5 - 3}{3} = \frac{4}{3},$$

and for the right member

$$\frac{2}{2} + \frac{1}{3} = 1 + \frac{1}{3} = \frac{3 + 1}{3} = \frac{4}{3}.$$

Hence, since both members are equal to $\frac{4}{3}$, $x = 2$ is a solution.

EXAMPLE 2

Solve the equation $\dfrac{4}{x - 1} - \dfrac{6 - 3x}{x(x - 1)} = 2 - \dfrac{2x - 3}{x}.$

Solution

1. The LCM of the denominators is $x(x - 1)$.

2. $\dfrac{x(x - 1)4}{x - 1} - \dfrac{x(x - 1)(6 - 3x)}{x(x - 1)} = x(x - 1)(2) - \dfrac{x(x - 1)(2x - 3)}{x}$.

3. $4x - (6 - 3x) = 2x(x - 1) - (x - 1)(2x - 3)$,

   $4x - 6 + 3x = 2x^2 - 2x - (2x^2 - 5x + 3)$,

   $4x - 6 + 3x = 2x^2 - 2x - 2x^2 + 5x - 3$.

4. $4x + 3x + 2x - 5x = -3 + 6$,

   $\qquad\qquad 4x = 3$.

5. $x = \frac{3}{4}$.

6. When we substitute $x = \frac{3}{4}$ in the left member of the original equation, we get

$$\dfrac{4}{\frac{3}{4} - 1} - \dfrac{6 - 3(\frac{3}{4})}{\frac{3}{4}(\frac{3}{4} - 1)} = \dfrac{16}{3 - 4} - \dfrac{96 - 36}{9 - 12} \qquad \text{(by the first method of Art. 31)}$$

$$= \dfrac{16}{-1} - \dfrac{60}{-3}$$

$$= -16 + 20 = 4.$$

Similarly, from the right member we have

$$2 - \dfrac{2(\frac{3}{4}) - 3}{\frac{3}{4}} = 2 - \dfrac{\frac{3}{2} - 3}{\frac{3}{4}} = 2 - \dfrac{6 - 12}{3} = 2 - \dfrac{-6}{3} = 2 + 2 = 4.$$

Hence, since the two members are equal, $x = \frac{3}{4}$ is a solution.

EXERCISE 16

Solve the following equations.

1. $\dfrac{5x}{4} - \dfrac{2x}{3} = \dfrac{7}{6}$.

2. $\dfrac{3x}{8} - \dfrac{2x}{3} = \dfrac{7}{12}$.

3. $\dfrac{5x}{6} = \dfrac{7x}{10} + \dfrac{4}{15}$.

4. $\dfrac{3x}{8} - \dfrac{2x}{9} - \dfrac{11}{12} = 0$.

5. $\dfrac{x}{5} - \dfrac{1}{4} = \dfrac{2x}{15} + \dfrac{1}{12}$.

6. $\dfrac{5x}{7} - \dfrac{1}{3} = \dfrac{9x}{14} + \dfrac{2}{21}$.

7. $\dfrac{7x}{2} + \dfrac{5}{6} = \dfrac{31x}{9} + \dfrac{2}{3}$.

8. $\dfrac{3x}{4} - \dfrac{5}{6} = \dfrac{2x}{3} - \dfrac{1}{2}$.

9. $\dfrac{3x - 2}{4} = \dfrac{5x}{6} - \dfrac{x}{3}$.

10. $\dfrac{2x - 5}{2} + \dfrac{3x}{4} = \dfrac{4x}{3}$.

11. $\dfrac{4x + 3}{3} + \dfrac{2x}{5} = \dfrac{19x}{10}$.

12. $\dfrac{5x - 2}{6} + \dfrac{7x}{8} - \dfrac{3x}{2} = 0$.

13. $\dfrac{4x + 1}{6} + \dfrac{3x}{4} = \dfrac{2x - 4}{3}.$

14. $\dfrac{3x - 5}{2} + \dfrac{5x - 29}{5} + \dfrac{4x}{15} = 0.$

15. $\dfrac{2x + 3}{4} + \dfrac{16x + 37}{12} = \dfrac{5x}{9}.$

16. $\dfrac{6x - 5}{3} - \dfrac{6x + 5}{6} = \dfrac{3x}{8}.$

17. $\dfrac{x + 5}{9} - \dfrac{2x + 2}{3} = x + 3.$

18. $\dfrac{4x - 3}{5} - \dfrac{3x - 2}{2} = 2x - 5.$

19. $\dfrac{6x - 1}{4} - 4x - 3 = \dfrac{10x + 1}{12}.$

20. $\dfrac{2x - 7}{6} = \dfrac{8x + 17}{18} + 5x + 3.$

21. $\dfrac{5x - 1}{3} - \dfrac{4x + 3}{4} = \dfrac{12x + 7}{12}.$

22. $\dfrac{2x + 3}{2} - \dfrac{5x - 2}{4} + \dfrac{4x + 3}{6} = 0.$

23. $\dfrac{3x - 1}{5} - \dfrac{5x + 3}{10} = \dfrac{x - 7}{15}.$

24. $\dfrac{2x - 3}{3} + \dfrac{x + 1}{12} = \dfrac{7x - 9}{9}.$

25. $\dfrac{1}{x} + \dfrac{2}{x + 4} = \dfrac{5}{3x}.$

26. $\dfrac{2}{3x} + \dfrac{6}{5x} = \dfrac{4}{2x + 1}.$

27. $\dfrac{3}{4x} = \dfrac{1}{12x} + \dfrac{2}{5x + 2}.$

28. $\dfrac{1}{2x} - \dfrac{7}{5x} + \dfrac{3}{2x - 3} = 0.$

29. $\dfrac{3}{3x + 2} + \dfrac{5x}{x + 3} = 5.$

30. $\dfrac{x}{x - 4} - \dfrac{4}{2x - 1} = 1.$

31. $\dfrac{x}{x + 3} + \dfrac{1}{x + 2} = 1.$

32. $\dfrac{3x}{x - 3} - \dfrac{27}{4x - 1} = 3.$

33. $\dfrac{3}{3x - 2} + \dfrac{3}{2x + 2} = \dfrac{5}{2x - 1}.$

34. $\dfrac{1}{x + 2} = \dfrac{2}{x - 1} - \dfrac{1}{x - 2}.$

35. $\dfrac{3}{2x - 3} - \dfrac{1}{2x - 1} = \dfrac{1}{x - 1}.$

36. $\dfrac{5}{3x + 1} = \dfrac{2}{3x - 1} + \dfrac{1}{x + 1}.$

37. $\dfrac{1}{x + 1} + \dfrac{1}{x + 4} = \dfrac{2}{x + 2}.$

38. $\dfrac{3}{x - 2} = \dfrac{2}{x - 1} + \dfrac{1}{x - 3}.$

39. $\dfrac{5}{2x - 2} = \dfrac{3}{2x - 1} + \dfrac{1}{x - 2}.$

40. $\dfrac{4}{x + 5} = \dfrac{3}{x + 6} + \dfrac{1}{x + 3}.$

41. $\dfrac{3x - 2}{4x + 3} + \dfrac{5x - 3}{2x - 2} = \dfrac{13}{4}.$

42. $\dfrac{3x - 8}{x - 2} + \dfrac{4x + 3}{2x - 1} = 5.$

43. $\dfrac{2x - 6}{3x - 1} - \dfrac{5x - 3}{4x + 3} = \dfrac{-7}{12}.$

44. $\dfrac{42x - 1}{6(6x - 5)} - \dfrac{4x + 3}{3x - 2} = -\dfrac{1}{6}.$

45. $\dfrac{2x + 1}{x - 2} - \dfrac{x - 1}{x + 2} = \dfrac{x^2 + x + 7}{x^2 - 4}.$

46. $\dfrac{3x + 2}{2x - 1} - \dfrac{3x - 1}{2x + 1} = \dfrac{5x + 15}{4x^2 - 1}.$

47. $\dfrac{3x + 4}{2x + 5} - \dfrac{5x^2 + 2x - 4}{6x^2 + 13x - 5} = \dfrac{2x - 3}{3x - 1}.$

48. $\dfrac{4x + 3}{3x - 2} - \dfrac{3x - 2}{2x + 5} + \dfrac{x^2 - 10x + 3}{6x^2 + 11x - 10} = 0.$

49. $\dfrac{x + 8}{(2x - 1)(x + 2)} + \dfrac{4x + 13}{x + 3} - \dfrac{8x - 1}{2x - 1} = 0.$

50. $\dfrac{3x + 2}{(x - 1)(x + 1)} - \dfrac{x + 1}{x - 1} + \dfrac{2x - 1}{2x + 1} = 0.$

51. $\dfrac{5x + 30}{(3x + 1)(x + 3)} - \dfrac{2x - 3}{x - 3} + \dfrac{6x + 6}{3x + 1} = 0.$

52. $\dfrac{3x + 1}{(x - 4)(2x - 5)} + \dfrac{x + 2}{x + 4} - \dfrac{2x - 6}{2x - 5} = 0.$

53. $\dfrac{2x + 4}{x + 1} + \dfrac{3x - 1}{x - 1} - \dfrac{10x + 13}{2x + 1} = 0.$

54. $\dfrac{8x - 15}{8(x - 2)} + \dfrac{x - 1}{x + 1} - \dfrac{16x + 17}{8(x + 2)} = 0.$

55. $\dfrac{6x - 5}{3(2x - 1)} + \dfrac{x - 2}{x - 1} - \dfrac{6x - 16}{3(x - 2)} = 0.$

56. $\dfrac{2x - 3}{2(x - 3)} + \dfrac{x + 3}{x + 2} - \dfrac{4x + 9}{2(x + 1)} = 0.$

57. $\dfrac{x}{x - 1} + \dfrac{x - 1}{x - 2} - \dfrac{2x - 4}{x - 3} = 0.$

58. $\dfrac{x + 7}{x + 1} + \dfrac{x - 2}{x + 2} - \dfrac{2x - 4}{x - 3} = 0.$

59. $\dfrac{x + 6}{x + 5} - \dfrac{2x - 1}{x - 4} + \dfrac{x + 4}{x - 2} = 0.$

60. $\dfrac{2x - 4}{x - 3} - \dfrac{x + 3}{x - 2} - \dfrac{x - 1}{x + 2} = 0.$

33. Problems leading to equations that involve fractions.
In Art. 6, we discussed methods for solving simple stated problems
by means of equations. As the problems become more difficult,
the equations for solving them grow more complicated. In this
article, we shall discuss problems which lead to fractional equations

and shall present examples illustrating various types of problems which often occur in this field.

1. *Work Problems.* Problems which involve the rate of doing certain things can often be solved by first finding the fractional part of the job done by each individual, or each agent, in one unit of time and then finding a relation between the fractional parts. When this method is used, the unit "one" represents the entire job that is to be done.

EXAMPLE 1

Mr. Brown can shingle a house in 5 days, and Mr. Smith can do it in $4\frac{1}{2}$ days. How long will it take them to shingle the house if they work together?

Solution

Let

x = the number of days required for both to shingle the house if they work together.

Then

$\dfrac{1}{x}$ = the part that both can shingle in 1 day.

Furthermore,

$\frac{1}{5}$ = the part that Mr. Brown can do in 1 day,

and

$\dfrac{1}{4\frac{1}{2}} = \dfrac{2}{9}$ = the part that Mr. Smith can do in 1 day.

Hence,

$$\frac{1}{5} + \frac{2}{9} = \frac{1}{x}.$$

Clearing of fractions, we have

$$9x + 10x = 45,$$
$$19x = 45,$$
$$x = 2\tfrac{7}{19} \text{ days.}$$

2. *Motion Problems Involving Uniform Rate.* Problems that involve uniform rate are usually solved by use of the formula

(1) $$D = RT,$$

where D represents distance, R represents rate, and T time. This formula can be solved for R or for T in order to obtain the following formulas:

(2)
$$R = \frac{D}{T}$$

and

(3)
$$T = \frac{D}{R},$$

respectively.   Problems involving these formulas usually state a relation between the times, the rates, or the distances involved.

EXAMPLE 2

A man must make a trip of 820 miles in exactly 7 hr.   If he travels part of the way in a plane at 200 miles per hr. and the remainder in a car at 55 miles per hr., find the distance traveled by each method.

Solution

In this problem, we know that the sum of the number of hours required for each part of the trip is 7.   Hence, we shall find an expression for the number of hours traveled in the plane and also the number traveled in the car; add these two and set the sum equal to 7.

Let

x = the number of miles traveled by plane.

Then

$820 - x$ = the number of miles by car.

Hence,

$\dfrac{x}{200}$ = the number of hours in the plane,

and

$\dfrac{820 - x}{55}$ = the number of hours in the car.

Therefore,

$$\frac{x}{200} + \frac{820 - x}{55} = 7.$$

If we clear of fractions by multiplying both members of the equation by the LCM of the denominators 2200, we get

$$11x + 32,800 - 40x = 15,400.$$

Hence,

$$-29x = -17,400,$$
$$x = 600 \text{ miles} \quad \text{(distance by plane)},$$

and

$$820 - 600 = 220 \text{ miles} \quad \text{(distance by car)}.$$

3. *Mixture Problems.* Many problems involve the combination of certain substances of known strengths, usually expressed in percentages, into a mixture of required strength in one of the substances. Others involve the mixing of certain commodities at a given price. In such problems, it should be remembered that the total amount of any given element in a mixture is equal to the sum of the amounts of that element in the substances combined, or that the value of any mixture is the sum of the values of the substances that are put together.

EXAMPLE 3

A man has a car with a 6-gal. radiator filled with a solution containing 10 per cent alcohol. He drains off a certain amount and replaces it with a solution that contains 70 per cent alcohol. How much was drained off if the solution then contained 20 per cent alcohol?

Solution

Here, the amount of alcohol in the radiator to start with minus the alcohol drained off plus the alcohol added is 20 per cent of 6 gal. In solving the problem, we shall express the percentage as decimal fractions.

$.10 \times 6 = .6$ gal. of alcohol in radiator originally.

Let

$x =$ the number of gallons drained off (also the number of gallons of 70 per cent solution added).

Then

$.10 \times x = .1x =$ the number of gallons of alcohol drained off,

and

$.70 \times x = .7x =$ the number of gallons of alcohol added.

Finally,

$.20 \times 6 = 1.2 =$ the number of gallons of alcohol at the end.

Hence,

$$.6 - .1x + .7x = 1.2.$$

We multiply each member by 10 to clear of fractions and get

$$6 - x + 7x = 12,$$
$$6x = 6,$$
$$x = 1 \text{ gal. (drained off).}$$

4. *Miscellaneous Problems.* Several problems in the exercise that is to follow cannot be classified as belonging to any one type, and only general directions can be given for solving them. The following example may be of assistance in understanding a method of attack.

EXAMPLE 4

A property owner fenced the front of two lots containing 7500 and 15,000 sq. ft., respectively. The total cost for the fencing was $137.50, and the price for the smaller lot was $1.25 per foot and for the larger $1 per foot. Find the dimensions of the lots if the depth of the smaller is $\frac{3}{4}$ that of the larger.

Solution

Let

$$x = \text{the depth of the larger lot.}$$

Then

$$\tfrac{3}{4}x = \text{the depth of the smaller lot.}$$

Furthermore,

$$\frac{7500}{\tfrac{3}{4}x} = \frac{10,000}{x} = \text{width of smaller lot,}$$

and

$$\frac{15,000}{x} = \text{width of larger.}$$

Hence,

$$1.25\left(\frac{10,000}{x}\right) + 1.00\left(\frac{15,000}{x}\right) = 137.50.$$

Clearing of fractions, we get

$$12,500 + 15,000 = 137.50x.$$

Hence,

$$137.50\,x = 27,500,$$
$$x = 200,$$
$$\tfrac{3}{4}x = 150.$$

Furthermore, $\frac{7500}{150} = 50$, and $\frac{15000}{200} = 75$. Therefore, the larger lot is 75 by 200 ft., and the smaller is 50 by 150 ft.

EXERCISE 17

1. Find the number such that the sum of $\frac{1}{3}$ and $\frac{1}{2}$ of it is 25.

2. Twice a number less $\frac{1}{2}$ of it is 18. Find the number.

3. If the difference between $\frac{2}{3}$ and $\frac{1}{4}$ of a number is 30, find the number.

4. One number is 3 times another, and $\frac{1}{2}$ their difference exceeds $\frac{1}{4}$ the larger number by 12. Find the numbers.

5. The difference between two numbers is 24, and their quotient is $\frac{3}{2}$. Find the numbers.

6. A certain number is added to 12 and subtracted from 36. Find the number if the quotient of the above sum and difference is 3.

7. Find a number such that its double divided by its excess over 8 is 10.

8. Find two numbers such that the larger is 1 less than twice the smaller and the quotient of their difference and sum is $\frac{3}{10}$.

Work Problems

9. A group of farm laborers picked a bale of cotton in 8 hr. Another group picked a bale in the same field in 12 hr. How long would it take the two groups working together to pick one bale?

10. A swimming pool has two intake pipes. One will fill the pool in 10 hr. and the other in 15 hr. If both pipes are open, how long will it take the pool to fill?

11. Two neighbors whose lots are equal in width spent 35 and 40 hr., respectively, building walls across the backs of their yards. How long will it take them to build a wall of equal length between their yards if they work together?

12. Joe polished $\frac{1}{3}$ of his car in 2 hr. He was then joined by Bob, and they finished the car in 2 more hours. How long would it have taken Bob to polish the car alone?

13. The editor can read the proof for the weekly edition of the college newspaper in $1\frac{1}{2}$ hr., and his assistant requires 2 hr. to read the same amount of proof. After they worked together for 30 min., the editor went to class, and the assistant finished the job. How long did it take him?

14. Two students, Jones and Brown, worked together for 3 hr. decorating a ballroom for a dance. Then Jones left, and Brown finished the work in 45 min. If Brown could have decorated the hall alone in 6 hr., how long would it have taken Jones to do it alone?

15. A lawn can be sprinkled with a $\frac{3}{4}$-in. hose in $1\frac{1}{3}$ hr. and with a $\frac{1}{2}$-in. hose in 2 hr.   A man sprinkled $\frac{1}{2}$ his lawn with the larger hose, and then his son joined him using the smaller.   How long did it take them to finish the job?

16. If Susan can make a dress in 3 days, Sarah in 2 days, and Sally in $1\frac{1}{2}$ days, how long would it take the three girls working together to make three dresses?

17. Three girls were on a committee to prepare a club supper.   Each of them could prepare the meal alone in 4 hr.   Jean started the work at 4 P.M.   Jane joined her at 4:30, and Janet came at 5 P.M.   What time was the supper ready?

18. A farmer can hoe a field of cotton in 6 days, his son can hoe the same field in 12 days, and the hired hand can hoe it in 8 days.   They started working in the field together, but after 1 day, the boy had to quit to start to school.   At the end of the third day the hired hand became ill.   How long did it take the farmer to finish the field?

19. An irrigation reservoir for a truck garden can be filled by the intake pipe in 6 hr. and emptied by the outlet in 8 hr.   How long would it take the reservoir to fill if both the intake and the outlet are open?

20. The intake pipe to a reservoir is controlled by an automatic valve that closes when the reservoir is full and opens again when $\frac{2}{3}$ of the water has been drained off.   The intake pipe can fill the reservoir in 8 hr., and the outlet can drain it in 12 hr.   If the outlet is open continuously, how much time elapses between two instants that the reservoir is full?

Motion Problems

21. A pilot flew from his home field to another at the rate of 180 miles per hr. and returned at the rate of 150 miles per hr.   If the outward trip required 1 hr. less time than the return trip, find the distance between the fields.

22. Two boys walked from their home to a boat landing on a lake and then crossed the lake in an outboard motorboat.   They walked at the rate of 3 miles per hr., and the boat moved at the rate of 12 miles per hr.   If the trip required 1 hr. and they traveled a distance of 6 miles, how far was it across the lake?

23. A passenger train left town A for town B 140 miles away at the same time that a freight left B for A, and the trains traveled on parallel tracks.   If the average speed of the passenger train was 64 miles per hr. and that of the freight was 48 miles per hr., how far were the trains from A when they met?

24. A rancher drove his truck to a town 60 miles away and returned with a load of supplies.   He spent 40 min. longer on the way home than on the way to town and drove $\frac{2}{3}$ as fast. How long did it take him to go to town?

25. A student going to his home 286 miles away rode 130 miles in a car and finished the trip on a bus. The speed of the bus was $\frac{4}{5}$ that of the car, and the second part of the trip required 1 hr. more than the first. How long did he ride in the car?

26. At 8 A.M. a salesman, traveling in a car, started for a town 280 miles away, where he had an appointment in the afternoon. He spent the first half of his traveling time going through mountainous country at an average speed of 45 miles per hr. He was then able to increase his speed to 60 miles per hr., and he finished the trip at this rate. How far did he travel in the mountains?

27. A boy walked from his home to the highway and then boarded a school bus and rode to a consolidated school that was 21 miles from his home. He walked at the rate of 3 miles per hr., and the bus averaged 30 miles per hr. If the entire trip required 1 hr. and there were no delays, find the distance that he walked.

28. A garage owner in Baton Rouge telephoned a wholesale house in Houston 245 miles away for a set of pistons. He learned that the pistons would be dispatched on a bus that would leave Houston at 11 A.M. The garage owner left Baton Rouge at 10 A.M., met the bus, and returned with the pistons, arriving at his garage at 4 P.M. Find the average speed of the car and that of the bus if the former was 10 miles per hr. greater than the latter.

29. A party of sportsmen traveled 160 miles on a paved highway and 120 miles on a graveled lane in order to reach their hunting camp and found that they had spent the same time on each part of the trip. Find their average speed on each road if they traveled 15 miles per hr. faster on the highway than on the lane.

30. A rancher drove from his headquarters to an airport at 45 miles per hr., waited 10 min., and continued his journey on a plane at 120 miles per hr. If the entire trip covered 240 miles and required 3 hr., find the distance from his headquarters to the airport.

31. A boy can paddle a canoe 3 miles downstream and 1 mile upstream in the same time. If the rate of the current is 2 miles per hr., find the rate of the canoe in still water.

32. A pilot flew from field A to field B that was 540 miles north of A, and the next day he continued his flight to field C that was 630 miles north of B. The wind blew from the north at the rate of 20 miles per hr. the first day and from the south at 10 miles per hr. the second. If the two parts of the trip required the same time, find the speed of the plane in still air.

Mixture Problems

33. How many quarts of distilled water must be added to 5 qts. of a solution that is 30 per cent nitric acid in order to obtain a 20 per cent solution?

34. How many quarts of alcohol must be added to 5 gal. of a solution that is 20 per cent alcohol in order to obtain a 30 per cent solution?

35. A 6-gal. radiator contains a solution that is 25 per cent antifreeze. How much must be drained off and replaced by pure antifreeze in order to obtain a solution that is $33\frac{1}{3}$ per cent antifreeze?

36. How many gallons of a 60 per cent hydrochloric acid solution must be added to 5 gal. of a 40 per cent solution in order to obtain a 50 per cent solution?

37. A dairy farmer mixed two grades of milk containing 3 and 5 per cent butterfat, respectively, in order to obtain 200 lb. of milk that contained $3\frac{1}{2}$ per cent butterfat. How many pounds of each grade were used?

38. After 20 lb. of milk containing 3 per cent butterfat was mixed with 30 lb. containing 4 per cent, a sufficient amount of cream that was 30 per cent butterfat was added to produce cereal cream that was 15 per cent butterfat. How many pounds of cream were added?

39. The radiator of a car developed a leak and a portion of the solution in it was lost. After the radiator was repaired, 2 gal. of a mixture of alcohol and water was required to fill it. If the capacity of the radiator was 5 gal. and the solution was 20 per cent alcohol before the leak and 30 per cent after it was refilled, find the percentage of alcohol in the solution added.

40. A man traveling in a car with a leaking radiator refilled it with water once on the trip. At the end of the trip 4 gal. of a solution that was 10 per cent alcohol was drained out in a repair shop. If the radiator held 5 gal. and was full of a solution that was 30 per cent alcohol at the start, how much water was added?

41. Two blocks of alloy containing 20 and 40 per cent silver, respectively, were melted together in order to produce 30 lb. of an alloy that was 35 per cent silver. How much did each block weigh?

42. A chemist mixed 20 cc. of a 20 per cent nitric acid solution with 30 cc. of a 15 per cent solution. He used a portion of the mixture and replaced it with distilled water. The new solution tested 13.6 per cent nitric acid. How much of the original mixture was used?

43. A portion of 12 bu. of a feed mix containing equal parts of corn chops, wheat, and maize was used. This was replaced by a mixture containing equal parts of corn chops and maize but no wheat. If $\frac{3}{8}$ of the new mixture was maize, how much of the original mix was used?

44. A block of metal containing 59 per cent copper was combined with 70 lb. of an alloy that was 83 per cent copper in order to obtain an alloy that was 73 per cent copper. How much did the first block weigh?

Miscellaneous Problems

45. Mr. Jones spent $\frac{1}{6}$ of his monthly salary for a suit of clothes and $\frac{1}{30}$ of it for a hat. If the suit and hat together cost $120, find his monthly salary.

46. After Joe traded Sam $\frac{1}{3}$ of his marbles for fishhooks, the latter had 3 times as many marbles as the former. If Sam had 50 marbles before the trade, how many did Joe have?

47. A carpenter sawed a piece of 2-by-4 lumber into three pieces. The first was 10 ft. in length, and the other two were, respectively, $\frac{1}{4}$ and $\frac{1}{3}$ as long as the original. Find the length of the piece before cutting.

48. One-fourth of the length of one of the posts of a barbed-wire fence is below the ground. The lower wire of the fence is 1 ft. from the ground, and the distance from the lower wire to the top of the post is $\frac{7}{12}$ of the length of the post. How long is the post?

49. A rancher has 2000 head of cattle in two pastures. Find the number in each if the number in the first is $\frac{3}{5}$ of that in the second.

50. Mr. Johnson bought a piece of land in 1930 for $25,600. In 1950, when the land had doubled in value, he sold a portion of it for $19,200 and had 800 acres left. Find the number of acres in the original piece and the price per acre paid for it.

51. A farmer received $3500 for a portion of his cotton crop and $1600 for the remainder. The number of bales in the first lot was twice that in the second, and the price per bale was $15 more. Find the number of bales in each lot.

52. A Sunday-school teacher was allotted $18 to buy Christmas presents for his class of boys. Before the presents were bought, two new boys joined the class, and, as a result, the teacher found that he must reduce the amount spent for each boy by $\frac{1}{4}$. How many boys were in the class originally?

53. A student purchased a textbook, a fountain pen, and a slide rule. The cost of the book was $\frac{1}{6}$ of the total bill, the cost of the pen was $4 more than that of the book, and the cost of the slide rule was twice that of the pen. Find the total amount spent.

54. A lot containing 7500 sq. ft. sold for $30 per front foot. Another lot $\frac{2}{3}$ as deep containing 6000 sq. ft. sold for $25 per front foot. Find the dimensions of each lot if the two sold for $3000.

55. A man who set aside $480 for a vacation found that the cost was $10 more per day than he expected, so he reduced his vacation time by

$\frac{1}{3}$ and thus saved $80. Find the length of the vacation as first planned and the expected cost per day.

56. When Mrs. James ordered $6 worth of cloth, the salesman found that if he filled her order, there would be only 3 yd. left in the bolt, so he proposed to reduce the price by 10 per cent and sell her the entire piece for $6.48. Find the number of yards Mrs. James intended to buy and the original price per yard.

CHAPTER 5

FUNCTIONS AND GRAPHS

34. Constants and variables. In Art. 1, we stated that the letters in a formula represent numbers. Some of these letters may represent values that never change, others may stand for quantities that do not change during a certain problem, and still others have values which vary within a certain range. For example, we shall consider the following problem:

Water is running into a cylindrical pail at the rate of 3 cubic inches per second. If the radius of the pail is 5 inches and its height is 10 inches, how fast is the water rising?

Since the water in the pail is in the form of a right circular cylinder, its volume is given by the formula

$$(1) \qquad\qquad V = \pi r^2 h,$$

in which $\pi = 3.1416$ (approximately), r is the radius, and h is the depth of the water. In this problem, $r = 5$, h varies from 0 to 10, and the value of π never changes. If we let t represent the number of seconds the water has been running, then the volume of water is $V = 3t$, and we have

$$(2) \qquad\qquad 3t = \pi(5)^2 h.$$

Now, since the rate at which the water rises is $\dfrac{h}{t}$, we solve (2) for h and get

$$(3) \qquad\qquad h = \frac{3t}{\pi(5)^2}.$$

Finally, dividing by t, we obtain

$$(4) \qquad\qquad \frac{h}{t} = \frac{3}{25\pi}.$$

Both letters on the left are constantly changing, but the values on the right are fixed. Hence, the value of the ratio $\frac{h}{t}$ is always the same.

This discussion illustrates the following definitions:

DEFINITION I.   *A variable is a symbol which represents a number that may vary within a given range.*

DEFINITION II.   *A constant is a symbol which represents a number that does not change in any discussion or situation.*

NOTE 1: The values of some symbols, such as π, 1, 2, 3, $\cdot$ $\cdot$ $\cdot$ never change, and these are called *absolute constants*.

NOTE 2: We frequently use a letter whose value is temporarily unknown, but which is fixed by the conditions of the problem. For example, in the equation

$$2x - 1 = 4x - 3$$

the value of x is unknown until the solution reveals that its value is 1.   Hence, in this problem, x is not a variable, but it is a constant whose value is to be determined.

35. Functions and functional notation.   If in (3) of Art. 34 we assign a value to t, the value of h is automatically fixed and can be calculated to as many decimal places as desired.   This situation is described mathematically by the statement "*h is a function of t,*" and it illustrates the following definition:

DEFINITION.   *One variable is a function of a second if at least one value of the first is determined whenever a value is assigned to the second.*

The variable to which values are assigned is called the *independent variable*, and the other is called the *dependent variable*.

Frequently functions are written without the dependent variable being explicitly shown.   For example, the expression $x^2 - 2x - 2$ is a variable since its value varies with x.   Furthermore, its value is determined whenever a definite number is assigned to x.   Hence, it is a function of x.   The statement "function of x" is often denoted by the symbol $f(x)$, which is read "f of x."   The letter enclosed in the parentheses is the independent variable in the function. Thus, if in a particular discussion, $f(x) = x^2 - 2x - 2$, then $f(z) = z^2 - 2z - 2$, $f(3) = 3^2 - 2(3) - 2$, and

$$f\left(\frac{1}{x}\right) = \left(\frac{1}{x}\right)^2 - 2\left(\frac{1}{x}\right) - 2.$$

If another function, such as $3x^2 - 1$, enters the same discussion, we may designate it by $F(x)$, $h(x)$, or by any letter other than f preceding (x).

EXAMPLES

1. If $f(x) = (x - 1)(x + 1)$, then $f(4) = (4 - 1)(4 + 1) = (3)(5) = 15$.
2. If $g(t) = 10t + 16t^2$, then $g(2) = 10(2) + 16(2)^2 = 84$, and $g(-1) = 10(-1) + 16(-1)^2 = 6$.
3. If $h(s) = s^3 - 3s - 2$, then $h(2) = 2^3 - 3(2) - 2 = 0$, and $h(3) = 3^3 - 3(3) - 2 = 16$.

EXERCISE 18

1. If $y(x) = 3x - 1$, find $y(4)$, $y(1)$, $y(\frac{1}{3})$, $y(-2)$.
2. If $h(x) = 2x + 7$, find $h(2)$, $h(\frac{1}{2})$, $h(0)$, $h(-3)$.
3. If $g(y) = 5y - 6$, find $g(3)$, $g(\frac{2}{5})$, $g(-3)$.
4. If $H(m) = -3m + 8$, find $H(4)$, $H(\frac{1}{3})$, $H(0)$, $H(-2)$.
5. If $q(x) = x^2 - 3x + 2$, find $q(2)$, $q(\frac{1}{2})$, $q(-1)$.
6. If $p(t) = 4t^2 + 2t - 1$, find $p(3)$, $p(\frac{1}{2})$, $p(-1)$.
7. If $s(a) = 2a^2 + 3a - 2$, find $s(8)$, $s(0)$, $s(\frac{1}{2})$.
8. If $M(s) = 6s^2 + 3s - 5$, find $M(\frac{1}{2})$, $M(0)$, $M(-2)$.
9. If $T(z) = \dfrac{2z^2 - z - 1}{z + 2}$, find $T(\frac{1}{2})$, $T(1)$, $T(-3)$.
10. If $F(b) = \dfrac{3b - 2}{6b^2 - 3b - 1}$, find $F(\frac{2}{3})$, $F(1)$, $F(-2)$.
11. If $N(T) = \dfrac{4T - 1}{T^2 + 2T - 1}$, find $N(\frac{1}{4})$, $N(0)$, $N(-3)$.
12. If $X(L) = \dfrac{3L^2 + 2L - 1}{2L - 3}$, find $X(\frac{1}{3})$, $X(-1)$, $X(2)$.
13. If $y(x) = 2x + 1$, find $y(a)$, $y(3b)$, $y(-2k)$.
14. If $T(p) = 5p - 2$, find $T(3a)$, $T(-a)$, $T(.2a)$.
15. If $f(a) = 3a - 4$, find $f(x)$, $f(2b)$, $f(-3c)$.
16. If $A(m) = 4m + 3$, find $A(2m)$, $A(3t)$, $A\left(\dfrac{s}{4}\right)$.
17. If $F(w) = 2w + 3$, find $F(x - 1)$, $F(2y - 3)$, $F(w - 2)$.
18. If $P(k) = 7k - 4$, find $P(t + 2)$, $P(a + 1)$, $P(k - 3)$.
19. If $S(a) = 2 - 3a$, find $S(b - 1)$, $S(k + 2)$, $S(a + 1)$.
20. If $J(c) = 3 + 2c$, find $J(a - 2)$, $J(2a + 1)$, $J(2c - 3)$.

21. If $X(y) = 3y + 2$, find $X(1) \div X(2)$.
22. If $y(z) = 5z - 1$, find $y(2) \times y(-1)$.
23. If $t(x) = 2x - 5$, find $t(x + 3) \div t(3x + 1)$.
24. If $L(s) = 3s - 4$, find $L(t + 1) \times L(t - 2)$.
25. If $q(x) = x^2 - 3x + 1$, find $q(y - 1)$, $q(2y + 1)$, $q(x + 1)$.
26. If $S(h) = 2h^2 + h - 1$, find $S(x - 2)$, $S(2y - 3)$, $S(h - 1)$.
27. If $I(w) = 3w^2 - 4w + 2$, find $I(b + 1)$, $I(y - 2)$, $I(a + 3)$.
28. If $h(x) = x^2 + 2x - 3$, find $h(2x + 1)$, $h(y - 3)$, $h(a - 1)$.
29. If $w(k) = k^2 - 3k + 2$, find $w(t + 1) \div w(2t - 1)$.
30. If $x(t) = t^2 + t$, find $x(1 - a) \div x(1 - 2a)$.
31. If $s(m) = m^2 + 2m - 3$, find $s(-x + 2) \div s(-5x + 2)$.
32. If $w(b) = b^2 - 5b - 6$, find $w(-2x + 1) \div w(5x + 1)$.

36. Graphical representation of functions. The manner in which a function varies as the independent variable changes is a subject of considerable importance in algebra. The behavior of a function can be studied very advantageously by means of a graph or a pictorial representation of the corresponding values of the variable and the function.

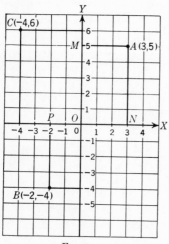

Fig. 2.

The graphical representation of functions depends upon a device known as the *rectangular coordinate system*. In order to set up such a system in a plane, we first select a horizontal and a vertical line in the plane and then choose a suitable scale on each. The horizontal line is called the *X-axis*, the vertical line is known as the *Y-axis*, and their intersection is called the *origin* (see Fig. 2). Next we shall agree that all horizontal distances measured to the right are positive, and all horizontal distances measured to the left are negative. Furthermore, all vertical distances directed upward are positive, and those directed downward are negative. Now we can see that every point in the plane determines two directed distances, namely, the directed distance from the Y-axis to the point and the directed distance from the X-axis to the point. This brings us to the following definition:

DEFINITION. *The **abscissa**, or **x-coordinate**, of a point in a plane is the directed distance from the Y-axis to the point. It is positive or negative according as the point is to the right or to the left of the Y-axis. The **ordinate**, or **y-coordinate**, of a point is the directed distance from the X-axis to the point, and it is positive or negative according as the point is above or below the X-axis.*

The abscissa and ordinate are called the *coordinates* of a point and are written as a pair of numbers enclosed in parentheses and separated by a comma. The abscissa is written first.

EXAMPLES

In Fig. 2, the abscissa of A is $MA = 3$ and the ordinate is $NA = 5$. Hence, we write the coordinates as $(3,5)$. Both coordinates are positive since A is to the right of the Y-axis and above the X-axis. Similarly, the coordinates of B are $(-2,-4)$.

We may locate the point C, whose coordinates are $(-4,6)$, by starting at O and counting 4 units to the left on the X-axis (Why?) and then 6 units upward.

When a point has been located by means of its coordinates, we say that the point has been *plotted*.

We are now in position to discuss the graphical representation of functions, and we shall illustrate the procedure by explaining the steps in the construction of the graph of $x^2 - 2x - 2$. We first let the function be represented by y and thus obtain

(1) $$y = x^2 - 2x - 2.$$

The next step is to assign several values to x and calculate each corresponding value of y. Before doing this, however, it is advisable to make a table like the one below in which the corresponding values of x and y can be recorded.

The values selected for x, in most cases, should be small, usually integers less than ten. In this case, we shall start with $x = 0$. Then let x equal $1, 2, 3$, and 4. Finally, let $x = -1$, and $x = -2$.

When $x = 0, y = (0)^2 - 2(0) - 2 = -2$;
$\quad\quad x = 1, y = (1)^2 - 2(1) - 2 = -3$;
$\quad\quad x = 2, y = (2)^2 - 2(2) - 2 = -2$.

This process is continued until the values of x mentioned above have been used. When a value is assigned to x, it should be recorded in the table and the corresponding value of y entered below it. The values of x should be entered in order of magnitude from left to right. When the value of y for each of the above values of x has been calculated and the results have been entered in the table, we have

x	-2	-1	0	1	2	3	4
y	6	1	-2	-3	-2	1	6

Now we take each pair of corresponding values of x and y as coordinates of a point and plot the points determined by the pairs of values in the above table. Finally, we connect the points thus determined by a smooth curve. Thus, we obtain the curve in Fig. 3. This curve is the graph of $x^2 - 2x - 2$, and it indicates the following facts about the behavior of the function:

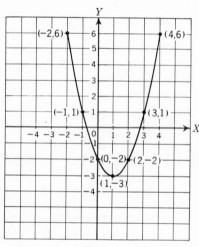

Fig. 3.

1. The value of the function is least, -3, when $x = 1$;

2. The value of the function increases rapidly both as x increases and decreases from 1;

3. The value of the function is zero when x is equal to the abscissas of the points where the graph crosses the X-axis or at $x = 2.7$ (approximately) and at $x = -.7$ (approximately).

A *zero* of a function is a value of the variable for which the function is zero. For example, the zero of $2x - 5$ is $x = 2\frac{1}{2}$. The zeros of many classes of functions can be obtained algebraically, but we must depend upon graphical methods for others. In the latter method, we construct the graph of the function and estimate the x-coordinate of each point where the graph crosses the X-axis. This estimate can be made as accurate as necessary by choosing a sufficiently large scale.

For the present, we shall be concerned with functions whose

graphs are curves of unlimited length. Hence, only a portion of the graph can be constructed, and we can usually obtain this portion by using comparatively small values of x. It is usually advisable to start with $x = 0$, assign several consecutive positive integral values to x, using a sufficient number of values to determine the general trend of the curve, and then proceed in a similar way by assigning consecutive negative values to x.

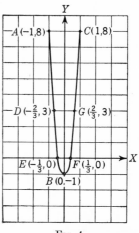

Fig. 4.

Some functions are such that the points obtained by assigning consecutive integral values to x are so far apart in the plane that we cannot tell how to draw the curve which connects them. For example, if we assign the values -1, 0, and 1 to x in the function $y = 9x^2 - 1$, we obtain the values 8, -1, and 8, respectively, for y and thus determine the points A, B, and C in Fig. 4. These points are not sufficient to determine the shape of the curve. However, by using $x = -\frac{2}{3}$, $x = -\frac{1}{3}$, $x = \frac{1}{3}$, and $x = \frac{2}{3}$, we obtain the additional points D, E, F, and G. Using these, together with A, B, and C, we can easily draw the curve.

On the other hand, we have functions that, for consecutive values of x, yield points that are clustered so closely together in the plane that only a small portion of the curve is determined. In such cases, instead of using consecutive integral values for x, we assign values that are more widely separated, probably numbers that differ by 2, 3, or 5. The idea is to use values for x that will yield a sufficient number of points so distributed in the plane that the approximate shape of the curve is determined. In the function $y = \dfrac{x}{5}$, the curve can be clearly defined by letting $x = -30$, -20, -10, 0, 10, 20, and 30.

37. Linear functions. A *linear function* of x is a function of the type $ax + b$ in which a and b are constants and a is not zero. It is proved in analytic geometry that the graph of a linear function is a straight line. Hence, the graph of a linear function is completely determined by two points. It is advisable, however, in obtaining the graph of such a function, to determine a third point as a check on the accuracy of the other two. It is also advisable to assign values to x that will determine points that are sufficiently far apart to determine accurately the direction of the graph.

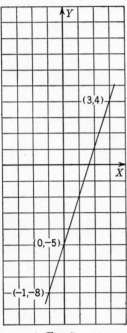

FIG. 5.

EXAMPLE

In order to construct the graph of $3x - 5$, we first set the function equal to y and obtain

$$(1) \qquad y = 3x - 5.$$

Now we assign the values -1, 0, and 3 to x and obtain the following table of corresponding values of x and y:

x	-1	0	3
y	-8	-5	4

When these points are plotted and connected by a straight line, we obtain the graph in Fig. 5.

If the three points obtained for the graph of a linear function do not lie along a straight line, one must check his computation, for certainly at least one error has been made.

EXERCISE 19

1. Plot the following points: $(3,2)$, $(-4,1)$, $(-2,-3)$, $(5,-1)$, $(2,0)$, $(0,3)$, $(4,-3)$, $(-6,3)$, $(7,-2)$, $(-5,0)$.

2. Plot the following points: $(3,-2)$, $(4,1)$, $(7,3)$, $(0,6)$, $(-5,-4)$, $(0,0)$, $(5,-3)$, $(-7,6)$, $(4,0)$, $(-8,-3)$.

3. State the quadrant in which each of the following points is located if k is positive: $(4,k)$, $(k,-3)$, (k^2,k), $(-k,k^3)$, $(k,-k)$, $(-k^2,-k)$.

4. State the quadrant in which each of the following points is located if k is negative: (k,k), $(-k,k)$, $(-k^2,-k)$, $(-k^3,k^2)$, $(k,-k)$, $(k^2,-k^2)$.

Plot the graphs of the functions given below and estimate the zero or zeros of each.

5. $y = 3x - 2$.   **6.** $y = 2x + 1$.   **7.** $y = -4x + 1$.

8. $y = 5x + 3$.   **9.** $y = -x + 3$.   **10.** $y = -2x - 1$.

11. $y = \frac{2}{3}x - 7$.   **12.** $y = -\frac{1}{2}x + 4$.   **13.** $x^2 - 4x + 2$.

14. $x^2 + 2x - 3$.   **15.** $x^2 - 3x + 1$.   **16.** $x^2 - 5x + 3$.

17. $2x^2 + 5x - 3$.   18. $x^2 + 5x + 2$.   19. $3x^2 - 6x + 2$.
20. $2x^2 + 4x + 1$.   21. $-x^2 - 2x$.   22. $-x^2 + 4x + 1$.
23. $-2x^2 + 6x + 5$.   24. $-2x^2 + 8x - 7$.

38. *Graphical representation of statistics.* Many tables of statistics or tables of scientific data set forth a set of related numbers. The information is usually written in two columns with corresponding quantities on the same horizontal line. For example, the following table shows the postal receipts for a small town for a period of 20 years:

Year	Postal receipts	Year	Postal receipts
1928	$5500	1938	$4800
1929	6000	1939	4600
1930	5700	1940	4600
1931	4800	1941	5000
1932	4400	1942	6300
1933	4000	1943	7900
1934	4400	1944	8600
1935	4400	1945	9000
1936	4400	1946	7300
1937	4800	1947	8400

This table establishes a functional relationship between two variables, the year and the postal receipts, since if any year between 1927 and 1948 is specified, the amount of the postal receipts is definitely determined and can be ascertained by looking at the table. This functional relationship is in no sense mathematical, and no mathematical formula exists that connects the two quantities. We can, however, use an adaptation of the previously discussed graphing method to obtain a graphical representation of these data. For this purpose, we choose a horizontal line in the plane and lay off 19 equal intervals on it (see Fig. 6), and let the successive left ends of each interval represent the years taken in order from 1928 to 1946, and the right end of the last interval represent 1947. Through the left end of the first interval, we draw a vertical line and lay off on it intervals of equal length whose upper extremities, taken in order, represent successive multiples of $1000. If graph paper is used, it is advisable to choose 10 of the shortest units on the paper as the length of each of the above intervals. Then the upper extremities of the short units represent multiples of $100. Now with respect to these two lines as axes, we may plot a point representing each year and the corresponding amount of the postal receipts listed in the table. For example, the point A represents the $5500 for 1928, and the points B, C, and D represent the amounts for 1931, 1934, and 1942, respectively. When the plotted points are joined by a curve, we obtain the graph in Fig. 6. While this curve is in no sense algebraic, it is a decided visual aid in interpreting the data. We notice at once the steady decline from 1929 to 1933, the leveling

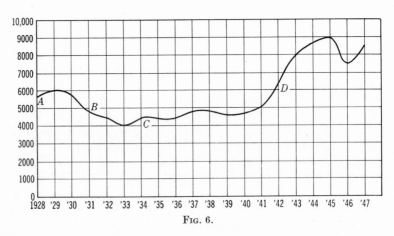

Fig. 6.

off from 1933 to 1940, and the sharp increase from 1941 to 1945. We would expect these decided trends since they occurred during the depression years, the period of recovery, and the war years, respectively.

The following table of values shows a set of readings from an exposure meter. The left column shows the measurement of the light intensity, and the right, the corresponding exposure time in seconds necessary to get a good picture with a camera using a given lens opening and a certain type of film.

Light intensity	Exposure in seconds
600	.0025
400	.004
300	.0057
200	.0087
150	.011
100	.017
75	.022
50	.033
25	.067

Figure 7 shows the graph of these data.   In this case, we obtain a smooth and regular curve, and this suggests that the length of the exposure might be a mathematical function of the light intensity.   In fact, it is, but the method of obtaining this relationship will not be discussed here.   We can use the curve, however, to obtain the exposure corresponding to light intensities not shown in the table.   For example, the exposure corresponding to the light intensity of 175 is approximately .009.

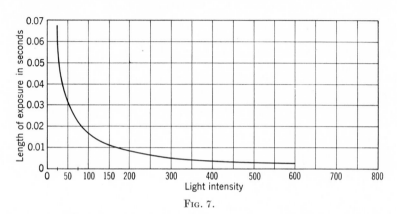

Fig. 7.

The graph of scientific data frequently leads to the discovery of a law.   When the curve is regular, advanced methods enable us to find an equation that fits the curve, or at least a portion of it. When we obtain the equation, we have the law governing the situation.

EXERCISE 20

1. The minimum number of calories needed per day by a boy of a given age is indicated in the table below.   Construct a graph showing this information.

Age	Calories	Age	Calories
8	1700	13	2500
9	1900	14	2600
10	2100	15	2700
11	2100	16	2700
12	2300	17	2800

2. The following table shows the pressure in centimeters of mercury

of saturated water vapor at the indicated centigrade temperature. Construct a graph showing this information.

Temperature	Pressure	Temperature	Pressure
0	0.46	60	14.9
10	0.92	80	35.5
20	1.75	100	76.0
30	3.17	120	148.9
40	5.51	140	270.9

3. The table below gives the normal weight of a man of age 30 years with the indicated height. Show this information graphically.

Height in inches	Weight in pounds	Height in inches	Weight in pounds
60	126	68	152
61	128	69	156
62	130	70	161
63	133	71	166
64	136	72	172
65	140	73	178
66	144	74	184
67	148	75	190

4. The osmotic pressure at the indicated concentration of a sucrose solution at 0°C. is given below. The concentration is given in moles per 1000 g., and the pressure is in atmospheres. Show this information graphically.

Concentration	Pressure	Concentration	Pressure
0.1	2.462	0.6	14.381
0.2	4.723	0.8	19.476
0.4	9.443	1.0	24.826

5. In the table below, the left column represents the temperature in degrees Fahrenheit and the right column the corresponding development time in minutes required to obtain a negative of required density from a certain type of film. Construct a graph showing these data.

Temperature	Time	Temperature	Time
55	15	75	7.4
60	12.8	80	6
65	10.9	85	4.5
70	9	90	3.6

6. The spectrophotometric curve for hydroquinone is made by using the wave length as the abscissa of a point and the corresponding density as the ordinate. Construct the curve from the data given below.

Wave length	Density	Wave length	Density
245	.01	260	.033
247	.03	264	.044
249	.02	270	.077
251	.01	280	.168
253	.03	288	.221
257	.033	300	.148

7. The following table shows the distance that a car traveling at the indicated speed will move after the brakes are applied. Show this information graphically.

Speed in miles per hour	Distance in feet	Speed in miles per hour	Distance in feet
10	29	60	230
20	39	70	300
30	70	80	380
40	110	90	470
50	160	100	560

8. In the following table, the left column indicates the measurement of light intensity and the right the corresponding exposure time in seconds necessary to get a good negative using a given lens opening and a certain type of film. Construct a graph showing this information.

Light intensity	Exposure time	Light intensity	Exposure time
10	.25	200	.0125
25	.1	400	.007
50	.05	600	.005
100	.025	800	.003

9. The following table shows the population (in millions) of the United States at intervals of 20 years from 1790 to 1930. Represent this information graphically.

Year	Population	Year	Population
1790	3.9	1870	38.6
1810	7.2	1890	62.9
1830	12.9	1910	92.0
1850	23.2	1930	122.8

10. The table below gives the number of divorces per **10,000** people in the United States granted in the indicated year. Construct the graph of these data.

Year	Divorces	Year	Divorces
1887	0.5	1922	1.4
1894	0.6	1929	1.7
1901	0.8	1936	1.8
1908	0.9	1943	2.6
1915	1.0	1950	2.9

11. The number of millions of pupils enrolled in the schools of the United States at intervals of **10** years from 1880 to 1950 is indicated in the table below. Construct the graph showing this information.

Year	Pupils	Year	Pupils
1880	9.9	1920	21.6
1890	12.7	1930	25.7
1900	15.5	1940	25.4
1910	17.8	1950	24.1

12. The following table gives the number of millions of motor vehicles in the United States at intervals of **2** years from 1936 to 1948. Construct the graph of these data.

Year	Vehicles	Year	Vehicles
1936	26.4	1944	30.5
1938	30.5	1946	34.4
1940	31.1	1948	41.2
1942	30.0		

13. The table below gives the number of passenger cars produced in the United States at intervals of **2** years from 1936 to 1948. Construct a graph showing this information.

Year	Cars	Year	Cars
1936	3.7	1944	0.0006
1938	2.0	1946	2.1
1940	3.7	1948	3.9
1942	0.2		

14. The number of millions of ounces of silver mined in the United States during the indicated year is given in the table below. Show this information graphically.

Year	Production	Year	Production
1920	55.4	1940	69.6
1925	66.1	1942	55.9
1930	50.7	1944	35.6
1935	45.9	1946	21.1

15. The salt production in the United States in millions of tons for the indicated year is given in the following table.   Construct the graph showing this information.

Year	Production	Year	Production
1941	12.7	1945	15.4
1942	13.7	1946	15.1
1943	15.2	1947	16.1
1944	15.7		

16. The number of thousands of families provided with new housing in the United States from 1930 to 1943 is given in the table below.   Show this information graphically.

Year	Families	Year	Families
1930	125	1937	117
1931	98	1938	157
1932	27	1939	203
1933	26	1940	221
1934	21	1941	232
1935	55	1942	143
1936	114	1943	115

CHAPTER 6

SIMULTANEOUS LINEAR EQUATIONS

39. *Linear equations in two unknowns.* If the dependent variable appears explicitly in a functional relationship, we have an equation in two unknowns. For example, the statement

$$(1) \qquad\qquad y = \tfrac{3}{4}x - 5$$

not only exhibits y as a linear function of x, but it also asserts that two quantities are equal, and hence it is an equation. Any pair of numbers, one for x and the other for y, for which the two members of (1) are equal is a *solution* of the equation. We can obtain as many solutions of (1) as we please by simply assigning values to x and then computing each corresponding value of y. Obviously, the coordinates of any point on the graph of (1) constitute a solution.

By Axioms I, II, and III of Art. 5, we know that any solution of (1) is also a solution of

$$(2) \quad 4y = 3x - 20 \qquad \text{[obtained by multiplying each member}$$
$$\text{of (1) by 4]}$$

and also of

$$(3) \quad 3x - 4y = 20. \qquad \text{(obtained by transposing } 3x \text{ and dividing}$$
$$\text{by } -1)$$

If each solution of a given equation is also a solution of a second equation and the second has no other solutions, we say that the two equations are *equivalent*.

In the next three articles, we shall discuss equations described in the following definition:

DEFINITION. *An equation that is equivalent to one of the type* $ax + by = c$, *where a, b, and c are constants, is called a* **linear equation in two unknowns**.

40. *Solution of two linear equations in two unknowns—graphical method.* We stated in the previous article that a linear equation in two unknowns has infinitely many solutions. Usually, however, only one pair of values will satisfy two such equations simultaneously. This pair of values is called the *solution* of the two equations.

Since the coordinates of any point on the graph of a linear equation in two unknowns satisfy the equation, the coordinates of the point of intersection of the graphs of two such equations form the solution of the two. This point is obtained by sketching the graphs of the two equations as in Art. 37 and then estimating the coordinates of their point of intersection.

EXAMPLE

Solve the equations

(1) $$3x + 2y = 14$$
(2) $$2x - y = 2$$

graphically.

Solution

First, we solve (1) and (2) for y and obtain

(3) $$y = -\tfrac{3}{2}x + 7$$

and

(4) $$y = 2x - 2.$$

Now, using the method of Art. 37, we assign the values -2, 0, and 4 to x in (3) and -3, 0, and 3 to x in (4) and obtain the following tables of corresponding values of x and y:

x	-2	0	4
y	10	7	1

from (3)   and

x	-3	0	3
y	-8	-2	4

from (4).

When we plot the points determined by these two tables and draw the graphs, we obtain Fig. 8. These graphs intersect at the point whose coordinates are approximately (2.6, 3.2). Hence, we say that, according to our graph, the solution of equations (1) and (2) is $x = 2.6$ and $y = 3.2$. This is as accurate as we can get the solution without using a larger scale. If we substitute these values in the left member of (1), we get

$$3(2.6) + 2(3.2) = 7.8 + 6.4 = 14.2.$$

Similarly, for the same values of x and y, the left member of (2) becomes

$$2(2.6) - 3.2 = 5.2 - 3.2 = 2.$$

Since the right members of (1) and (2) are 14 and 2, respectively, we see

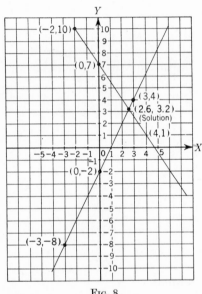

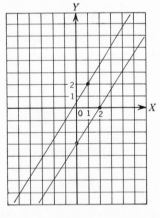

FIG. 8.   FIG. 9.

that the pair of values $x = 2.6$, $y = 3.2$, is not the exact solution of the two equations, but, to one decimal place, these values are probably correct.

It may happen that the graphs of two linear equations are parallel lines. For example, the graphs of the equations

(5) $\qquad\qquad\qquad 3x - 2y = 6$

and

(6) $\qquad\qquad\qquad 9x - 6y = -3$

shown in Fig. 9 are parallel lines. Hence, the equations have no solution. This fact can be seen algebraically if one observes that the left member of (6) is exactly 3 times the left member of (5). Hence, any pair of values which makes the left member of (5) equal to 6 makes the left member of (6) equal to 18, and not -3.

Again, we might have two equations whose graphs coincide. Then every pair of values which satisfies the first equation also satisfies the second, and the pair of equations has an infinite number of solutions.

If two equations in two unknowns have one and only one solution, they are called *consistent equations*. If they have no solution, they are called *inconsistent equations*, and if they have an infinite number of solutions, they are called *dependent equations*.

Although the graphical approach helps us to understand the above three types of pairs of linear equations, it is not an efficient method for obtaining the solution when one exists. In the first place, it is too cumbersome. In the second, the accuracy of the method depends upon the solver's skill in constructing the two graphs and in estimating the coordinates of their point of intersection. The two algebraic methods which we shall next present can be performed more easily and they yield the solution, when it exists, with absolute accuracy.

EXERCISE 21

Find the solutions of the following pairs of equations to one decimal place using the graphical method. Identify the pairs that are inconsistent and those that are dependent.

1. $2x + 3y = 9$
   $2x - y = 5.$

2. $x + 2y = -1$
   $3x + 2y = 5.$

3. $2x + y = 1$
   $4x - 2y = -10.$

4. $x + 2y = 8$
   $3x + y = 14.$

5. $2x + y = 3$
   $4x - 2y = -2.$

6. $x + 4y = 8$
   $3x + 2y = 9.$

7. $x + 2y = 2$
   $2x - 2y = 1.$

8. $2x + 2y = 11$
   $2x - 3y = -4.$

9. $x + 3y = 4$
   $x + 6y = 1.$

10. $2x + y = 6$
    $2x - 2y = 10.$

11. $x + 2y = 4$
    $3x + 6y = -2.$

12. $3x - 3y = 4$
    $3x - 3y = -4.$

13. $x + 4y = 2$
    $3x + 12y = 6.$

14. $4x - 2y = 6$
    $6x - 3y = 9.$

15. $6x + 3y = 4$
    $4x + 6y = 12.$

16. $x + 4y = 15$
    $2x + 2y = 10.$

17. $4x + 2y = 2$
    $6x + 3y = -3.$

18. $6x - 9y = 4$
    $4x - 6y = 6.$

19. $7x + 2y = 14$
    $7x + 5y = 21.$

20. $4x - 6y = 12$
    $6x + 3y = 26.$

21. $5x - 2y = 5$
    $6x + 3y = 12.$

22. $x + 4y = 11$
    $4x - 2y = 16.$

23. $4x + 2y = 6$
    $6x + 3y = 9.$

24. $9x - 12y = 18$
    $6x - 8y = 12.$

25. $4x + y = -1$
  $2x + y = 0.$
26. $2x + 3y = 1$
  $4x + 3y = -4.$
27. $3x + 4y = 12$
  $x - y = 1.$
28. $3x - 2y = 6$
  $3x - 2y = -6.$
29. $2x - 5y = 10$
  $x + 2y = -2.$
30. $3x - 6y = 4$
  $2x - 4y = 3$
31. $7x - 5y = 3$
  $5x + 7y = 2.$
32. $3x - 9y = 6$
  $2x + y = 4.$

41. Elimination of a variable by addition or subtraction. In order to solve two linear equations in two unknowns, we first *eliminate* one of the variables. That is, we obtain from the two given equations a third equation in one unknown whose solution is one of the values sought. We then substitute this value in one of the given equations and solve for the other unknown. Probably the method most often used is the one known as *elimination by addition or subtraction*, and we shall explain the process by applying it to the equations

(1) $$2x - 3y = 6$$
(2) $$3x + 2y = 12.$$

We assume at the start that there is a value of x and an associated value of y that will satisfy both of these equations. Then, by Axiom II of Art. 5, the same pair of values will satisfy

(3) $4x - 6y = 12$ [obtained by multiplying each member of (1) by 2]
(4) $9x + 6y = 36.$ [obtained by multiplying each member of (2) by 3]

Furthermore, by Axiom I of Art. 5, the equation obtained by adding the corresponding members of (3) and (4) will also be satisfied by the same pair of values. However, this addition yields

(5) $$13x = 48,$$

which contains only one variable x, and the solution is

(6) $$x = \tfrac{48}{13}.$$

This is the value of x sought. We can complete the process by substituting $\tfrac{48}{13}$ for x in either of the given equations and then solving for y. If we use Eq. (1), we get

$$2(\tfrac{48}{13}) - 3y = 6$$

or

$$\tfrac{96}{13} - 3y = 6.$$

Transposing $\tfrac{96}{13}$, we get

$$-3y = 6 - \tfrac{96}{13}$$
$$= \frac{78 - 96}{13}$$
$$= -\tfrac{18}{13}.$$

Hence,

$$y = -\tfrac{18}{13} \div (-3)$$
$$= \tfrac{6}{13}.$$

Therefore, the solution is $x = \tfrac{48}{13}$, $y = \tfrac{6}{13}$.

Since we used equation (1) to obtain the value of y, the above solution will satisfy (1) unless an error was made in computation. However, if the solution satisfies (2), we can be reasonably certain that it is correct. For the above values of x and y, the left member of (2) becomes

$$3(\tfrac{48}{13}) + 2(\tfrac{6}{13}) = \tfrac{144}{13} + \tfrac{12}{13} = \tfrac{156}{13} = 12.$$

Hence, since the right member of (2) is 12, the solution checks.

We could have solved this problem with about the same amount of computation if we had started by eliminating x instead of y. Often, however, the process of elimination will be slightly longer for one variable than for the other. Hence, it is advisable to study the problem before starting, so as to select the method that will involve the least amount of computation.

The steps in the solution of two linear equations in two unknowns may be summarized as follows:

1. *Select the unknown that will be easier to eliminate.*
2. *Find the LCM of the two coefficients of this unknown.*
3. *Multiply both members of each equation by the quotient of the above LCM and the coefficient of the selected variable in that equation.*
4. *Add or subtract the corresponding members of the equations obtained in Step 3 according as the terms containing the selected unknown have unlike or like signs.*
5. *Solve the resulting equation for the variable that remains.*
6. *Substitute the value obtained in Step 5 in one of the given equations and solve for the other unknown.*

7. *Write as the solution, x = _____, y = _____, filling the blanks with the values obtained in Steps 5 and 6.*

8. *Check by substituting the values of Step 7 in the original equation not used in Step 6.*

EXAMPLE

Solve the equations

$$(7) \qquad\qquad 4x - 11y = -3$$
$$(8) \qquad\qquad 6x + 7y = 19.$$

Solution

The least common multiples of the coefficients of x and of y are 12 and 77, respectively. Hence, we shall introduce smaller numbers if we eliminate x instead of y.

If we divide 12 by 4 and then by 6, we get 3 and 2, respectively. Hence, we multiply both members of (7) by 3, and both members of (8) by 2 and get

$$(9) \qquad\qquad 12x - 33y = -9$$
$$(10) \qquad\qquad 12x + 14y = 38.$$

Since the terms involving x have the same sign, we subtract (10) from (9) and get

$$(11) \qquad\qquad -47y = -47.$$

Hence,

$$y = 1.$$

Substituting $y = 1$ in (7), we get

$$(12) \qquad\qquad 4x - 11 = -3.$$

Therefore,

$$4x = 11 - 3 = 8$$

and

$$x = 2.$$

Hence, the solution is $x = 2$, $y = 1$.

Since Eq. (7) was used in the process of obtaining the value of x, we must check our solution by the use of (8). When $x = 2$ and $y = 1$, the left member of (8) becomes

$$6(2) + 7(1) = 12 + 7 = 19.$$

Hence, since the right member of (8) is 19, the solution checks.

42. *Elimination of a variable by substitution.* We shall list below the steps in the method of elimination by substitution, and then we shall illustrate the application of these steps by means of two examples. For the sake of definiteness, we shall assume that y is the variable to be eliminated. However, the directions below can be used for the elimination of x by interchanging x and y in each of the following steps:

1. *Solve one of the equations for y in terms of x.*
2. *Substitute this linear function of x for y in the other equation, thus obtaining an equation that contains only the unknown x.*
3. *Solve the latter equation for x.*
4. *Substitute this value of x in the function obtained in Step 1, and then calculate the value of y.*
5. *State the solution as $x = $ _____, $y = $ _____, filling the blanks with the values obtained in Steps 3 and 4.*
6. *Check by substituting the solution in the equation not used in Step 1.*

EXAMPLE 1

Solve the equations

(1) $$5x + 3y = 13$$
(2) $$3x - y = 5$$

simultaneously.

Solution

1. We note here that if we solve Eq. (2) for y, we do not obtain fractions. If this is done, we get

(3) $$y = 3x - 5.$$

2. Next we substitute $3x - 5$ for y in Eq. (1) and get

$$5x + 3(3x - 5) = 13.$$

3. Solving this equation, we have

$$5x + 9x - 15 = 13,$$
$$14x = 28,$$
$$x = 2.$$

4. Now we substitute 2 for x in Eq. (3) and obtain

$$y = 3(2) - 5$$

and

$$y = 1.$$

5. Hence, the solution is $x = 2$, $y = 1$.

6. Since we used Eq. (2) in Step 1, we shall check by substituting the above solution in the left member of Eq. (1). Thus, we get

$$5(2) + 3(1) = 10 + 3 = 13.$$

Hence, since the right member of (2) is 13, the solution checks.

EXAMPLE 2

Solve the equations

(4) $6x + 5y = 13$
(5) $7x - 4y = 25$

simultaneously.

Solution

1. Since we cannot avoid fractions in the first step in the solution of these two equations, it makes little difference which equation we start with or which unknown we solve for. Hence, we shall arbitrarily start with (4) and solve it for x and obtain

(6) $x = \dfrac{13 - 5y}{6}.$

2. When the right member of (6) is substituted for x in (5), we have

(7) $7\left(\dfrac{13 - 5y}{6}\right) - 4y = 25.$

3. Clearing (7) of fractions by multiplying each of its members by 6, we have

$$7(13 - 5y) - 24y = 150$$

or

$$91 - 35y - 24y = 150.$$

Combining and transposing, we have

$$-59y = 150 - 91$$
$$= 59.$$

Hence,

$$y = -1.$$

4. Substituting -1 for y in (6), we have

$$x = \frac{13 - 5(-1)}{6}$$
$$= \frac{13 + 5}{6}$$
$$= 3.$$

5. Hence, the solution is $x = 3$, $y = -1$.

6. Now we check by substituting this solution in the left member of (5) and get

$$7(3) - 4(-1) = 25.$$

Hence, since the right member of (5) is 25, the solution checks.

EXERCISE 22

Solve the pair of equations in each of Problems 1 to 16 by the method of addition or subtraction.

1. $2x + y = 5$
   $3x - 2y = -3.$

2. $2x + 5y = 9$
   $4x - y = 7.$

3. $3x - 6y = -3$
   $x + 3y = 9.$

4. $4x + 4y = 20.$
   $2x - y = 7.$

5. $3x + 2y = 16$
   $2x - 3y = -11.$

6. $5x + 3y = 27$
   $3x - 4y = -7.$

7. $7x + 5y = 50$
   $3x + 4y = 27.$

8. $3x + 6y = 36$
   $5x + 4y = 18.$

9. $2x + 2y = 5$
   $2x - y = 2.$

10. $3x + 4y = 15$
    $6x - 12y = -5.$

11. $4x - 9y = -11$
    $6x - 12y = -13.$

12. $2x - 4y = -5$
    $6x + 12y = 36.$

13. $\frac{1}{4}x + \frac{1}{3}y = 2$
    $\frac{3}{2}x - \frac{2}{3}y = 4.$

14. $\frac{2}{5}x + \frac{3}{2}y = 8$
    $\frac{3}{5}x - \frac{1}{4}y = 2.$

15. $\frac{2}{3}x + y = 10$
    $\frac{3}{4}x - 3y = 3.$

16. $x + \frac{5}{6}y = 18$
    $2x - \frac{2}{9}y = 2.$

Solve the pair of equations in each of Problems 17 to 32 by substitution.

17. $3x - y = 9$
    $4x + 3y = 25.$

18. $x + 2y = -2$
    $3x + 5y = -9.$

19. $2x + 5y = 11$
    $5x - y = 14.$

20. $x + 4y = 13$
    $2x - 3y = 4.$

21. $3x + 2y = 4$
    $4x + 3y = 5.$

22. $5x + 3y = -1$
    $3x + 4y = 6.$

23. $6x + 7y = 4$
    $5x + 3y = 10.$

24. $4x + 3y = 10$
    $3x - 2y = 16.$

25. $3x + 6y = 9$
    $6x - 12y = -2.$

26. $8x + 3y = 8$
    $12x + 12y = 17.$

27. $2x + 3y = 10$
    $4x + 9y = 27.$

28. $18x + 24y = 19$
    $12x + 9y = 8.$

29. $\frac{1}{3}x + \frac{3}{4}y = 5$
    $x - y = 2.$

30. $\frac{3}{5}x + \frac{2}{3}y = 5$
    $2x - 3y = 1.$

31. $\frac{1}{2}x + \frac{4}{5}y = 6$
    $2x - y = 3.$

32. $\frac{2}{3}x + \frac{1}{2}y = 5$
    $4x - 3y = -6.$

Solve the pair of equations in each of Problems 33 to 52 by either method.

33. $\dfrac{x + y}{3} + \dfrac{y}{2} = 4$
    $3x - y = 2.$

34. $\dfrac{x}{4} + \dfrac{x - 3y}{6} = \dfrac{3}{4}$
    $2x + 2y = 8.$

35. $\dfrac{x + y}{8} + \dfrac{2x - 3y}{4} = 1\tfrac{1}{4}$

$2x - y = 7.$

36. $\dfrac{2x - y}{3} + \dfrac{x + y}{4} = 2$

$3x + 2y = 24.$

37. $\dfrac{x - 2y + 1}{2x - 5y + 2} = 2$

$x - 2y = 1.$

38. $\dfrac{2x - y + 3}{3x - y + 2} = \dfrac{1}{2}$

$7x - 2y = 2.$

39. $\dfrac{x - 2y + 4}{2x - 2y + 1} = \dfrac{1}{3}$

$4x - 3y = 8.$

40. $\dfrac{x + 2y - 3}{2x - 3y + 1} = \dfrac{5}{3}$

$2x + 3y = 14.$

41. $\dfrac{2x - 2y}{2} + \dfrac{x - y}{3} = -\dfrac{4}{3}$

$\dfrac{x + 2y}{4} + \dfrac{3x + 2y}{3} = 6.$

42. $\dfrac{x + y}{2} + \dfrac{3x + 2y}{3} = \dfrac{1}{6}$

$\dfrac{2x + y}{3} - \dfrac{4x + 3y}{2} = -\dfrac{2}{3}.$

43. $\dfrac{2x + y}{4} + \dfrac{x + y}{6} = \dfrac{3}{4}$

$\dfrac{2x + 2y}{3} - \dfrac{3x + 2y}{2} = 0.$

44. $\dfrac{x + 3y}{6} + \dfrac{2x + 2y}{4} = \dfrac{4}{3}$

$\dfrac{2x + y}{4} - \dfrac{x + 2y}{2} = -3.$

45. $\dfrac{2x - y}{3} + \dfrac{x + 2y}{2} = 1$

$\dfrac{x - y}{2} - \dfrac{2x + y}{3} = \dfrac{4}{3}.$

46. $\dfrac{4x - y}{3} - \dfrac{2x + y}{2} = -\dfrac{13}{6}$

$\dfrac{x + 2y}{4} + \dfrac{3x - 4y}{3} = -\dfrac{5}{4}.$

47. $\dfrac{3x - 4y}{5} - \dfrac{2x - 3y}{3} = \dfrac{1}{3}$

$\dfrac{2x + 5y}{3} - \dfrac{2x - y}{6} = \dfrac{7}{6}.$

48. $\dfrac{4x - y}{6} - \dfrac{2x + 5y}{4} = \dfrac{10}{5}$

$\dfrac{5x - 2y}{3} - \dfrac{3x - y}{9} = \dfrac{46}{9}.$

49. $ax + by = a$
$a^2x + b^2y = a^2.$

50. $a^2x - b^2y = -br$
$b^2x + aby = ar.$

51. $ax + (a + b)y = 2a$
$abx - (a - b)y = 2ab.$

52. $ax - by = 2b$
$abx + b^2y = 2ab.$

In Problems 53 to 60, solve for $\dfrac{1}{x}$ and $\dfrac{1}{y}$ and then for x and y.

53. $\dfrac{3}{x} + \dfrac{1}{y} = 1$

$\dfrac{9}{x} - \dfrac{1}{y} = 1.$

54. $\dfrac{5}{x} + \dfrac{6}{y} = 3$

$\dfrac{10}{x} - \dfrac{9}{y} = -1.$

55. $\dfrac{2}{x} + \dfrac{4}{y} = 6$

$\dfrac{3}{x} + \dfrac{3}{y} = 5.$

56. $\dfrac{4}{x} + \dfrac{4}{y} = 6$

$\dfrac{3}{x} + \dfrac{6}{y} = 6.$

57. $\dfrac{7}{x} + \dfrac{6}{y} = 2$

$\dfrac{21}{x} - \dfrac{12}{y} = 1.$

58. $\dfrac{5}{x} + \dfrac{9}{y} = 3$

$\dfrac{7}{x} + \dfrac{12}{y} = 5.$

59. $\dfrac{8}{x} - \dfrac{9}{y} = -16$

$\dfrac{9}{x} - \dfrac{4}{y} = 31.$

60. $\dfrac{4}{x} - \dfrac{6}{y} = 4$

$\dfrac{6}{x} + \dfrac{9}{y} = 48.$

43. *Three linear equations in three unknowns.* The solution of three linear equations in three unknowns, when it exists, consists of three numbers, one for each of the unknowns which satisfy all of the given equations. In order to determine this solution, we first eliminate one of the variables. That is, we obtain from the given equations two linear equations in two unknowns, whose solution is two of the numbers sought. The value of the third unknown can then be determined by substitution.

The method most often used for eliminating the first unknown is that of addition or subtraction, and we shall illustrate it by means of the following examples:

EXAMPLE 1

Solve the equations

(1)	$3x - 2y + 3z = 16$
(2)	$x + 3y - 6z = -23$
(3)	$5x + 4y - 2z = -9$

simultaneously.

Solution

Since the coefficient of z in (2) is divisible by the coefficients of z in (1) and (3), we shall start by eliminating z. We accomplish this by first multiplying (1) by 2 and then adding (2); thus,

(4)	$6x - 4y + 6z = \quad 32$ [Eq. (1) $\times$ 2]
(2)	$\underline{x + 3y - 6z = -23}$
(5)	$7x - y \qquad\quad = \quad 9.$ [Eq. (4) + Eq. (2)]

Next we multiply Eq. (3) by 3 and subtract the result from Eq. (2) and get

(2)	$x + 3y - 6z = -23$	
(6)	$15x + 12y - 6z = -27$	[Eq. (3) × 3]
(7)	$-14x - 9y \quad\quad = 4.$	[Eq. (2) − Eq. (6)]

Now we have Eqs. (5) and (7) which contain x and y only, and we can solve them by the method of Art. 41, as indicated below.

(8)	$14x - 2y = 18$	[Eq. (5) × 2]
(7)	$-14x - 9y = 4$	
	$-11y = 22$	[Eq. (8) + Eq. (7)]
	$y = -2.$	

Substituting $y = -2$ in (5), we get

$$7x - (-2) = 9,$$
$$7x + 2 = 9,$$
$$7x = 7,$$
$$x = 1.$$

Hence, $x = 1$, $y = -2$ are two of the values sought. We may obtain z by substituting these values in any one of the three original equations. We shall choose (1), and, after substituting, we have

$$3(1) - 2(-2) + 3z = 16$$

or

$$3 + 4 + 3z = 16.$$

Combining, transposing, and solving for z, we get

$$3z = 16 - 7,$$
$$3z = 9,$$
$$z = 3.$$

Hence, the solution is $x = 1$, $y = -2$, $z = 3$. This solution may be checked by substituting in either (2) or (3).

EXAMPLE 2

Solve the equations

(9)	$3x + 4y - 5z = 37$	
(10)	$2x - 3y + 2z = -8$	
(11)	$x \quad\quad - 2z = 11$	

simultaneously.

Solution

Since Eq. (11) contains x and z only, we shall eliminate y from (9) and (10) and solve the resulting equation with (11). The steps in this process follow.

(12)	$9x + 12y - 15z = 111$	[Eq. (9) × 3]
(13)	$8x - 12y + 8z = -32$	[Eq. (10) × 4]
(14)	$17x \qquad - 7z = 79.$	[Eq. (12) + Eq. (13)]

We shall next eliminate x from (11) and (14) and solve for z.

(15)	$17x - 34z = 187$	[Eq. (11) × 17]
(14)	$17x - 7z = 79$	
	$-27z = 108$	[Eq. (15) − Eq. (14)]
	$z = -4.$	

Substituting $z = -4$ in (11), we have

$$x - 2(-4) = 11,$$
$$x + 8 = 11,$$
$$x = 3.$$

Finally, we substitute $x = 3$, $z = -4$ in (9) and get

$$3(3) + 4y - 5(-4) = 37,$$
$$9 + 4y + 20 = 37,$$
$$4y = 37 - 29 = 8,$$
$$y = 2.$$

Thus, the solution is $x = 3$, $y = 2$, $z = -4$.

This solution may be checked by substituting these values in Eq. (10).

The method of elimination by substitution may also be employed in the solution of three linear equations in three unknowns. In fact, it is advisable to use this method when two of the equations contain only two variables.

EXAMPLE 3

Solve the equations

(16)	$2x - y \qquad = 11$	
(17)	$3x \qquad + 5z = 17$	
(18)	$2x + 5y + 4z = -3$	

simultaneously.

Solution

We shall solve (16) for y in terms of x, and (17) for z in terms of x. Then we shall substitute the resulting expressions for y and z in (18) and thus get one equation in one unknown. Solving (16) for y, we have

(19) $y = 2x - 11.$

Similarly, solving (17) for z, we get

(20) $z = \dfrac{17 - 3x}{5}.$

Now we substitute the right members of (19) and (20) for y and z, respectively, in (18) and have

(21) $2x + 5(2x - 11) + 4\left(\dfrac{17 - 3x}{5}\right) = -3.$

In order to solve (21), we first perform the indicated multiplication; then we clear of fractions by multiplying both members of the resulting equation by 5; and finally we transpose, combine terms, and solve for x. The steps just indicated follow.

$$2x + 10x - 55 + \frac{68 - 12x}{5} = -3,$$
$$10x + 50x - 275 + 68 - 12x = -15,$$
$$10x + 50x - 12x = -15 + 275 - 68,$$
$$48x = 192,$$
$$x = 4.$$

Now we substitute $x = 4$ in (19) and (20) and get

$$y = 2(4) - 11 = 8 - 11 = -3$$

and

$$z = \frac{17 - 3(4)}{5} = \frac{17 - 12}{5} = \frac{5}{5} = 1.$$

Hence, the solution is $x = 4$, $y = -3$, and $z = 1$.

Since (19) and (20) are equivalent to (16) and (17), respectively, we may check the above solution by substituting in (18).

EXERCISE 23

Solve the following equations simultaneously for x, y, and z.

1. $2x + 3y + z = 11$
$\ 3x - 2y - z = 2$
$\ 4x - 3y - z = 1.$

2. $3x + y - 2z = 2$
$\ 2x - y + 3z = 17$
$\ 2x + y - 2z = -1.$

3. $x - y + z = 9$
$2x + 3y + z = 1$
$4x + 3y - z = 5.$

4. $x + 2y - z = 7$
$x - 3y + 2z = 5$
$x + 3y - 3z = -1.$

5. $x - 2y + 3z = 1$
$2x + 3y - 2z = 20$
$x - 3y + 4z = -2.$

6. $3x + y + 4z = 5$
$2x - y + 3z = -7$
$2x + 2y + 5z = 22.$

7. $2x + y + z = 7$
$3x + 2y - 2z = -4$
$3x + 3y - z = 7.$

8. $x - 2y + z = 9$
$3x + y - 2z = 11$
$2x + 3y - z = 14.$

9. $3x + 4y - 2z = 4$
$2x + 7y - 8z = -13$
$5x + 3y + 5z = 28.$

10. $4x + 3y + 6z = 7$
$5x + 5y - 4z = 1$
$3x - 2y + 7z = -5.$

11. $3x + 5y + 6z = 7$
$2x - 7y - 9z = 20$
$7x + 3y - 4z = 15.$

12. $6x + 5y + 7z = -2$
$5x + 3y + 6z = -10$
$4x - 4y - 2z = 8.$

13. $3x + 4y - 2z = 4$
$6x - 8y + 4z = 0$
$9x + 12y + 2z = 16.$

14. $5x + 3y - 6z = -1$
$10x - 6y + 12z = 14$
$15x + 9y - 6z = 7.$

15. $6x - 5y + 8z = 1$
$18x + 10y - 12z = 2$
$12x + 5y - 8z = 2.$

16. $12x + 7y - 12z = 3$
$16x - 14y + 18z = 19$
$8x - 7y + 12z = 12.$

17. $3x - 10y + 8z = 4$
$6x + 5y - 12z = -3$
$12x + 15y - 12z = 5.$

18. $3x + 4y - 4z = 5$
$9x - 8y + 12z = 15$
$6x - 4y - 8z = -8.$

19. $10x - 8y + 2z = 5$
$5x + 8y - 6z = 2$
$5x + 12y - 4z = 4.$

20. $5x + 6y + 7z = 9$
$15x - 9y - 21z = -9$
$10x + 6y - 7z = 5.$

21. $4x + 3y + 2z = 6$
$2x - 6y + z = -7$
$6x + 9y - 3z = 0.$

22. $10x + 5y - 4z = 6$
$x + y + 4z = 2$
$6x + y - 8z = 1.$

23. $6x - 3y - 4z = -4$
$2x - y + 4z = 8$
$3x - 6y + 2z = 2.$

24. $8x - 6y + 4z = 5$
$4x + 9y - 8z = 5$
$6x + 3y + 3z = 10.$

25. $x + 2y = 14$
$3y + z = 8$
$x - 2y + 3z = -27.$

26. $3x - y = 9$
$2x + 4y - 3z = 5$
$2x + z = 13.$

27. $x + 2z = 9$
$y + 4z = 18$
$3x + 2y - 3z = -5.$

28. $x - 3z = 4$
$y + 2z = -1$
$2x - 3y + 2z = -3.$

29. $2x + y = 11$
$y + 2z = 13$
$2x - 2y + z = 7.$

30. $3x + z = 13$
$3y - z = -13$
$4x + 2y - 4z = -10.$

31. $2x + 3y \quad\quad = 14$
$\quad\quad 2y + 3z = 19$
$\quad 3x - 5y + 4z = 22.$

32. $2x + 4y \quad\quad = 12$
$\quad 3x \quad\quad - 4z = -2$
$\quad 4x - 3y + 5z = 12.$

44. Problems leading to systems of linear equations. Many stated problems involve more than one unknown quantity, and often the symbolic statement for solving such a problem can be more easily obtained if more than one unknown letter is introduced. However, before the problem can be completely solved, the number of equations formed must be equal to the number of unknown letters used. The general procedure for obtaining the equations is the same as that in Art. 6, and the student is advised to reread that article before he studies the following examples or attempts the problems in Exercise 24.

EXAMPLE 1

A real-estate dealer received $1200 in rents on two dwellings in 1956, and one of them brought $10 per month more than the other. How much did he receive per month for each if the more expensive house was vacant for 2 months?

Solution

If we let
$\quad\quad x =$ the monthly rental on the more expensive house
and
$\quad\quad y =$ the monthly rental on the other,
then

(1) $\quad\quad\quad\quad\quad\quad\quad x - y = 10$

since one rented for $10 more per month than the other. Furthermore, since the first of the above houses was rented for 10 months and the other was rented for 12 months, we know that $10x + 12y$ is the total amount received in rentals. Hence,

(2) $\quad\quad\quad\quad\quad\quad\quad 10x + 12y = 1200.$

We now have the two equations (1) and (2) in the unknowns x and y and we shall solve them simultaneously by eliminating y. The solution follows.

(3) $\quad\quad 12x - 12y = \quad 120 \quad$ [Eq. (1) $\times$ 12]
(2) $\quad\quad \underline{10x + 12y = 1200}$
$\quad\quad\quad 22x \quad\quad = 1320. \quad$ [Eq. (3) + Eq. (2)]

Hence,
$\quad\quad\quad\quad\quad x \quad\quad = 60.$

Substituting 60 for x in (1), we get

$$60 - y = 10.$$

Hence,

$$-y = 10 - 60 = -50,$$

and

$$y = 50.$$

Therefore, the monthly rentals were $60 and $50, respectively.

EXAMPLE 2

A tobacco dealer mixed one grade of tobacco worth $1.40 per pound with another worth $1.80 per pound in order to obtain 50 lb. of a blend that sold for $1.56 per pound. How much of each grade did he use?

Solution

We shall let

$x = $ the number of pounds of the $1.40 grade used

and

$y = $ the number of pounds of the $1.80 grade.

Then

(4) $$x + y = 50,$$

since there were 50 lb. in the mixture. Furthermore, $1.40x$ is the value in dollars of the first grade, $1.80y$ is the value in dollars of the second, and $(1.56)50 = 78$ is the value in dollars of the mixture. Therefore,

(5) $$1.40x + 1.80y = 78.$$

Hence, (4) and (5) are the two required equations and we shall solve them by eliminating x.

(6) $\quad\quad 1.40x + 1.40y = \quad 70 \quad\quad$ [Eq. (4) $\times$ 1.40]

(5) $\quad\quad \underline{1.40x + 1.80y = \quad 78}$

$\quad\quad\quad\quad\quad - .40y = -8. \quad\quad$ [Eq. (6) $-$ Eq. (5)]

Therefore,

$$y = \frac{-8}{-.40} = 20.$$

Substituting 20 for y in (4), we have

$$x + 20 = 50,$$
$$x = 30.$$

Hence, the dealer used 30 lb. of the $1.40 grade and 20 lb. of the $1.80 grade in the mixture.

EXAMPLE 3

Two airfields A and B are 400 miles apart and B is due east of A. A plane flew from A to B in 2 hr. and then returned to A in $2\frac{1}{2}$ hr. If the wind blew with a constant velocity from the west during the entire trip, find the speed of the plane in still air and the speed of the wind.

Solution

Let
$$x = \text{the speed of the plane in still air}$$
and
$$y = \text{the speed of the wind.}$$

Then, since the wind was blowing from the west,

$$x + y = \text{the speed of the plane from } A \text{ to } B,$$
and
$$x - y = \text{the speed of the plane on the return trip.}$$

Hence,
$$\frac{400}{x + y} = \text{the time required for the first half of the trip,}$$
and
$$\frac{400}{x - y} = \text{the time required to return.}$$

Therefore,

$$(7) \qquad \frac{400}{x + y} = 2,$$

$$(8) \qquad \frac{400}{x - y} = 2\frac{1}{2}.$$

Now we clear of fractions by multiplying both members of (7) by $x + y$ and of (8) by $2(x - y)$ and get

$$(9) \qquad\qquad 400 = 2x + 2y$$

and

$$(10) \qquad\qquad 800 = 5x - 5y.$$

We shall solve (9) and (10) simultaneously by first eliminating y.

(11) $2000 = 10x + 10y$ [Eq. (9) × 5]
(12) $1600 = 10x - 10y$ [Eq. (10) × 2]
$\overline{}$
          $3600 = 20x.$ [Eq. (11) + Eq. (12)]

Hence,

$$x = 180.$$

Substituting 180 for x in (9), we have

$$400 = 2(180) + 2y,$$
$$400 = 360 + 2y,$$
$$2y = 40,$$
$$y = 20.$$

Hence, the speed of the plane in still air was 180 miles per hr. and the speed of the wind was 20 miles per hr.

EXAMPLE 4

A cash drawer contains $50 in nickels, dimes, and quarters. There are 802 coins in all, and 10 times as many nickels as dimes. How many coins of each denomination are in the drawer?

Solution

Let

$$q = \text{the number of quarters,}$$
$$d = \text{the number of dimes,}$$

and

$$n = \text{the number of nickels.}$$

We now form the following three linear equations in q, d, and n:

(13) $$25q + 10d + 5n = 5000,$$

since $50 = 5000 cents;

(14) $$q + d + n = 802,$$

since there were 802 coins in all;

(15) $$n = 10d,$$

since there were 10 times as many nickels as dimes.

If we substitute $10d$ for n [given by Eq. (15)] in Eqs. (13) and (14), we obtain two linear equations in q and d. From (13), we get

$$25q + 10d + 5(10d) = 5000,$$

which reduces to

(16) $$25q + 60d = 5000.$$

Furthermore, from (14) we have

$$q + d + 10d = 802$$

or

(17) $q + 11d = 802.$

We may eliminate q from (16) and (17) as shown below.

(16) $25q + 60d = 5,000$
(18) $\underline{25q + 275d = 20,050}$ [Eq. (17) × 25]
                $ - 215d = -15,050$ [Eq. (16) − Eq. (18)]
                $d = 70.$

Now, substituting 70 for d in (15), we get

$$n = 10(70) = 700.$$

Finally, substituting $d = 70$ in (17), we have

$$q + 11(70) = 802.$$

Hence,

$$q = 802 - 770 = 32.$$

Consequently, there were 32 quarters, 70 dimes, and 700 nickels in the cash drawer.

EXERCISE 24

1. A professor has 75 students enrolled in two classes. Find the size of each class if one has 5 more students than the other.

2. A student bought a textbook in grammar and a book of essays for his English class. The price of the essays was 75 cents more than that of the grammar, and the total cost of the two books was $8.25. Find the cost of each.

3. James spent $80 for camping equipment and a camera. If the camping equipment cost $5 more than half the price of the camera, find the amount spent for each.

4. On one examination a student scored 5 points more than the passing grade, and on another he scored 5 points less than a pass. If his total score on the two was 140 points, find the grade made on each.

5. During one season a football team scored 108 points in touchdowns and conversion points. If this team was successful in converting after $\frac{3}{4}$ of the touchdowns, how many points were scored by each method?

6. Frank earned $550 by working 60 days of his summer vacation. During the first portion of this time he earned $8 per day, and then his daily wage was raised to $10. How many days did he work for each wage?

7. A campus organization raised $222.50 by selling tickets to a neighboring theater and by serving a buffet supper. A total of 364 tickets to the two events was sold. If the price of each theater ticket was 50 cents and that of the buffet supper was $1.25 per person, find the number of tickets sold for each.

8. A student found that he had spent $9.67 for 43 gal. of gasoline on his spring vacation. If the price of ethyl gasoline was 25 cents per gallon and that of regular was 21 cents, how many gallons of each grade were purchased?

9. A homeowner received $890 in rents from two bedrooms during a certain year, and the cheaper room was vacant for 2 months. If the total monthly rental when both were occupied was $80, find the price per month on each.

10. Jane figured that the total cost of a new dress and a pair of shoes would be $25. By shopping at a sale, she was able to save $\frac{1}{9}$ of the estimated cost of the dress and $\frac{1}{7}$ of the estimated cost of the shoes, and these savings totaled $3. What was the estimated cost of her dress and of her shoes?

11. Two boys made a canoe trip to a picnic grounds 6 miles up a river. If the upward trip required 3 hr. and the return trip 1 hr., find the speed of the current and the speed the boys could paddle in still water.

12. A total of 400 freshmen bought tickets for the annual picnic, and 250 of them bought tickets for the trip to the picnic grounds on chartered buses. If the combined cost of a picnic ticket and a bus ticket was $1 and $362.50 was collected from the sales of both types, find the price of each.

13. Two campers set out in opposite directions for a trip around a lake. One traveled on horseback, and the other walked. When they met on the opposite side of the lake, the rider had traveled $9\frac{3}{8}$ miles and the hiker $5\frac{5}{8}$ miles. Find the speed of each if the former reached camp 2 hr. ahead of the latter.

14. A high school band of 60 members made a trip to a neighboring town using several private cars and a chartered bus. If bus tickets were $1.25 apiece and each car owner received 75 cents per passenger, and if the total transportation cost was $65, how many traveled by each method?

15. Tom earned $50 more from his summer job than Harry. If Tom saved 25 per cent of his earnings and Harry saved 20 per cent of his, how much did each earn if the total savings were $170?

16. A college student drove from the campus to his home in 9 hr. He averaged 45 miles per hr. over a portion of the trip and 50 miles per hr. over the remainder. If his home was 430 miles from the campus, find the distance traveled at each rate.

17. Los Angeles and Long Beach are 20 miles apart. A local interurban left Long Beach for Los Angeles at 9 A.M., and an express interurban left Los Angeles for Long Beach at 9:30 A.M. They met at 9:40. They met again on their return trips at 10:40. If each interurban had a 20-min. wait at its destination, find the speed of each.

18. A baker had two grades of cookies, one worth 36 cents per dozen and the other 24 cents per dozen. He combined two batches of each grade into 10 doz. of a mixture that sold for 30 cents per dozen. How many of each grade were included?

19. At the end of a day's motion-picture-film processing, it was found by chemical analysis that the hydroquinone concentration of the negative developer was 4 g. per liter. If the negative-developing system required 2400 liters of developer, how much replenisher with hydroquinone concentration of 8 g. per liter must be mixed with the old developer in order to produce a solution containing 5 g. per liter?

20. Water is drawn continuously from a reservoir at the rate of 40 cu. ft. per sec. When the reservoir has been depleted by 20,000 cu. ft., a pump automatically starts delivering water to the reservoir at the rate of 50 cu. ft. per sec. and then cuts off when the reservoir is full. Find the period of time that elapses between two instants when the reservoir is full and the length of time the pump operates during this period.

21. A professor and his assistant performed a laboratory experiment in 3 hr. When they repeated the experiment, the professor had to leave at the end of 2 hr., and the assistant finished in another 3 hr. How long would it take each to do the job alone?

22. A certain city devotes 5 per cent of its land area to public parks. The city planning commission wants to annex some adjacent countryside and at the same time set aside 16 per cent of it for parks, and this would bring the park percentage of the whole city up to 10 per cent. If the city limits would include 66,000 acres after the annexation, how many acres are included now, and how many acres does the commission plan to annex?

23. A vending machine releases either a ball of chewing gum or a prize when a penny is inserted in it. The gum costs the owner .5 cent per ball, and the prizes cost .9 cent each. At the end of a certain week the owner removed 500 pennies from the machine and figured that he had earned $2 on the merchandise sold. How many gum balls and how many prizes were delivered by the machine for this sum?

24. A traveling salesman is allowed 8 cents per mile for the use of his car and $6 per day for hotel accommodation. On a certain trip his hotel bill was $78 less than his mileage charge, and the two totaled $114. Find the number of miles traveled and the number of nights spent in hotels.

25. Jean spent $220 for luggage, new clothes, and a camera. If the combined cost of the luggage and camera was $20 more than the cost of her new wardrobe and the combined cost of the new clothes and the camera was $20 less than twice the cost of the luggage, how much was spent for each?

26. A professor found that the 30 students in a certain class had mid-semester grades of A, B, or C. If there were four times as many B's as A's and half as many C's as A's and B's together, how many students earned each grade?

27. A college allowed 3 grade points per semester hour for a grade of A, 2 grade points per hour for the grade of B, and 1 grade point per hour for a grade of C. A student earned a grade point average of 1.5 on a semester when he carried a load of 16 hours. If the number of hours on which he earned an A was 1 greater than the number on which he earned a B, on how many hours did he earn each of the three grades?

28. Tickets to a campus dramatic production were priced at 50 cents for students, 75 cents for faculty members, and $1 for the general public. A total of 550 people attended the performance, and $337.50 was collected from the ticket sales. If twice as much was collected from students as from noncampus sales, how many tickets of each type were sold?

29. It was found that the average age of a class of 20 members was 18.8 years. All members of the class were either 18, 19, or 20 years of age. The number of 18-year-old students was 2 less than the number of 19- and 20-year-olds combined. How many of each age were in the class?

30. A student walked to the bus station at the rate of 3 miles per hr. and took a bus that averaged 40 miles per hr. to a nearby city, where he boarded a plane that flew to his home town at the average rate of 170 miles per hr. The entire trip of 381.5 miles required $3\frac{1}{2}$ hr., and the plane trip required $\frac{1}{2}$ hr. longer than the other two parts of the journey together. How much time was spent in each mode of travel?

31. Tom, Dick, and Harry obtained permission to repaint their dormitory rooms. Working together, all three boys painted Tom's room in $1\frac{1}{3}$ hr. Dick and Harry painted the former's room in 2 hr., and Tom and Harry painted the latter's room in $1\frac{5}{7}$ hr. How long would it have taken each boy to paint his own room alone?

32. A confectioner had three grades of chocolate candy worth 60 cents, 70 cents, and $1 per pound, respectively. He mixed one-third of the 70-cent candy with the 60-cent grade and priced it at 65 cents per pound. He then mixed the remainder of the 70-cent grade with the $1 grade and priced this combination at 80 cents per pound. If there was 50 lb. in the two mixtures, how many pounds of each grade were in each combination?

CHAPTER 7

EXPONENTS AND RADICALS

45. *Laws of positive integral exponents.* In this chapter, we shall extend the definition of exponents and develop several laws for their use. For the convenience of the reader, we shall repeat several definitions and laws previously considered.

If n is a positive integer,

(1) $$a^n = a \times a \times a \cdots \textit{to n factors.}$$

(definition V, Art. 3)

In (1), the symbol a is called the *base* and n is the *exponent*.

(2) $$a^0 = 1. \qquad \text{(Art. 14)}$$
(3) $$a^m \times a^n = a^{m+n}. \qquad \text{(Art. 9)}$$

(4) $$\frac{a^m}{a^n} = a^{m-n}, \qquad m \geqq n. \qquad \text{(Art. 13)}$$

By use of (1), we can derive three other important laws of exponents which give the value of a power of a power, a power of a product, and a power of a quotient. If we apply (1) to $(a^m)^n$, we have

$$(a^m)^n = a^m \times a^m \times a^m \cdots \textit{to n factors}$$
$$= a^{m+m+m} \cdots \textit{to n terms} \qquad \text{[by (3)]}$$
$$= a^{nm}.$$

Hence,

(5) $$(a^m)^n = a^{nm}.$$

Again, if we apply (1) to $(ab)^n$, we get

$$(ab)^n = (ab) \times (ab) \times (ab) \cdots \textit{to n factors}$$
$$= (a \times a \times a \cdots \textit{to n factors})(b \times b \times b \cdots \textit{to n factors})$$
$$\text{(by the commutative law of multiplication)}$$
$$= a^n b^n. \qquad \text{[by (1)]}$$

132

Hence, we have

(6) $$(ab)^n = a^n b^n.$$

Finally, by (1)

$$\left(\frac{a}{b}\right)^n = \frac{a}{b} \times \frac{a}{b} \times \frac{a}{b} \cdots \text{ to } n \text{ factors}$$

$$= \frac{a \times a \times a \cdots \text{ to } n \text{ factors}}{b \times b \times b \cdots \text{ to } n \text{ factors}}$$

$$= \frac{a^n}{b^n}. \quad [\text{by } (1)]$$

Hence,

(7) $$\left(\frac{a}{b}\right)^n = \frac{a^n}{b^n}.$$

EXAMPLES

1. $(a^4)^3 = a^{3\times4} = a^{12}.$
2. $(3a)^4 = 3^4 a^4 = 81a^4.$
3. $(2a^2b^3)^4 = 2^4(a^2)^4(b^3)^4 = 16a^8b^{12}.$
4. $\left(\dfrac{a^3}{2b^2}\right)^5 = \dfrac{(a^3)^5}{2^5(b^2)^5} = \dfrac{a^{15}}{32b^{10}}.$

In order to simplify an expression involving positive integral exponents, we perform all possible operations by means of Laws 1 to 7. If the result is a fraction, we reduce it to the lowest terms.

EXAMPLE 5

Simplify $\left(\dfrac{2a^2c^3}{b^2}\right)^4 \left(\dfrac{3b^3c^2}{2a^3}\right)^2.$

Solution

We shall perform the following steps in the solution:
1. Apply (6) and (7) to the expressions in the parentheses.
2. Apply (5) to all expressions thus obtained that are in the form "power of a power."
3. Perform the indicated multiplication in the expressions thus obtained.
4. Reduce the result obtained in Step 3 to lowest terms by dividing the numerator and denominator by the highest common factor of the two.

When we carry out these operations, we get

$$\left(\frac{2a^2c^3}{b^2}\right)^4 \left(\frac{3b^3c^2}{2a^3}\right)^2 = \left[\frac{2^4(a^2)^4(c^3)^4}{(b^2)^4}\right]\left[\frac{3^2(b^3)^2(c^2)^2}{2^2(a^3)^2}\right] \quad \text{[by (6) and (7)]}$$

$$= \left(\frac{16a^8c^{12}}{b^8}\right)\left(\frac{9b^6c^4}{4a^6}\right) \qquad \text{[by (5)]}$$

$$= \frac{144a^8b^6c^{16}}{4a^6b^8} \qquad \text{[by (3)]}$$

$$= \frac{36a^2c^{16}}{b^2}. \qquad \text{(by dividing the numerator and denominator by } 4a^6b^6\text{)}$$

EXAMPLE 6

Simplify $\left(\dfrac{12x^{2a-2}}{6x^{a-2}}\right)^4 \left(\dfrac{1}{2x^{2a}}\right)^2.$

Solution

It is easier to simplify this expression by first applying (4) to the expression in the first parentheses. Then we use (6) and (5) and finally simplify the result thus obtained. These operations yield

$$\left(\frac{12x^{2a-2}}{6x^{a-2}}\right)^4 \left(\frac{1}{2x^{2a}}\right)^2 = [2x^{(2a-2)-(a-2)}]^4 \left(\frac{1}{2x^{2a}}\right)^2 \quad \text{[by (4)]}$$

$$= (2x^{2a-2-a+2})^4 \left(\frac{1}{2x^{2a}}\right)^2$$

$$= (2x^a)^4 \left(\frac{1}{2x^{2a}}\right)^2$$

$$= (16x^{4a}) \left(\frac{1}{4x^{4a}}\right) \qquad \text{[by (6) and (5)]}$$

$$= \frac{16x^{4a}}{4x^{4a}}$$

$$= 4x^0 \qquad \text{[by (4)]}$$

$$= 4(1) = 4. \qquad \text{[by (2)]}$$

The converse of (6) is

(8) $$a^n b^n = (ab)^n.$$

When multiplying equal powers of two or more expressions, it is frequently more efficient to apply (8) first and then proceed with the multiplication.

EXAMPLE 7

Simplify $\left(\dfrac{2a^2c^3}{15b^4}\right)^3 \left(\dfrac{30b^6}{4a^2c^2}\right)^3.$

Solution

Each of the expressions in the parentheses is raised to the third power. Hence, by (8), we can multiply them and then raise the product to the third power. After this is done, we can complete the simplification. The solution follows.

$$\left(\frac{2a^2c^3}{15b^4}\right)^3 \left(\frac{30b^6}{4a^2c^2}\right)^3 = \left[\left(\frac{2a^2c^3}{15b^4}\right)\left(\frac{30b^6}{4a^2c^2}\right)\right]^3 \qquad \text{[by (8)]}$$

$$= \left(\frac{60a^2b^6c^3}{60a^2b^4c^2}\right)^3$$

$$= (a^0b^2c)^3 \qquad \text{[by (4)]}$$
$$= (b^2c)^3 \qquad \text{[by (2)]}$$
$$= b^6c^3. \qquad \text{[by (5)]}$$

The converse of (7) may be used in a similar manner.

NOTE 1: In the application of (5), it should be noted that the exponent inside the parentheses is multiplied by the one on the outside. It is not raised to the power indicated by the outside exponent. For example,

$$(2a^2)^3 = 8a^{2(3)} = 8a^6, \qquad not \ 8a^{2^3} = 8a^8.$$

NOTE 2: When we multiply two powers of the same base, we *hold that base* and add the exponents. For example,

$$(2a^2)^3(2a^2)^2 = (2a^2)^5, \qquad not \ (4a^4)^5.$$

NOTE 3: When we multiply two equal powers of different bases, we *hold the exponent* and multiply the bases. For example,

$$(3a^2)^3(2a^4)^3 = (6a^6)^3, \qquad not \ (6a^6)^6.$$

Simplify the expression in each of Problems 1 to 20.

1. $3^2 3^3.$ 2. $2^5 2^2.$ 3. $4(4^3).$ 4. $5^3 5^2.$

5. $\dfrac{7^4}{7^3}.$ 6. $\dfrac{5^6}{5^2}.$ 7. $\dfrac{3^8}{3^5}.$ 8. $\dfrac{2^7}{2^3}.$

9. $(2^2)^3$.   **10.** $(3^3)^2$.   **11.** $(5^4)^2$.   **12.** $(2^2)^5$.

13. $(2^3 3^2)^2$.   **14.** $(3^2 2^4)^2$.   **15.** $(3^0 5)^2$.   **16.** $(2^2 3)^3$.

17. $\left(\dfrac{3^2}{2^3}\right)^2$.   **18.** $\left(\dfrac{5^3}{2^4}\right)^2$.   **19.** $\left(\dfrac{4^2}{2^3}\right)^3$.   **20.** $\left(\dfrac{6^0}{3^4}\right)^2$.

Simplify the following exponential expressions.

21. $\left(\dfrac{a^2 b}{c^3}\right)^4$.   **22.** $\left(\dfrac{a^3 b^2}{c^4}\right)^3$.   **23.** $\left(\dfrac{-2u^4 v^0}{3w^2}\right)^5$.   **24.** $\left(\dfrac{3c^3}{2d^2}\right)^4$.

25. $(2a^2 b)(3a^3 b^2)$.   **26.** $(4x^3 y^2)(-2x^2 y^5)$.

27. $(-5x^5 y^2 z)(-2x^2 y^3 z^2)$.   **28.** $(-3u^3 v^2 w^4)(2uv^3 w^2)$.

29. $\dfrac{12a^6 b^3}{8a^2 b^5}$ **30.** $\dfrac{20c^2 d^2}{15c^4 d^0}$ **31.** $\dfrac{18p^5 q^4}{24p^3 q^6}$ **32.** $\dfrac{36x^2 y^7}{12x^5 y^5}$

33. $\dfrac{a^5 b^3 c^7}{a^4 bc^3}$.   **34.** $\dfrac{x^6 y^5 z^2}{x^2 y^3 z^0}$.   **35.** $\dfrac{r^3 s^2 t^0}{r^2 st}$.   **36.** $\dfrac{a^7 x^3 i^2}{ax^4 t^5}$.

37. $(r^2 s^3 t)^4 (rs^2)$.   **38.** $(2a^3 b^2 c^4)^2 (3a^0 b)$.

39. $(x^2 y)(2x^3 y^2)^4$.   **40.** $(3a^2 b^3)(2ab^0 c^3)^2$.

41. $\dfrac{(u^2 vw^0)^3}{(uv^2 w)^2}$.   **42.** $\dfrac{(a^3 x^2 v^4)^2}{(a^2 xv^3)^3}$.

43. $\dfrac{(2a^3 y^2)^4}{(4ay^0)^2}$.   **44.** $\dfrac{(3b^2 x^3)^3}{(9bx^2)^4}$.

45. $\left(\dfrac{9a^2 y^3}{4b}\right)^2 \left(\dfrac{2b^3}{3ay^2}\right)^3$.   **46.** $\left(\dfrac{4b^2 u^2}{s^3}\right)^4 \left(\dfrac{s^2}{2bu^3}\right)^5$.

47. $\left(\dfrac{9m^3 v^2}{25t^4}\right)^2 \left(\dfrac{5t^3}{3m^2 v}\right)^3$.   **48.** $\left(\dfrac{a^5 x^3}{t^0}\right)^6 \left(\dfrac{t^4}{a^8 x^5}\right)^4$.

49. $\left(\dfrac{a^3 b^2}{c^4}\right)^2 \div \left(\dfrac{a^2 b}{c^3}\right)^3$.   **50.** $\left(\dfrac{m^5 p^7}{9n^4}\right)^2 \div \left(\dfrac{m^4 p^6}{3n^3}\right)^3$.

51. $\left(\dfrac{s^4 t^2}{2x^3}\right)^3 \div \left(\dfrac{s^6 t^4}{4x^5}\right)^2$.   **52.** $\left(\dfrac{a^2 b^3}{3c^2}\right)^4 \div \left(\dfrac{ab^0}{9c^3}\right)^2$.

53. $\left[(2x)^3 \left(\dfrac{y}{4x^2}\right)^2\right]^3$.   **54.** $\left[\left(\dfrac{3a^2}{4b^3}\right)^2 \left(\dfrac{8b^7}{9a^5}\right)\right]^4$.

55. $\left[\left(\dfrac{12u^2 v}{25w^2}\right)\left(\dfrac{5w^3}{4uv^2}\right)^2\right]^3$.   **56.** $\left[\left(\dfrac{2pq^2}{3r^3}\right)^4 \left(\dfrac{27r^6}{4p^2 q^3}\right)^2\right]^5$.

57. $\left[\left(\dfrac{2a^2}{3b}\right)^3 \left(\dfrac{9b}{4a^3}\right)^2\right]^3$.   **58.** $\left[\left(\dfrac{8x^4}{9y}\right)^2 \left(\dfrac{3y^2}{4x^3}\right)^3\right]^4$.

59. $\left[\left(\dfrac{2c^3}{5d^0}\right)^4 \left(\dfrac{25d}{8c^4}\right)^2\right]^5$.   **60.** $\left[\left(\dfrac{4p^4}{3q^3}\right)^4 \left(\dfrac{3q^2}{4p^5}\right)^3\right]^3$.

61. $2^{1+n} 2^{1-n}$.   **62.** $3^{2+n} 3^{2-n}$.   **63.** $2^{2-2n} 4^{1+n}$.   **64.** $27^{1-a} 3^{3+3a}$.

65. $3^{2n+3} 3^{2n-3}$.   **66.** $4^{n-3} 4^{2n+3}$.   **67.** $5^{2n-4} 5^{n+4}$.   **68.** $4^{5n-3} 4^{2n+3}$.

69. $\dfrac{a^{3n+2}}{a^{3n-1}}.$ **70.** $\dfrac{a^{3m+1}}{a^{2m+1}}.$ **71.** $\dfrac{r^{c+5}}{r^{2-c}}.$ **72.** $\dfrac{s^{9-t}}{s^{5+t}}.$

73. $(s^{t+2})^2.$ **74.** $(b^{r-1})^4.$ **75.** $(c^{n+3})^4.$ **76.** $(c^{n+3})^3.$

77. $\dfrac{(a^{x+2}b^{x-1})^3}{a^{3x-2}b^{x-3}}.$ **78.** $\dfrac{(a^{y+1}b^{y+2})^2}{a^{2y}b^4}.$

79. $\dfrac{(m^{2x+3}n^{3x})^3}{m^{6x}n^{5x}}.$ **80.** $\dfrac{(b^{3a+c}d^{y})^2}{b^{2c}d^{2y}}.$

46. Negative integral exponents. We shall now extend our interpretation of exponents so as to include exponents that are negative integers. We shall do so in such a way that all of the laws of positive exponents remain valid for the negative ones.

We shall first assume that a^{-n}, $a \neq 0$, represents a number and shall multiply it by $\dfrac{a^n}{a^n} = 1$ and obtain

$$a^{-n} = a^{-n}\left(\frac{a^n}{a^n}\right) = \frac{a^{-n+n}}{a^n} \qquad \text{[by (3), Art. 45]}$$

$$= \frac{a^0}{a^n}$$

$$= \frac{1}{a^n}. \qquad \text{[by (2), Art. 45]}$$

Hence, we shall define a^{-n} as follows:

DEFINITION. *If* $a \neq 0$ *and* **n** *is a positive integer, then*

(1) $$a^{-n} = \frac{1}{a^n}.$$

We may now remove the restriction $m \geqq n$ in (4), Art. 45, since we have an interpretation for negative exponents. Furthermore, it can be shown that Laws 3 to 7 of Art. 45 hold for this interpretation. We shall illustrate the general method for proving this by applying it to Law 3 as shown below.

$$a^{-m} \times a^{-n} = \frac{1}{a^m} \times \frac{1}{a^n} = \frac{1}{a^{m+n}} = a^{-(m+n)} = a^{-m-n}.$$

By use of (1) of this article and Laws 2 to 7 of Art. 45, we can change any expression which involves negative exponents into an equivalent expression with all exponents positive.

1. $3^{-2} = \dfrac{1}{3^2} = \dfrac{1}{9}.$

2. $3^{-2} \times 3^{-3} = 3^{-5} = \dfrac{1}{3^5} = \dfrac{1}{243}.$

3. $\dfrac{3^{-5}}{3^{-2}} = 3^{-5-(-2)} = 3^{-5+2} = 3^{-3} = \dfrac{1}{3^3} = \dfrac{1}{27}.$

4. $\dfrac{3a^m b^{-n}}{d^{-t}} = \dfrac{3a^m \left(\dfrac{1}{b^n}\right)}{\dfrac{1}{d^t}} = \dfrac{\dfrac{3a^m}{b^n}}{\dfrac{1}{d^t}} = \dfrac{\dfrac{3a^m}{b^n}(b^n d^t)}{\dfrac{1}{d^t}(b^n d^t)} = \dfrac{3a^m d^t}{b^n}.$

In Example 4, we note that letters which had negative exponents in the original fraction were moved from one member of the fraction to the other in the simplification process, and the sign of the exponent was changed. This is an illustration of the following general rule for changing a fraction involving negative exponents into another which contains only positive exponents.

RULE FOR FRACTIONS INVOLVING NEGATIVE EXPONENTS. *Any factor in one member of a fraction can be moved to the other member, provided the sign of the exponent of that factor is changed.*

EXAMPLE 5

$$\frac{2a^{-2}b}{c^{-3}} = \frac{2bc^3}{a^2}.$$

NOTE: The above rule applies to *factors, not to terms.* For example,

$$\frac{a^{-1} + b^{-1}}{c^{-3}} \text{ is not equal to } \frac{c^3}{a + b},$$

since if we apply (1) of this article to the original fraction, we get

$$\frac{a^{-1} + b^{-1}}{c^{-3}} = \frac{\dfrac{1}{a} + \dfrac{1}{b}}{\dfrac{1}{c^3}} = \frac{\dfrac{b + a}{ab}}{\dfrac{1}{c^3}} = \frac{bc^3 + ac^3}{ab}.$$

We shall agree that an expression involving negative exponents is simplified when all combinations by use of Laws 2 to 7 of Art. 45

have been made, and the result has been expressed without zero or negative exponents. If the final result is a fraction, it should be reduced to lowest terms.

EXAMPLE 6

Simplify $\left(\dfrac{2x^{-3}y^2}{x^2z^{-3}}\right)^{-4}$.

Solution

$$\left(\frac{2x^{-3}y^2}{x^2z^{-3}}\right)^{-4} = \frac{2^{-4}(x^{-3})^{-4}(y^2)^{-4}}{(x^2)^{-4}(z^{-3})^{-4}} \qquad \text{[by (7) and (6), Art. 45]}$$

$$= \frac{2^{-4}x^{12}y^{-8}}{x^{-8}z^{12}} \qquad \text{[by (5), Art. 45]}$$

$$= \frac{x^8x^{12}}{2^4y^8z^{12}} \qquad \text{(by the rule preceding Example 5)}$$

$$= \frac{x^{20}}{16y^8z^{12}}. \qquad \text{[by (3), Art. 45]}$$

EXAMPLE 7

Simplify $\dfrac{x^{-1}+y^{-2}}{x^{-3}}$.

Solution

By (1) of this article, $x^{-1} = \dfrac{1}{x}$, $y^{-2} = \dfrac{1}{y^2}$, and $x^{-3} = \dfrac{1}{x^3}$. Hence,

$$\frac{x^{-1}+y^{-2}}{x^{-3}} = \frac{\dfrac{1}{x}+\dfrac{1}{y^2}}{\dfrac{1}{x^3}}$$

$$= \frac{\left(\dfrac{1}{x}+\dfrac{1}{y^2}\right)x^3y^2}{\left(\dfrac{1}{x^3}\right)x^3y^2} \qquad \text{(multiplying numerator and denominator by the LCM of the denominators)}$$

$$= \frac{x^2y^2+x^3}{y^2}.$$

Find the value of the expression in each of Problems 1 to 24.

1. 3^{-2}.   **2.** 4^{-1}.   **3.** 5^{-3}.   **4.** 2^{-4}.

5. $2^{-1}2^{-2}$.   **6.** $3^{-3}3$.   **7.** $5^{-4}5^0$.   **8.** $7^{-5}7^3$.

9. $\dfrac{3^{-3}}{3^{-2}}.$ 10. $\dfrac{2^{-4}}{2^{-1}}.$ 11. $\dfrac{7^0}{7^{-3}}.$ 12. $\dfrac{5^{-2}}{5}.$

13. $(2^{-2})^3.$ 14. $(3^{-1})^{-2}.$ 15. $(5^{-2})^{-1}.$ 16. $(7^2)^{-2}.$

17. $(\frac{2}{3})^{-2}.$ 18. $(\frac{3}{5})^{-1}.$ 19. $(\frac{2}{5})^{-3}.$ 20. $(\frac{4}{7})^{-3}.$

21. $(2^2 3^{-1})^{-1}.$ 22. $(3^0 2^{-3})^{-2}.$ 23. $(5^2 2^{-1})^2.$ 24. $(2^{-1} 3^{-2})^{-3}.$

By use of negative exponents, write the expressions in each of Problems 25 to 32 without denominators.

25. $\dfrac{4x^2}{y^3}.$ 26. $\dfrac{3a^3}{b^4}.$ 27. $\dfrac{2c^5}{de^2}.$ 28. $\dfrac{5pq^3}{rt^3}.$

29. $\dfrac{3a^2 b}{2c^{-1} d^2}.$ 30. $\dfrac{4x^2 y^3}{3^0 w^{-2} z}.$ 31. $\dfrac{r^3 s^2 t}{3u^0 v^{-3} t^{-2}}.$ 32. $\dfrac{6pq^2 r^3}{5^{-1} s^2 t u^{-2}}.$

Simplify the following exponential expressions.

33. $2a^{-1} a^{-2}.$ 34. $4c^0 c^{-2}.$ 35. $6x^{-2} x^{-3}.$

36. $5m^2 m^{-5}.$ 37. $\dfrac{x^{-2}}{x^{-1}}$ 38. $\dfrac{x^2}{x^{-3}}.$

39. $\dfrac{y^0}{y^{-4}}.$ 40. $\dfrac{a^{-7}}{a^{-4}}.$ 41. $\dfrac{p^{-2} d^{-1} q^0}{p^{-4} d^{-3} q^{-2}}.$

42. $\dfrac{r^{-2} s^{-1} t^2}{r^{-1} s^{-2} t^{-3}}.$ 43. $\dfrac{p^{-3} e^{-2} n^{-5}}{p^0 e^{-4} n^{-2}}.$ 44. $\dfrac{a^{-2} b^2 c^0}{ab^{-3} c^{-1}}.$

45. $\dfrac{2^{-1} r^{-1} a^2 t^{-3}}{3^{-2} r^3 a^{-1} t^{-2}}.$ 46. $\dfrac{3^{-2} p^{-1} e^0 r^{-2}}{2^{-3} p e^{-2} r^{-4}}.$ 47. $\dfrac{2^{-2} a^{-2} r^{-1} e^0}{3^{-1} a^{-3} r e^{-4}}.$

48. $\dfrac{5^{-1} b^{-2} a h^0}{2^{-3} b a^{-2} h^{-3}}.$ 49. $\dfrac{3ab^{-2} c}{2^{-1} a^{-3} b c^{-4}}.$ 50. $\dfrac{4x^{-3} y^{-2} z^4}{2^{-2} x y^4 z^{-2}}.$

51. $\dfrac{5^{-1} p^{-2} q^4 r^{-4}}{2^0 p q^{-1} r^{-3}}.$ 52. $\dfrac{2c^{-3} d^{-2} e^4}{3c^{-4} d e^{-1}}.$ 53. $\left(\dfrac{x^{-1} y^2}{x^2 y^{-3}}\right)^{-1}.$

54. $\left(\dfrac{b^{-3} m^2}{b m^0}\right)^{-2}.$ 55. $\left(\dfrac{a^{-2} m^{-1}}{a^2 m}\right)^{-3}.$ 56. $\left(\dfrac{s^{-1} y^{-2}}{s^0 y^{-1}}\right)^{-2}.$

57. $\left(\dfrac{4^{-1} x^{-2} y^{-3}}{2^{-3} x^{-4} y^{-1}}\right)^{-3}.$ 58. $\left(\dfrac{3^{-3} a b^{-3}}{9^{-1} a^{-2} b^0}\right)^{-4}.$ 59. $\left(\dfrac{25^{-1} c^2 d^{-3}}{5^{-3} c^{-3} d^{-2}}\right)^{-2}.$

60. $\left(\dfrac{3^{-4} a^{-1} b^{-3}}{9^{-1} a b^{-2}}\right)^{-1}.$ 61. $x^a - \dfrac{2}{x^{-a}}.$ 62. $x^{-a} - \dfrac{2}{x^a}.$

63. $x^a - \dfrac{2^{-1}}{x^{-a}}.$ 64. $x^{-a} - \dfrac{2}{x^{-a}}.$ 65. $\dfrac{a}{b} + \dfrac{b^{-1}}{a^{-1}}.$

66. $\dfrac{a}{b} + \dfrac{a^{-1}}{b^{-1}}.$ 67. $\dfrac{a}{b^{-1}} + \dfrac{a^{-1}}{b}.$ 68. $\dfrac{a^{-1}}{b^{-1}} + \dfrac{a^{-1}}{b}.$

69. $\dfrac{a^{-1} + b^{-1}}{a^{-2}}.$

70. $\dfrac{a^{-1} - b^{-1}}{a^{-3}}.$

71. $\dfrac{a^{-2} - b^{-2}}{a^{-1} - b^{-1}}.$

72. $\dfrac{x^{-1}y^{-3} - x^{-3}y^{-1}}{x^{-2}y^{-3} + x^{-3}y^{-2}}.$

73. $-3(x + 1)^2(x - 1)^{-4} + 2(x + 1)(x - 1)^{-3}.$

74. $6(x + 2)^{-2}(2x + 1)^2 - 2(2x + 1)^3(x + 2)^{-3}.$

75. $8(x + 1)^{-1}(2x - 3)^3 - (x + 1)^{-2}(2x - 3)^4.$

76. $6(x - 3)^{-2}(3x - 1) - 2(x - 3)^{-3}(3x - 1)^2.$

77. $(2x + 3)^{-2}(3 - x)^{-2} - 4(2x + 3)^{-3}(3 - x)^{-1}.$

78. $(3x - 1)^{-2}(2 - x)^{-2} - 6(3x - 1)^{-3}(2 - x)^{-1}.$

79. $6(2x + 5)^2(x + 3)^{-2} - 2(x + 3)^{-3}(2x + 5)^3.$

80. $8(2x - 1)^3(x + 2)^{-1} - (x + 2)^{-2}(2x - 1)^4.$

47. Roots of numbers. In arithmetic, the following terminology is customary. Since $8^2 = 64$ and $(-8)^2 = 64$, we call each of the numbers 8 and -8 a *square root* of 64. Furthermore, since $4^3 = 64$, we call 4 a *cube root* of 64; and since $2^6 = 64$, we call 2 a *sixth root* of 64. We note that in each case the root is one of a set of equal factors of 64. These examples illustrate the following general definition.

DEFINITION. *An **nth** root of a number is a second number whose **nth** power is the given number.*

In the above paragraph, we stated that 64 has the two square roots 8 and -8. Since $(-n)^2 = n^2$, it is true that any positive number has two square roots, one positive and the other negative, with their numerical values equal. It is also true, but we shall not prove it here, that every number has three cube roots, four fourth roots, and, in general, n nth roots. Usually all n of these roots are not real numbers.[1] In fact, in many cases, no one of the n roots is a real number. Since any even power of a positive or a negative number is positive, there is no real square root of $-a$, no real fourth root of $-a$, and, in general, no real nth root of $-a$, where n is an even integer and a is positive. We shall call such roots *imaginary* numbers and shall discuss them more fully in later articles.

If there is a *positive real* nth root of a number, it is called the *principal nth root*. If there is a negative but no positive nth real root of a number, the negative root is called the principal nth root.

[1] At this point, the reader should review definitions I, II, III, and IV of Art. 2.

For example, 2 is the principal square root of 4, and -2 is the principal cube root of -8.

The customary notation for the principal nth root of a is $\sqrt[n]{a}$. This symbol is called a *radical of order n*. The letter a is the *radicand*, and n is the *index* of the radical.

By the above definition,

(1) $$(\sqrt[n]{a})^n = a.$$

If a is not the nth power of a rational number, the value of $\sqrt[n]{a}$ cannot be expressed exactly as an integer or a fraction. Often it can be expressed in other forms but never exactly without the use of the radical. However, if $\sqrt[n]{a}$ is real, its value can be expressed approximately as a decimal fraction.

48. Fractional exponents. In this article, we shall give an interpretation to fractional exponents so that Laws 3 to 7 of Art. 45 will hold. If we assume that

$$(a^m)^n = a^{mn} \qquad [(5), \text{ Art. 45}]$$

holds when $m = \dfrac{1}{n}$, we have

$$(a^{\frac{1}{n}})^n = a^{\frac{n}{n}} = a.$$

Hence, by the definition of an nth root of a number, we have

(1) $$a^{\frac{1}{n}} = \sqrt[n]{a}.$$

Consequently, we accept (1) as the definition of a fractional exponent when the numerator is one. Furthermore, if (5) of Art. 45 is to hold when $m = \dfrac{1}{p}$ and $n = q$, we have

$$(a^{\frac{1}{p}})^q = a^{\frac{q}{p}}.$$

Hence, by (1), we have

(2) $$a^{\frac{q}{p}} = (\sqrt[p]{a})^q.$$

Therefore, *we define a number with a fractional exponent as a power of a radical. The denominator of the fraction is the index of the radical and the numerator denotes the power to which the radical is raised.*

If $\sqrt[p]{a}$ is a real number,[1] it can be proved[2] that
$$(\sqrt[p]{a})^q = \sqrt[p]{a^q}.$$

Hence, we have

(3) $\qquad a^{\frac{q}{p}} = (\sqrt[p]{a})^q = \sqrt[p]{a^q}$ *when* $\sqrt[p]{a}$ *is real.*

EXAMPLES

1. $125^{\frac{2}{3}} = (\sqrt[3]{125})^2 = 5^2 = 25.$

2. $8^{\frac{3}{4}} = (\sqrt[4]{8})^3.$ Since there is no rational fourth root of 8, we cannot express $(\sqrt[4]{8})^3$ without the use of a radical. However, by use of (3), we can express it in another form; thus,
$$(\sqrt[4]{8})^3 = \sqrt[4]{8^3} = \sqrt[4]{512}.$$

In a later article, we shall show how to express $\sqrt[4]{512}$ in a simpler form.

If all radicals of the type $\sqrt[q]{a} = a^{\frac{1}{q}}$ are real, it can be proved that Laws 3, 4, 5, 6, and 7 of Art. 45 are valid for fractional exponents. We shall prove below that Law 5 holds. The validity of the others can be established in a similar manner.

If we raise $(a^{\frac{p}{q}})^{\frac{s}{r}}$ to the qrth power, we have

$$[(a^{\frac{p}{q}})^{\frac{s}{r}}]^{qr} = \{[(a^{\frac{p}{q}})^s]^{\frac{1}{r}}\}^{qr} \qquad \text{[by (3)]}$$
$$= [(a^{\frac{p}{q}})^s]^{\frac{qr}{r}} \qquad \text{[by (5), Art. 45]}$$
$$= [(a^{\frac{p}{q}})^s]^q$$
$$= (a^{\frac{p}{q}})^{sq} \qquad \text{[by (5), Art. 45]}$$
$$= [(a^{\frac{p}{q}})^p]^{sq} \qquad \text{[by (3)]}$$
$$= (a^{\frac{psq}{q}}) \qquad \text{[by (5), Art. 45, and (3)]}$$
$$= a^{ps}.$$

[1] This excludes only the case in which a is negative and p is an even integer.

[2] In order to prove this statement, we raise $(\sqrt[p]{a})^q$ to the pth power and get
$$[(\sqrt[p]{a})^q]^p = (\sqrt[p]{a})^{qp} \qquad \text{[by (5), Art 45]}$$
$$= (a^{\frac{1}{p}})^{qp} = a^{\frac{qp}{p}} \qquad \text{[by (5), Art 45]}$$
$$= a^q.$$

Hence, $(\sqrt[p]{a})^q$ is a pth root of a^q. Furthermore, it can be readily verified that, except for the case excluded above, $(\sqrt[p]{a})^q$ and $\sqrt[p]{a^q}$ have the same sign. Hence, the two expressions are equal.

Hence, $(a^{\frac{p}{q}})^{\frac{s}{r}}$ is a qrth root of a^{ps}. Furthermore, it can be readily verified that for admissible values of a, q, and r (that is, all values except even values of either q or r when a is negative), $(a^{\frac{p}{q}})^{\frac{s}{r}}$ and $a^{\frac{ps}{qr}}$ have the same sign. Hence,

$$(a^{\frac{p}{q}})^{\frac{s}{r}} = a^{\frac{ps}{qr}}.$$

We are now in position to express radicals in terms of fractional exponents, or vice versa, when it is desirable to do so.

EXAMPLE 1

Write the expression $\dfrac{\sqrt{3a^4b^3}}{\sqrt[3]{c^2d^6}}$ without radicals.

Solution

$$\frac{\sqrt{3a^4b^3}}{\sqrt[3]{c^2d^6}} = \frac{(3a^4b^3)^{\frac{1}{2}}}{(c^2d^6)^{\frac{1}{3}}} = \frac{3^{\frac{1}{2}}a^{\frac{4}{2}}b^{\frac{3}{2}}}{c^{\frac{2}{3}}d^{\frac{6}{3}}} = \frac{3^{\frac{1}{2}}a^2b^{\frac{3}{2}}}{c^{\frac{2}{3}}d^2}.$$

EXAMPLE 2

Write $\dfrac{2a^{\frac{1}{2}}b^{\frac{3}{2}}}{c^{\frac{2}{3}}}$ without fractional exponents.

Solution

$$\frac{2a^{\frac{1}{2}}b^{\frac{3}{2}}}{c^{\frac{2}{3}}} = \frac{2(ab^3)^{\frac{1}{2}}}{(c^2)^{\frac{1}{3}}} = \frac{2\sqrt{ab^3}}{\sqrt[3]{c^2}}.$$

EXAMPLE 3

Write $a^{\frac{2}{3}}y^{-\frac{3}{4}}$ without fractional exponents.

Solution

$$a^{\frac{2}{3}}y^{-\frac{3}{4}} = \frac{a^{\frac{2}{3}}}{y^{\frac{3}{4}}}$$

$$= \frac{\sqrt[3]{a^2}}{\sqrt[4]{y^3}}.$$

Write the value of the expression in each of Problems 1 to 16 without the use of exponents or radicals.

1. $4^{\frac{1}{2}}$.
2. $25^{\frac{1}{2}}$.
3. $27^{\frac{1}{3}}$.
4. $16^{\frac{1}{4}}$.
5. $.01^{\frac{1}{2}}$.
6. $.36^{\frac{1}{2}}$.
7. $.125^{\frac{1}{3}}$.
8. $.00032^{\frac{1}{5}}$.
9. $27^{\frac{2}{3}}$.
10. $32^{\frac{3}{5}}$.
11. $.09^{\frac{3}{2}}$.
12. $.008^{\frac{2}{3}}$.
13. $9^{-\frac{1}{2}}$.
14. $8^{-\frac{2}{3}}$.
15. $16^{-\frac{3}{4}}$.
16. $32^{-\frac{2}{5}}$.

Write the expression in each of Problems 17 to 44 without the use of radicals.

17. $\sqrt{9}$.
18. $\sqrt{16}$.
19. $\sqrt[3]{8}$.
20. $\sqrt{4^3}$.
21. $\sqrt{36a^2}$.
22. $\sqrt{9b^4}$.
23. $\sqrt[3]{8x^6}$.
24. $\sqrt[4]{16y^{12}}$.
25. $\sqrt{\dfrac{x^4}{y^6}}$.
26. $\sqrt{\dfrac{4x^2}{9y^8}}$.
27. $\sqrt[3]{\dfrac{8y^9}{27a^6}}$.
28. $\sqrt[5]{\dfrac{32a^{15}}{b^{10}c^0}}$.
29. $\sqrt{a^3}$.
30. $\sqrt[3]{b^2}$.
31. $\sqrt[4]{b^2}$.
32. $\sqrt[6]{a^{12}}$.
33. $\sqrt{8}$.
34. $\sqrt[3]{16}$.
35. $\sqrt[4]{64}$.
36. $\sqrt[6]{81}$.
37. $\sqrt{4a^3b^4}$.
38. $\sqrt[3]{8x^6y^2z}$.
39. $\sqrt[6]{64a^4b^{12}c^3}$.
40. $\sqrt[4]{9u^6v^8z}$.
41. $\sqrt[3]{\dfrac{8a^2}{27b}}$.
42. $\sqrt[4]{\dfrac{a^0b^3}{16w^8}}$.
43. $\sqrt[3]{\dfrac{64a^2}{27c^5}}$.
44. $\sqrt[3]{\dfrac{8x^2}{81y^4}}$.

Write the expression in each of Problems 45 to 76 without the use of fractional or negative exponents.

45. $a^{\frac{2}{3}}$.
46. $b^{\frac{3}{4}}$.
47. $c^{\frac{2}{5}}$.
48. $d^{\frac{3}{7}}$.
49. $x^{-\frac{1}{2}}$.
50. $y^{-\frac{2}{3}}$.
51. $z^{-\frac{3}{5}}$.
52. $w^{-\frac{4}{7}}$.
53. $a^{\frac{3}{5}}b^{\frac{2}{3}}$.
54. $x^{\frac{2}{5}}y^{\frac{3}{8}}$.
55. $y^{\frac{2}{7}}w^{\frac{4}{7}}$.
56. $s^{\frac{3}{8}}t^{\frac{5}{8}}$.
57. $4^{\frac{1}{2}}a^{\frac{2}{3}}$.
58. $27^{\frac{1}{3}}x^{\frac{1}{2}}y^{\frac{3}{2}}$.
59. $16^{\frac{3}{4}}z^{\frac{1}{4}}w^{\frac{3}{4}}$.
60. $9^{\frac{3}{2}}u^{\frac{2}{3}}v^{\frac{1}{3}}$.
61. $8^{\frac{2}{3}}b^{-\frac{1}{3}}$.
62. $16^{\frac{3}{4}}y^{-\frac{1}{4}}$.
63. $27^{\frac{1}{3}}a^{\frac{2}{3}}y^{-\frac{1}{3}}$.
64. $32^{\frac{2}{5}}x^{\frac{3}{5}}y^{-\frac{4}{5}}$.
65. $x^{\frac{1}{2}}y^{\frac{1}{4}}$.   HINT: Reduce the fractional exponents to a common denominator.
66. $a^{\frac{1}{2}}b^{\frac{1}{3}}$.
67. $p^{\frac{2}{3}}q^{\frac{3}{4}}$.
68. $x^{\frac{3}{2}}y^{\frac{2}{3}}z^{\frac{3}{4}}$.
69. $3c^{\frac{1}{3}}y^{\frac{2}{5}}$.
70. $2x^{\frac{1}{2}}y^{\frac{2}{3}}$.
71. $a^{\frac{1}{2}}y^{\frac{1}{5}}w^{\frac{1}{3}}$.
72. $b^{\frac{2}{3}}c^{\frac{3}{5}}d^{\frac{1}{2}}$.
73. $8^{\frac{1}{3}}a^{\frac{1}{4}}b^{\frac{1}{2}}$.
74. $16^{\frac{1}{4}}x^{\frac{3}{2}}y^{\frac{1}{3}}$.
75. $32^{\frac{1}{5}}c^{\frac{1}{3}}d^{\frac{5}{6}}e^{\frac{1}{2}}$.
76. $81^{\frac{1}{4}}u^{\frac{3}{5}}v^{\frac{1}{2}}w^{\frac{3}{4}}$.

49. Simplification of exponential expressions. We shall agree that an exponential expression is simplified if the following steps are performed:

1. *Make all possible combinations by means of (2) to (7), Art. 45.*
2. *Express the result without zero or negative exponents.*

In many problems, it is more efficient to perform Step 2 first. However, after some practice, it is often possible to perform the two steps simultaneously.

In order to simplify an exponential expression that also contains radicals, we first change the radicals to fractional exponents and then apply Steps 1 and 2.

EXAMPLE 1

Simplify $\dfrac{3a^2b^4c^{-2}}{12a^{-2}b^3}$.

Solution

We first apply (4), Art. 45, to the powers of a and b and get

$$\frac{3a^2b^4c^{-2}}{12a^{-2}b^3} = \frac{3a^{2-(-2)}b^{4-3}c^{-2}}{12} = \frac{3a^4bc^{-2}}{12}.$$

Now we move the factor c^{-2} to the denominator, change the sign of the exponent, then divide the numerator and denominator by 3, and obtain

$$\frac{3a^4bc^{-2}}{12} = \frac{a^4b}{4c^2}.$$

EXAMPLE 2

Simplify $\dfrac{5x^3y^{-2}z^{-\frac{1}{2}}}{10x^{\frac{2}{3}}y^{\frac{1}{4}}}$.

Solution

In this problem, we shall apply (4), Art. 45, to the powers of x and also move the factors y^{-2} and $z^{-\frac{1}{2}}$ into the denominator by changing the signs of the exponents. Thus, we get

$$\frac{5x^3y^{-2}z^{-\frac{1}{2}}}{10x^{\frac{2}{3}}y^{\frac{1}{4}}} = \frac{5x^{3-\frac{2}{3}}}{10y^{\frac{1}{4}}y^2z^{\frac{1}{2}}}$$

$$= \frac{5x^{\frac{7}{3}}}{10y^{2+\frac{1}{4}}z^{\frac{1}{2}}}$$

$$= \frac{x^{\frac{7}{3}}}{2y^{\frac{9}{4}}z^{\frac{1}{2}}}.$$

EXAMPLE 3

Simplify $\left(\dfrac{2a^3b^{\frac{1}{2}}c^2}{3a^{\frac{1}{3}}c^4}\right)\left(\dfrac{a^{-\frac{1}{2}}b^{\frac{3}{2}}}{c^{-1}}\right)^2$.

Solution

We shall first square the expression in the second parentheses, then multiply the result by the expression in the first parentheses, and finally simplify the product thus obtained.

$$\left(\frac{2a^3b^{\frac{1}{2}}c^2}{3a^{\frac{1}{3}}c^4}\right)\left(\frac{a^{-\frac{1}{2}}b^{\frac{3}{2}}}{c^{-1}}\right)^2 = \left(\frac{2a^3b^{\frac{1}{2}}c^2}{3a^{\frac{1}{3}}c^4}\right)\left[\frac{a^{(-\frac{1}{2})2}b^{(\frac{3}{2})2}}{c^{(-1)2}}\right]$$

$$= \left(\frac{2a^3b^{\frac{1}{2}}c^2}{3a^{\frac{1}{3}}c^4}\right)\left(\frac{a^{-1}b^3}{c^{-2}}\right)$$

$$= \frac{2a^{3-1}b^{\frac{1}{2}+3}c^2}{3a^{\frac{1}{3}}c^{4-2}}$$

$$= \frac{2a^2b^{\frac{7}{2}}c^2}{3a^{\frac{1}{3}}c^2}$$

$$= \tfrac{2}{3}a^{\frac{5}{3}}b^{\frac{7}{2}}c^0 = \tfrac{2}{3}a^{\frac{5}{3}}b^{\frac{7}{2}}.$$

EXAMPLE 4

Simplify $\left(\dfrac{a^{-1}b^{-1}}{a^{-1}-b^{-1}}\right)^{-2}$.

Solution

Since the denominator is the difference of two terms, we must use (1), Art. 46, and replace each term having a negative exponent with an equivalent term in which the exponents are positive. When this is done, we have

$$\left(\frac{a^{-1}b^{-1}}{a^{-1}-b^{-1}}\right)^{-2} = \left[\frac{\left(\frac{1}{a}\right)\left(\frac{1}{b}\right)}{\frac{1}{a}-\frac{1}{b}}\right]^{-2}$$

$$= \left[\frac{ab\left(\frac{1}{ab}\right)}{ab\left(\frac{1}{a}-\frac{1}{b}\right)}\right]^{-2} \qquad \text{(multiplying numerator and denominator by } ab)$$

$$= \left(\frac{1}{b-a}\right)^{-2}$$

$$= \frac{1^{-2}}{(b-1)^{-2}} \qquad \text{[by (7), Art. 45]}$$

$$= \frac{(b-a)^2}{1^2} \qquad \text{[by (1), Art. 46]}$$

$$= (b-a)^2.$$

EXERCISE 28

Simplify the expression in each of Problems 1 to 80.

1. $a^{\frac{1}{3}}a^{\frac{2}{3}}$.

2. $x^{\frac{5}{4}}x^{\frac{3}{4}}$.

3. $c^{\frac{1}{6}}c^{\frac{5}{6}}$.

4. $y^{\frac{7}{6}}y^{\frac{3}{5}}$.

5. $a^{\frac{1}{4}}a^{\frac{1}{2}}$.

6. $d^{\frac{2}{3}}d^{\frac{1}{4}}$.

7. $z^{\frac{1}{5}}z^{\frac{3}{10}}$.

8. $w^{\frac{2}{3}}w^{\frac{1}{6}}$.

9. $\dfrac{b^{\frac{3}{2}}}{b^{\frac{1}{2}}}$.

10. $\dfrac{m^{\frac{2}{3}}}{m^{-\frac{1}{3}}}$.

11. $\dfrac{r^{\frac{3}{4}}}{r^{\frac{1}{2}}}$.

12. $\dfrac{t^{\frac{5}{4}}}{t^{\frac{3}{8}}}$.

13. $(2a^{\frac{1}{2}}b^{\frac{3}{4}})(3a^{-\frac{1}{2}}b^{-\frac{1}{4}})$.

14. $(\frac{1}{2}x^{\frac{2}{3}}y^{-\frac{1}{3}})(4x^{\frac{1}{3}}y^{\frac{2}{3}})$.

15. $(6w^{\frac{3}{5}}z^{-\frac{1}{4}})(2w^{-\frac{2}{5}}z^{\frac{3}{4}})$.

16. $(4xy^{\frac{1}{3}})(2x^{-2}y^{\frac{2}{3}})$.

17. $(4a^2b^{\frac{2}{3}})^{\frac{1}{2}}$.

18. $(27m^{\frac{3}{4}}n^6)^{\frac{1}{3}}$.

19. $(16x^8y^{\frac{4}{3}}z^{\frac{2}{3}})^{\frac{1}{4}}$.

20. $(8m^2n^{\frac{2}{3}})^{\frac{2}{3}}$.

21. $(a^4y^{-1})^{\frac{1}{2}}$.

22. $(p^{-1}t^{-3})^{\frac{1}{3}}$.

23. $(e^{-2}m^3)^{\frac{1}{4}}$.

24. $(s^{-6}y^{-1})^{-\frac{1}{2}}$.

25. $(2a^{-\frac{1}{2}}b^{\frac{3}{4}})^{-4}$.

26. $(8x^{-6}y^9)^{-\frac{1}{3}}$.

27. $(3^{-\frac{1}{2}}a^{-\frac{3}{2}}x^{\frac{5}{2}})^{-2}$.

28. $(32c^{\frac{5}{2}}d^{-5})^{-\frac{2}{5}}$.

29. $\dfrac{4^{\frac{1}{2}}a^{\frac{2}{3}}b^{\frac{5}{4}}}{2a^{\frac{1}{3}}b^{\frac{1}{4}}}$.

30. $\dfrac{3x^{\frac{5}{8}}y^{\frac{3}{4}}}{27^{\frac{2}{3}}x^{\frac{1}{8}}y^{\frac{1}{4}}}$.

31. $\dfrac{16^{\frac{1}{2}}c^{\frac{5}{6}}d^{\frac{3}{2}}}{8^{\frac{1}{3}}c^{\frac{3}{6}}d^{\frac{1}{2}}}$.

32. $\dfrac{16^{\frac{3}{4}}m^{\frac{5}{6}}n^{\frac{1}{4}}}{64^{\frac{1}{2}}m^{\frac{1}{6}}n^{\frac{1}{4}}}$.

33. $\dfrac{25^{-\frac{1}{2}}u^{-\frac{1}{2}}v^{\frac{2}{3}}}{5u^{\frac{3}{2}}v^{-\frac{1}{3}}}$.

34. $\dfrac{9^{\frac{3}{2}}r^{\frac{3}{4}}s^{-\frac{5}{8}}}{3^2r^{-\frac{1}{4}}s^{\frac{3}{8}}}$.

35. $\dfrac{25^{\frac{3}{2}}a^{-\frac{5}{6}}b^{\frac{2}{3}}}{5^3a^{\frac{1}{6}}b^{-\frac{2}{5}}}$.

36. $\dfrac{64^{\frac{5}{6}}w^{\frac{3}{8}}z^{-\frac{2}{3}}}{4^{\frac{3}{2}}w^{-\frac{1}{8}}z^{-\frac{2}{3}}}$.

37. $\left(\dfrac{2x^{\frac{2}{3}}y^{\frac{1}{4}}}{2^{-1}x^{-\frac{1}{3}}y^{\frac{3}{4}}}\right)(16^{-\frac{1}{2}}y^{\frac{1}{2}})$.

38. $\left(\dfrac{3^{\frac{1}{2}}m^{\frac{1}{4}}}{27^{-\frac{1}{3}}n^{-\frac{3}{8}}}\right)(m^{-\frac{1}{2}}n^{\frac{1}{4}})$.

39. $\left(\dfrac{8^{\frac{2}{3}}p^{-\frac{3}{8}}}{4^{-\frac{1}{2}}q^{\frac{3}{4}}}\right)(2^{-3}p^{-\frac{1}{8}}q^{\frac{1}{4}})$.

40. $\left(\dfrac{16^{-\frac{1}{4}}a^{\frac{2}{3}}b^{-\frac{1}{8}}}{4^{\frac{1}{2}}a^{-\frac{3}{5}}b^{\frac{5}{8}}}\right)(64a^{-1}b^{-\frac{1}{4}})$.

41. $(2a^{-4}b^{\frac{1}{3}})^{\frac{1}{2}}(2a^{-1}b^{\frac{1}{3}})^{-2}$.

42. $(9c^{\frac{2}{3}}d^{-6})^{-\frac{3}{2}}(3c^{\frac{1}{3}}d^{-2})^3$.

43. $(8a^{-\frac{3}{4}}b^{-\frac{1}{2}})^{-\frac{2}{3}}(2a^{\frac{1}{4}}b^{\frac{1}{6}})^{-2}$.

44. $(16x^{\frac{8}{3}}y^{\frac{2}{3}})^{\frac{3}{4}}(2^{-1}x^{-\frac{1}{3}}y^{\frac{1}{2}})^3$.

45. $(2u^{\frac{1}{2}}v^{-1})^2(u^{-2}v^{\frac{5}{3}})^{\frac{1}{2}}$.

46. $(3x^{\frac{1}{3}}y^{-2})^3(4x^{\frac{1}{2}}y^{-1})^{\frac{1}{2}}$.

47. $(2s^{\frac{2}{3}}y^{\frac{5}{8}})^6(27s^3y^{-3})^{-\frac{1}{3}}$.

48. $(3a^{-\frac{1}{3}}y^0)^3(9a^{-1}y^{\frac{1}{2}})^{-\frac{1}{2}}$.

49. $\dfrac{8^{\frac{1}{3}}a^{\frac{3}{4}}bc^0}{4a^{\frac{1}{2}}b^{-1}c^{-\frac{1}{2}}}$.

50. $\dfrac{16^{\frac{1}{2}}r^{-\frac{1}{3}}s^{\frac{2}{5}}t^0}{8^{\frac{1}{3}}r^{\frac{2}{3}}s^{-\frac{1}{5}}}$.

51. $\dfrac{27^{\frac{1}{3}}x^{\frac{3}{7}}y^{-\frac{2}{5}}}{9^{\frac{1}{2}}x^{-\frac{2}{7}}y^{\frac{3}{5}}}$.

52. $\dfrac{16^{\frac{3}{4}}m^{\frac{1}{4}}n^{-\frac{3}{7}}y}{4m^{-\frac{1}{3}}n^{\frac{1}{7}}y^{-\frac{1}{2}}}$.

53. $\dfrac{8^{\frac{2}{3}}a^{-\frac{1}{2}}y^{\frac{2}{3}}x^0}{4a^{\frac{3}{2}}y^{\frac{1}{3}}x^{-\frac{1}{5}}}$.

54. $\dfrac{32^{\frac{2}{5}}s^{-\frac{2}{3}}x^{-\frac{1}{4}}}{8s^{\frac{1}{3}}x^{\frac{3}{4}}}$.

55. $\dfrac{64^{\frac{2}{3}}p^{-\frac{2}{5}}d^{-\frac{1}{3}}q^{\frac{1}{2}}}{32^{\frac{1}{5}}p^{\frac{3}{5}}d^{-1}q^{-\frac{1}{2}}}$.

56. $\dfrac{4^{\frac{3}{2}}w^{-\frac{1}{3}}h^{\frac{2}{3}}y^{\frac{3}{5}}}{16^{\frac{1}{4}}w^{\frac{2}{3}}h^{\frac{1}{3}}y^{\frac{1}{5}}}$.

57. $\dfrac{d^{\frac{1}{2}}y^{\frac{5}{6}}}{d^{\frac{1}{3}}y^{\frac{1}{2}}}$.

58. $\dfrac{m^{-\frac{2}{3}}y^{\frac{3}{5}}}{m^{\frac{1}{2}}y^{\frac{1}{3}}}$.

59. $\dfrac{s^{\frac{1}{2}}x^{-\frac{3}{5}}}{s^{\frac{1}{3}}x^{\frac{1}{4}}}$.

60. $\dfrac{y^{\frac{3}{4}}w^{-\frac{1}{3}}}{y^{\frac{1}{3}}w^{\frac{2}{5}}}$.

61. $\left(\dfrac{3a^2b^{\frac{1}{2}}}{2a^{-1}b^{-\frac{1}{2}}}\right)\left(\dfrac{a^{-1}b^{-2}}{a^0}\right)^3$.

62. $\left(\dfrac{3s^{-\frac{1}{2}}a^2}{s^{-1}a^{-3}}\right)^2\left(\dfrac{a^{-1}s}{a^{\frac{1}{2}}}\right)$.

63. $\left(\dfrac{2^{-1}b^{-\frac{1}{2}}c}{b^{-1}c^{-\frac{1}{2}}}\right)^2\left(\dfrac{4b^0c^{\frac{1}{2}}}{b^{\frac{1}{2}}c^2}\right).$

64. $\left(\dfrac{3^{-2}x^{-\frac{1}{2}}y}{x^2y^{-\frac{1}{2}}}\right)^2\left(\dfrac{27x^{\frac{1}{2}}}{x^{-\frac{1}{2}}y}\right).$

65. $\left(\dfrac{a^{\frac{1}{2}}b^{\frac{2}{5}}}{a^{\frac{2}{3}}b^{\frac{3}{5}}}\right)^{-2}.$

66. $\left(\dfrac{e^{-\frac{1}{3}}f^{\frac{2}{5}}}{e^{\frac{1}{2}}f^{\frac{3}{4}}}\right)^{-12}.$

67. $\left(\dfrac{t^{\frac{2}{5}}y^{-\frac{1}{4}}}{t^{\frac{1}{2}}y^{\frac{1}{5}}}\right)^{-10}.$

68. $\left(\dfrac{a^{\frac{3}{7}}b^{-\frac{1}{4}}}{a^{\frac{1}{2}}b^{-\frac{1}{3}}}\right)^{-14}.$

69. $\left(\dfrac{a^{-1}-b^{-1}}{a^{-1}+b^{-1}}\right)^{-1}.$

70. $\left(\dfrac{a^{-2}-b^{-2}}{a^{-1}-b^{-1}}\right)^{-1}.$

71. $\left(\dfrac{a^{-2}-b^{-2}}{a^{-1}+b^{-1}}\right)^{-2}.$

72. $\left(\dfrac{a^{-2}b^{-2}}{a^{-1}-b^{-1}}\right)^{-1}.$

73. $\left(\dfrac{x^{a-2b}}{x^{-b}}\right)^{\frac{1}{a-b}}.$

74. $\left(\dfrac{x^{2a+b}}{x^a}\right)^{\frac{a}{a+b}}.$

75. $\left(\dfrac{y^{m-n}}{y^m}\right)^{\frac{m-n}{n}}.$

76. $\left(\dfrac{y^{3m+n}}{y^{m-n}}\right)^{\frac{2}{m+n}}.$

77. $(2x-1)^{\frac{1}{2}}(3x-4)^{-\frac{2}{3}}+(2x-1)^{-\frac{1}{2}}(3x-4)^{\frac{1}{3}}.$

78. $3(3x+1)^{\frac{2}{3}}(4x-3)^{-\frac{1}{4}}+2(3x+1)^{-\frac{1}{3}}(4x-3)^{\frac{3}{4}}.$

79. $(5x-2)^{\frac{2}{5}}(2x-3)^{-\frac{1}{2}}+2(5x-2)^{-\frac{3}{5}}(2x-3)^{\frac{1}{2}}.$

80. $(6x-5)^{\frac{1}{3}}(5x-6)^{-\frac{4}{5}}+2(6x-5)^{-\frac{2}{3}}(5x-6)^{\frac{1}{5}}.$

50. Simplification of radical expressions. Since (6), Art. 45, holds for fractional exponents, we have $(ab)^{\frac{1}{n}}=a^{\frac{1}{n}}b^{\frac{1}{n}}$. Hence, when this relation is expressed in radical form, we have

$$(1) \qquad\qquad \sqrt[n]{ab}=\sqrt[n]{a}\,\sqrt[n]{b}.$$

We may use (1) for simplifying a radical of order n provided the radicand has a factor that is the nth power of a number.

EXAMPLES

1. $\sqrt[3]{243}=\sqrt[3]{(27)(9)}=\sqrt[3]{27}\,\sqrt[3]{9}=3\sqrt[3]{9}.$

2. $\sqrt{72a^3b^5}=\sqrt{(36a^2b^4)(2ab)}=\sqrt{(6ab^2)^2}\,\sqrt{2ab}=6ab^2\sqrt{2ab}.$

We may also use (1) for obtaining and simplifying the product of two or more radicals of the same order.

EXAMPLES

3. $\sqrt{6}\,\sqrt{15}=\sqrt{90}=\sqrt{(9)(10)}=\sqrt{9}\,\sqrt{10}=3\sqrt{10}.$

4. $\sqrt[3]{4a^2b}\,\sqrt[3]{16ab^4}=\sqrt[3]{64a^3b^5}=\sqrt[3]{(64a^3b^3)b^2}=\sqrt[3]{64a^3b^3}\,\sqrt[3]{b^2}$
$\qquad = 4ab\sqrt[3]{b^2}.$

By use of (1), Art. 48, and (7), Art. 45, we may derive a formula for finding the quotient of two radicals of the same order, as follows:

$$\frac{\sqrt[n]{a}}{\sqrt[n]{b}} = \frac{a^{\frac{1}{n}}}{b^{\frac{1}{n}}} \qquad \text{[by (1), Art. 48]}$$

$$= \left(\frac{a}{b}\right)^{\frac{1}{n}} \qquad \text{[by (7), Art. 45]}$$

$$= \sqrt[n]{\frac{a}{b}}. \qquad \text{[by (1), Art. 48]}$$

Hence, we have

(2) $$\frac{\sqrt[n]{a}}{\sqrt[n]{b}} = \sqrt[n]{\frac{a}{b}}.$$

EXAMPLE

$$\frac{\sqrt{54a^3b}}{\sqrt{3ab^3}} = \sqrt{\frac{54a^3b}{3ab^3}} \qquad \text{[by (2)]}$$

$$= \sqrt{\frac{18a^2}{b^2}} \qquad \text{(by dividing numerator and denominator by } 3ab\text{)}$$

$$= \sqrt{\frac{9a^2}{b^2}}\,\sqrt{2} \qquad \text{[by (1)]}$$

$$= \frac{3a}{b}\,\sqrt{2}.$$

In order to simplify expressions which involve only multiplication or division of radicals of the nth order, we *first perform all possible operations by use of* (1) *and* (2) *and the laws of exponents, thus obtaining a single radical of the nth order; second, if the radicand thus obtained has factors that are nth powers, we take the nth roots of these factors, thus removing them from the radical. We then write the product of these nth roots as the coefficient of the radical.*

EXAMPLE

Simplify $\dfrac{\sqrt{27a^3b^2c}\,\sqrt{15ab^3c^5}}{\sqrt{3a^2bc^3}}.$

Solution

We shall first combine the radicals by means of (1) and (2) and then simplify the radical thus obtained.

$$\frac{\sqrt{27a^3b^2c} \; \sqrt{15ab^3c^5}}{\sqrt{3a^2bc^3}} = \sqrt{\frac{(27a^3b^2c)(15ab^3c^5)}{3a^2bc^3}} \qquad \text{[by (1) and (2)]}$$

$$= \sqrt{\frac{(3^3)(3)(5)a^4b^5c^6}{3a^2bc^3}} \qquad \begin{array}{l}(\text{since} \quad 27 = 3^3 \quad \text{and} \\ 15 = 3 \times 5)\end{array}$$

$$= \sqrt{3^3(5)a^2b^4c^3}$$

$$= \sqrt{(3ab^2c)^2(3)(5)c}$$

$$= 3ab^2c \; \sqrt{15c}.$$

EXERCISE 29

Simplify the following radical expressions.

1. $\sqrt{16}$. 2. $\sqrt{49}$. 3. $\sqrt{256}$. 4. $\sqrt{324}$.

5. $\sqrt{50}$. 6. $\sqrt{54}$. 7. $\sqrt{147}$. 8. $\sqrt{63}$.

9. $\sqrt{128}$. 10. $\sqrt{200}$. 11. $\sqrt{192}$. 12. $\sqrt{512}$.

13. $\sqrt[3]{24}$. 14. $\sqrt[3]{81}$. 15. $\sqrt[3]{297}$. 16. $\sqrt[3]{1024}$.

17. $\sqrt[4]{162}$. 18. $\sqrt[4]{1875}$. 19. $\sqrt[4]{405}$. 20. $\sqrt[4]{1024}$.

21. $\sqrt{50a^2y^3}$. 22. $\sqrt{18a^3y^4}$. 23. $\sqrt{27x^6y^7}$. 24. $\sqrt{48c^0d^3}$.

25. $\sqrt[3]{54x^4y^3}$. 26. $\sqrt[3]{24a^2t^6}$. 27. $\sqrt[4]{48m^7r^5}$. 28. $\sqrt[4]{162s^9t^7}$.

29. $\sqrt[5]{u^7v^9w^{11}}$. 30. $\sqrt[5]{m^5n^7w^{12}}$. 31. $\sqrt[6]{g^7h^9k^{13}}$. 32. $\sqrt[6]{a^9b^6c^7}$.

33. $\sqrt[3]{16a^4b^9c^5}$. 34. $\sqrt[4]{48x^7y^8z^9}$. 35. $\sqrt[5]{64c^{10}d^6e^8}$.

36. $\sqrt[5]{243r^{15}s^7t^{11}}$. 37. $\sqrt{\dfrac{45xy^2}{x^{-1}}}$. 38. $\sqrt{\dfrac{80x^4y^{-2}}{x^{-1}y^{-3}}}$.

39. $\sqrt{\dfrac{98a^{-1}s^3}{a^{-3}s^{-2}}}$. 40. $\sqrt{\dfrac{75b^{-1}c^3}{b^3c^{-1}}}$. 41. $\sqrt{\dfrac{8a^2b^{-2}c^3}{9a^{-1}b^2c^{-1}}}$.

42. $\sqrt[3]{\dfrac{24m^2n^{-2}p^4}{125m^{-1}n^4}}$. 43. $\sqrt[3]{\dfrac{32r^6s^3t^{-4}}{108r^2s^{-1}t^2}}$. 44. $\sqrt[4]{\dfrac{162x^6y^{-3}z^2}{625x^2y^5z^{-7}}}$.

45. $\sqrt{18} \, \sqrt{8}$. 46. $\sqrt{3} \, \sqrt{27}$. 47. $\sqrt{6} \, \sqrt{54}$. 48. $\sqrt{14} \, \sqrt{56}$.

49. $\sqrt[3]{4} \, \sqrt[3]{16}$. 50. $\sqrt[3]{5} \, \sqrt[3]{25}$. 51. $\sqrt[4]{8} \, \sqrt[4]{2}$. 52. $\sqrt[4]{48} \, \sqrt[4]{27}$.

53. $\sqrt{8r^3t} \, \sqrt{2rt^5}$. 54. $\sqrt{18a^2b} \, \sqrt{2ab^3}$. 55. $\sqrt{20x^3y} \, \sqrt{5x^5y^2}$.

56. $\sqrt{27m^3y} \, \sqrt{12my^3}$. 57. $\sqrt[3]{8x^4y^2} \, \sqrt[3]{x^2y}$.

58. $\sqrt[3]{54a^7c^0} \, \sqrt[3]{4a^2c^6}$. 59. $\sqrt[4]{a^8b^3} \, \sqrt[4]{a^3b^5c^5}$.

60. $\sqrt[4]{t^3s^2} \, \sqrt[4]{t^5s^3}$. 61. $\dfrac{\sqrt{128}}{\sqrt{2}}$. 62. $\dfrac{\sqrt{27}}{\sqrt{3}}$.

63. $\dfrac{\sqrt{108}}{\sqrt{3}}.$

64. $\dfrac{\sqrt{54}}{\sqrt{6}}.$

65. $\dfrac{\sqrt{63x^2y^3}}{\sqrt{7x^4y}}.$

66. $\dfrac{\sqrt{252x^{-1}y^3}}{\sqrt{28x^5y}}.$

67. $\dfrac{\sqrt{245x^7y^3}}{\sqrt{125xy^5}}.$

68. $\dfrac{\sqrt{567m^3n}}{\sqrt{63mn^3}}.$

69. $\dfrac{\sqrt{20a^2b^3c^4}}{\sqrt{5ab^{-1}c}}.$

70. $\dfrac{\sqrt{26x^{-2}y^5z^0}}{\sqrt{13x^4yz^{-1}}}.$

71. $\dfrac{\sqrt{28u^6v^2z^{-3}}}{\sqrt{7u^{-1}v^4z}}.$

72. $\dfrac{\sqrt{48x^3y^{-5}z^2}}{\sqrt{8xyz^4}}.$

73. $\dfrac{\sqrt{6}\sqrt{18}}{\sqrt{24}}.$

74. $\dfrac{\sqrt[3]{16}\sqrt[3]{81}}{\sqrt[3]{6}}.$

75. $\dfrac{\sqrt{28}\sqrt{14}}{\sqrt{126}}.$

76. $\dfrac{\sqrt[4]{32}\sqrt[4]{27}}{\sqrt[4]{6}}.$

77. $\dfrac{\sqrt{8x^2y^5}\sqrt{3xy^4}}{\sqrt{6x^3y^3}}.$

78. $\dfrac{\sqrt{28a^3b^4}\sqrt{14a^4b^5}}{\sqrt{2a^2b^3}}.$

79. $\dfrac{\sqrt{56w^6z^{-1}}\sqrt{108w^{-3}z^3}}{\sqrt{21wz^{-5}}}.$

80. $\dfrac{\sqrt{96c^6d^{-3}}\sqrt{75c^{-3}d^4}}{\sqrt{60c^2d^{-5}}}.$

51. Rationalizing denominators. Frequently it is desirable to change a fraction whose denominator contains radicals to an equal fraction in which the denominator is free of radicals. This process is called *rationalizing the denominator*. We shall discuss the cases in which (1) the denominator is either a single radical or has radical factors; and (2) the denominator is the sum of two or more terms at least one of which contains a radical of the second order. We shall illustrate the method for each situation by several examples.

EXAMPLE 1

We shall first consider the fraction $\sqrt{\tfrac{2}{3}}$. The index of the radical here is 2. Hence, in order to rationalize the denominator of this fraction, we change the denominator of the radicand to $3^2 = 9$ by multiplying the numerator and denominator by 3. Thus, we get

$$\sqrt{\frac{2}{3}} = \sqrt{\frac{2\times 3}{3\times 3}} = \sqrt{\frac{6}{9}} = \frac{\sqrt{6}}{\sqrt{9}} = \frac{\sqrt{6}}{3}.$$

EXAMPLE 2

In order to rationalize the denominator of $\sqrt[5]{\dfrac{a}{b^3}}$, we must convert the denominator of the radicand into a fifth power, since the index of the radical is 5. Hence, we multiply both the numerator and the denominator of the radicand by b^2 and obtain

$$\sqrt[5]{\frac{a}{b^3}} = \sqrt[5]{\frac{ab^2}{b^3b^2}} = \sqrt[5]{\frac{ab^2}{b^5}} = \frac{\sqrt[5]{ab^2}}{b}.$$

EXAMPLE 3

We rationalize the denominator of $\dfrac{a^2 - b^2}{3a \sqrt{a + b}}$ by multiplying the numerator and denominator by $\sqrt{a + b}$, thus obtaining

$$\frac{a^2 - b^2}{3a \sqrt{a + b}} = \frac{(a^2 - b^2) \sqrt{a + b}}{3a \sqrt{a + b} \sqrt{a + b}}$$

$$= \frac{(a^2 - b^2) \sqrt{a + b}}{3a \sqrt{(a + b)^2}} \quad \text{[by (1), Art. 50]}$$

$$= \frac{(a - b)(a + b) \sqrt{a + b}}{3a(a + b)} = \frac{(a - b) \sqrt{a + b}}{3a}.$$

We see from the above examples that when the denominator of a fraction has a factor that is a radical of order n, we rationalize it by multiplying numerator and denominator by the number required to make the radicand an nth power.

If the denominator of a fraction is the sum or difference of two terms at least one of which contains a radical of the second order, we rationalize the denominator by the method illustrated below.

EXAMPLE 4

Rationalize the denominator of $\dfrac{2}{\sqrt{3} - 1}$.

Solution

Since the product of the sum and difference of two numbers is the difference of their squares, we multiply the numerator and denominator of this fraction by $\sqrt{3} + 1$ and obtain

$$\frac{2}{\sqrt{3} - 1} = \frac{2(\sqrt{3} + 1)}{(\sqrt{3} - 1)(\sqrt{3} + 1)} = \frac{2(\sqrt{3} + 1)}{(\sqrt{3})^2 - 1} = \frac{2(\sqrt{3} + 1)}{3 - 1}$$

$$= \frac{2(\sqrt{3} + 1)}{2} = \sqrt{3} + 1.$$

EXAMPLE 5

Rationalize the denominator of $\dfrac{2\sqrt{3}-\sqrt{2}}{\sqrt{3}+\sqrt{2}}$.

Solution

In this problem, we multiply the numerator and denominator by $\sqrt{3}-\sqrt{2}$ and get

$$\frac{2\sqrt{3}-\sqrt{2}}{\sqrt{3}+\sqrt{2}} = \frac{(2\sqrt{3}-\sqrt{2})(\sqrt{3}-\sqrt{2})}{(\sqrt{3}+\sqrt{2})(\sqrt{3}-\sqrt{2})}$$

$$= \frac{2(\sqrt{3})^2 - 3\sqrt{3}\sqrt{2} + (\sqrt{2})^2}{(\sqrt{3})^2 - (\sqrt{2})^2}$$

$$= \frac{2(3) - 3\sqrt{6} + 2}{3 - 2}$$

$$= 8 - 3\sqrt{6}.$$

In the above examples, the desired rationalization was accomplished by multiplying both members of the fraction by a binomial containing the same terms as the denominator, but with the sign between them changed. If we apply this procedure to any fraction having a binomial denominator that contains a radical of the second order, we obtain an equivalent fraction whose denominator is the difference of the squares of the terms of the original binomial. Hence, it contains no radicals.

EXERCISE 30

Simplify the radical expression in each of the following problems and rationalize all denominators.

1. $\sqrt{\frac{3}{2}}$. 2. $\sqrt{\frac{5}{7}}$. 3. $\sqrt{\frac{3}{5}}$. 4. $\sqrt{\frac{2}{13}}$.

5. $\sqrt{\frac{7}{8}}$. 6. $\sqrt{\frac{5}{18}}$. 7. $\sqrt{\frac{3}{20}}$. 8. $\sqrt{\frac{2}{75}}$.

9. $\sqrt{\frac{8}{27}}$. 10. $\sqrt{\frac{20}{63}}$. 11. $\sqrt{\frac{32}{45}}$. 12. $\sqrt{\frac{27}{80}}$.

13. $\sqrt[3]{\frac{1}{4}}$. 14. $\sqrt[3]{\frac{3}{2}}$. 15. $\sqrt[3]{\frac{2}{5}}$. 16. $\sqrt[3]{\frac{4}{9}}$.

17. $\sqrt[3]{\frac{81}{16}}$. 18. $\sqrt[3]{\frac{24}{49}}$. 19. $\sqrt[3]{\frac{54}{25}}$. 20. $\sqrt[3]{\frac{128}{81}}$.

21. $\sqrt{\frac{3}{5}}\sqrt{\frac{2}{3}}$. 22. $\sqrt{\frac{7}{3}}\sqrt{\frac{3}{8}}$. 23. $\sqrt{\frac{3}{2}}\sqrt{\frac{4}{5}}$. 24. $\sqrt{\frac{21}{8}}\sqrt{\frac{3}{7}}$.

25. $\sqrt{\dfrac{a}{c}}$. 26. $\sqrt{\dfrac{2x^3}{y}}$. 27. $\sqrt{\dfrac{s^2}{3t}}$. 28. $\sqrt{\dfrac{m^3}{5u}}$.

29. $\dfrac{\sqrt{8a^3b^2}}{\sqrt{36ab^3}}$. 30. $\dfrac{\sqrt{125a^7b^2}}{\sqrt{75a^5b^5}}$. 31. $\dfrac{\sqrt{28x^3y}}{\sqrt{35x^5y^3}}$. 32. $\dfrac{\sqrt{108c^2d^4e^3}}{\sqrt{32c^3de^2}}$.

33. $\sqrt{\dfrac{x^{-1}}{cy}}.$ **34.** $\sqrt{\dfrac{2a^{-1}}{3x^{-2}}}.$ **35.** $\sqrt{\dfrac{3^{-1}d}{x^{-2}4^{-2}}}.$ **36.** $\sqrt{\dfrac{2^{-3}s}{t^{-1}u}}.$

37. $\sqrt[3]{\dfrac{2b}{c^2d}}.$ **38.** $\sqrt[3]{\dfrac{3x}{4y}}.$ **39.** $\sqrt[3]{\dfrac{5a^4}{9b}}.$ **40.** $\sqrt[3]{\dfrac{3s}{16t^2}}.$

41. $\sqrt{\dfrac{2x}{3a}}\sqrt{\dfrac{4a^3}{2x^4}}.$ **42.** $\sqrt{\dfrac{6ab}{a^{-1}b^2}}\sqrt{\dfrac{2a}{a^2b}}.$ **43.** $\sqrt[3]{\dfrac{m^2s}{ab^2}}\sqrt[3]{\dfrac{ms}{ab}}.$

44. $\sqrt[3]{\dfrac{a^2b^4}{cd^4}}\sqrt[3]{\dfrac{ab}{cd^2}}.$ **45.** $\dfrac{a^2-b^2}{\sqrt{a-b}}.$ **46.** $\dfrac{a+b}{(a-b)\sqrt{a+b}}.$

47. $\dfrac{(x-y)\sqrt{x-y}}{\sqrt{x^2-y^2}}.$ **48.** $\dfrac{c+d}{\sqrt{c^2-d^2}}.$ **49.** $\dfrac{1}{\sqrt{2}-1}.$

50. $\dfrac{2}{\sqrt{3}+1}.$ **51.** $\dfrac{4}{1-\sqrt{5}}.$ **52.** $\dfrac{5}{2+\sqrt{7}}.$

53. $\dfrac{\sqrt{3}+\sqrt{2}}{\sqrt{3}-\sqrt{2}}.$ **54.** $\dfrac{2+\sqrt{2}}{2-\sqrt{2}}.$ **55.** $\dfrac{\sqrt{6}-2}{\sqrt{6}+2}.$

56. $\dfrac{\sqrt{3}+2}{\sqrt{3}-2}.$ **57.** $\dfrac{\sqrt{6}+\sqrt{3}}{\sqrt{6}-\sqrt{3}}.$ **58.** $\dfrac{\sqrt{8}-\sqrt{6}}{\sqrt{8}+\sqrt{6}}.$

59. $\dfrac{\sqrt{7}+\sqrt{5}}{\sqrt{7}-\sqrt{5}}.$ **60.** $\dfrac{\sqrt{10}+\sqrt{5}}{\sqrt{10}-\sqrt{5}}.$

52. Addition of radicals. In order to find the sum of two or more radicals, we

1. *Simplify all radicals;*
2. *Rationalize all denominators in the terms of the sum;*
3. *Combine all radicals which have the same index and the same radicand by adding coefficients.*

EXAMPLE

$$\sqrt{32}+\sqrt{54}-3\sqrt{8}-\frac{3}{\sqrt{24}}=\sqrt{16\times 2}+\sqrt{9\times 6}-3\sqrt{4\times 2}-\frac{3\sqrt{24}}{24}$$

$$=4\sqrt{2}+3\sqrt{6}-(3\times 2)\sqrt{2}-\frac{3\sqrt{4\times 6}}{24}$$

$$=4\sqrt{2}+3\sqrt{6}-6\sqrt{2}-\frac{\sqrt{6}}{4}$$

$$=(4-6)\sqrt{2}+(3-\tfrac{1}{4})\sqrt{6}$$

$$=-2\sqrt{2}+\tfrac{11}{4}\sqrt{6}.$$

53. *Changing the order of a radical.*   We shall use (5), Art. 45, and (1), Art. 48, to derive a formula which will enable us to express any radical as a radical with a different index.   The derivation follows.

$$\sqrt[mn]{a} = a^{\frac{1}{mn}} \qquad \text{[by (1), Art. 48]}$$
$$= (a^{\frac{1}{m}})^{\frac{1}{n}} \qquad \text{[by (5), Art. 45]}$$
$$= \sqrt[n]{\sqrt[m]{a}}. \qquad \text{[by (1), Art. 48]}$$

Hence, we have

(1) $$\sqrt[mn]{a} = \sqrt[n]{\sqrt[m]{a}}.$$

If $a = b^m$, then

$$\sqrt[mn]{a} = \sqrt[n]{\sqrt[m]{b^m}} = \sqrt[n]{b}.$$

Thus, *if the radicand can be expressed as a power whose exponent is a factor of the index of the radical, the order of the radical can be reduced.*

EXAMPLE 1

Express $\sqrt[4]{4a^2b^6}$ as a radical of lower order.

Solution

Since the radicand, $4a^2b^6$, is equal to $(2ab^3)^2$ and the exponent 2 is a factor of the index 4, we write

$$\sqrt[4]{4a^2b^6} = \sqrt{\sqrt{(2ab^3)^2}} = \sqrt{2ab^3}.$$

EXAMPLE 2

Express $\sqrt[6]{\dfrac{27a^9b^{12}}{8c^3}}$ as a radical of lower order.

Solution

In this problem, the radicand can be expressed as a third power since

$$\frac{27a^9b^{12}}{8c^3} = \left(\frac{3a^3b^4}{2c}\right)^3.$$

Furthermore, the index 6 is divisible by 3; hence,

$$\sqrt[6]{\frac{27a^9b^{12}}{8c^3}} = \sqrt[3]{\sqrt{\left(\frac{3a^3b^4}{2c}\right)^3}} = \sqrt{\frac{3a^3b^4}{2c}}.$$

It is sometimes desirable to express a given radical as another radical of higher order, and (1) can be used for this purpose also. For example, $\sqrt[p]{a} = \sqrt[p]{\sqrt[n]{a^n}} = \sqrt[pn]{a^n}$. Hence, *we see that we may multiply the index of a radical by any number* n *provided we raise the radicand to the nth power.*

EXAMPLE 3

Express $\sqrt[3]{2a^2b}$ as a radical of order 12.

Solution

The problem requires us to multiply the given index by 4; hence, we must also raise the radicand to the fourth power. This operation yields

$$\sqrt[3]{2a^2b} = \sqrt[3]{\sqrt[4]{(2a^2b)^4}} = \sqrt[12]{16a^8b^4}.$$

EXAMPLE 4

Express $\sqrt{3x}$, $\sqrt[3]{4y^2}$, and $\sqrt[4]{4x^3}$ as radicals of the same order.

Solution

Since the LCM of the given indices 2, 3, and 4 is 12, we shall express each of the given radicals as a radical of order 12. Hence, we must multiply the first index by 6, the second by 4, and the third by 3, and raise the respective radicands to the corresponding powers. When this is done, we have

$$\sqrt{3x} = \sqrt{\sqrt[6]{(3x)^6}} = \sqrt[12]{729x^6};$$
$$\sqrt[3]{4y^2} = \sqrt[3]{\sqrt[4]{(4y^2)^4}} = \sqrt[12]{256y^8};$$
$$\sqrt[4]{4x^3} = \sqrt[4]{\sqrt[3]{(4x^3)^3}} = \sqrt[12]{64x^9}.$$

EXERCISE 31

Simplify the radicals in Problems 1 to 24 and then make all possible combinations.

1. $\sqrt{3} + \sqrt{12} + \sqrt{27}$.
2. $\sqrt{2} + \sqrt{72} - \sqrt{50}$.
3. $\sqrt{5} + \sqrt{20} - \sqrt{45}$.
4. $\sqrt{24} - \sqrt{54} + \sqrt{150}$.
5. $\sqrt{18} + \sqrt{12} + \sqrt{50} - \sqrt{75}$.

6. $\sqrt{32} + \sqrt{45} - \sqrt{98} - \sqrt{125}.$

7. $\sqrt{63} - \sqrt{28} + \sqrt{147} - \sqrt{48}.$

8. $\sqrt{50} - \sqrt{245} - \sqrt{125} + \sqrt{80}.$

9. $\sqrt[3]{2} + \sqrt[3]{16} - \sqrt[3]{54}.$ **10.** $\sqrt[3]{3} + \sqrt[3]{24} + \sqrt[3]{81}.$

11. $\sqrt[3]{6} + \sqrt[3]{48} + \sqrt[3]{162}.$ **12.** $\sqrt[3]{40} - \sqrt[3]{135} + \sqrt[3]{625}.$

13. $a\sqrt{a^2b} + \sqrt{a^4b} + a^2\sqrt{9b}.$ **14.** $\sqrt{m^4p} + 2\sqrt{m^2p^3} + \sqrt{p^5}.$

15. $y\sqrt{4x^3y} - x\sqrt{9xy^3} + \sqrt{25x^3y^3}.$

16. $ab\sqrt{9a^3b^3} - 2a\sqrt{4a^3b^5} + \sqrt{4a^5b^5}.$

17. $2c^2d^3\sqrt{4c^3d} - 2c\sqrt{9c^5d^7} - d^2\sqrt{4c^7d^3} + 3\sqrt{9c^7d^7}.$

18. $4u\sqrt{4u^3v^5} - 2v\sqrt{9u^5v^3} + 4\sqrt{u^5v^5} - uv\sqrt{25u^3v^3}.$

19. $4w\sqrt{9w^5z^5} + 3z\sqrt{9w^7z^3} - 5wz\sqrt{9w^5z^3} - 2\sqrt{16w^7z^5}.$

20. $3m^2\sqrt{4mn^7} - m^2n^3\sqrt{9mn} - 2n\sqrt{4m^5n^5} - 2n^2\sqrt{m^5n^3}.$

21. $3x\sqrt{\dfrac{y^3}{4}} + y\sqrt{\dfrac{x^2y}{9}} - \dfrac{xy}{2}\sqrt{\dfrac{25y}{16}} - \dfrac{1}{2}\sqrt{\dfrac{x^2y^3}{4}}.$

22. $3\sqrt{\dfrac{b^2}{2a}} + \dfrac{b}{a}\sqrt{\dfrac{a}{2}} - \dfrac{4}{a}\sqrt{\dfrac{ab^2}{18}}.$ **23.** $\sqrt{\dfrac{5x}{y}} + \sqrt{\dfrac{16y}{5x}} - \sqrt{\dfrac{5y}{x}} - \sqrt{\dfrac{x}{5y}}.$

24. $\sqrt{\dfrac{3t}{2s^3}} + 3\sqrt{\dfrac{3s}{8t^3}} - \dfrac{1}{s}\sqrt{\dfrac{2t}{3s}} - \dfrac{1}{2t}\sqrt{\dfrac{3s}{2t}}.$

Express the radicals in Problems 25 to 40 in terms of radicals of lower order and simplify.

25. $\sqrt[4]{x^6y^4}.$ **26.** $\sqrt[6]{x^3y^9}.$ **27.** $\sqrt[8]{a^4b^6}.$ **28.** $\sqrt[9]{a^6b^{12}}.$

29. $\sqrt[9]{27x^3y^6}.$ **30.** $\sqrt[6]{64x^2y^4}.$ **31.** $\sqrt[12]{16a^4b^8}.$ **32.** $\sqrt[9]{x^3y^9}.$

33. $\sqrt[4]{\dfrac{81x^2y}{y^{-3}}}.$ **34.** $\sqrt[6]{\dfrac{8m^3n^2}{27n^{-1}}}.$ **35.** $\sqrt[14]{\dfrac{128x^6y^3}{x^{-1}y^{-4}}}.$ **36.** $\sqrt[12]{\dfrac{9x^6y^4}{3^{-1}y^{-2}}}.$

37. $\sqrt[4]{\dfrac{9ab^3}{4a^3b}}.$ **38.** $\sqrt[9]{\dfrac{64m^3n^6}{125m^{12}n^3}}.$ **39.** $\sqrt[6]{\dfrac{27x^5y}{8x^2y^4}}.$ **40.** $\sqrt[8]{\dfrac{16c^2d^3e^5}{81c^{10}d^7e}}.$

Change the radicals in each of Problems 41 to 52 to the same order.

41. $\sqrt{x},\ \sqrt[4]{x^2y^6}.$ **42.** $\sqrt[3]{a^2b},\ \sqrt[6]{a^4b^2}.$ **43.** $\sqrt[3]{p^2q},\ \sqrt[6]{pq^2}.$

44. $\sqrt{st},\ \sqrt[4]{s^2y^3}.$ **45.** $\sqrt{x^2y},\ \sqrt[3]{2xy^2}.$ **46.** $\sqrt[4]{3ab^3},\ \sqrt[6]{2a^2b^2}.$

47. $\sqrt[6]{2z^2w^3},\ \sqrt[8]{3zw}.$ **48.** $\sqrt[6]{4cd^2e^3},\ \sqrt[9]{2c^2d^4e}.$

49. $\sqrt{a},\ \sqrt[3]{a},\ \sqrt[6]{a}.$ **50.** $\sqrt{2xy},\ \sqrt[4]{3x^3y^2},\ \sqrt[6]{2x^5y^3}.$

51. $\sqrt{ab},\ \sqrt[3]{a^2b},\ \sqrt[8]{a^3b^5}.$ **52.** $\sqrt[3]{s^2t},\ \sqrt[4]{s^3t^2},\ \sqrt[6]{s^5t^4}.$

Change the radicals in each of Problems 53 to 56 to the same order, perform the indicated operations, and simplify.

53. $(\sqrt{8x^3})(\sqrt[3]{4x^2})(\sqrt[4]{2x})$.   **54.** $(\sqrt{s^3t})(\sqrt[4]{8st^2})(\sqrt[6]{4s^2t^3})$.

55. $(\sqrt[3]{9by^2})(\sqrt[4]{27b^3y})(\sqrt[6]{81b^3y^3})$.

56. $(\sqrt[6]{288x^5y^3})(\sqrt[8]{81x^3y^5})(\sqrt[12]{36xy^2})$.

CHAPTER 8

QUADRATIC EQUATIONS

54. *Introduction.* An equation in one unknown that involves the second but no higher power of the unknown is called a *quadratic equation.* Equations that involve both the first and second powers of the unknown are called *affected quadratic equations*, and those that contain only the second power are called *pure quadratic equations.*

EXAMPLES

Affected quadratic equations:

$$2x^2 - 3x + 2 = 0,$$
$$4x^2 = 2x - 1.$$

Pure quadratic equations:

$$3x^2 = 4,$$
$$2x^2 - 9 = 0.$$

55. *Solution of pure quadratic equations.* We obtain the roots of a pure quadratic equation by first solving it for the second power of the unknown. Then the roots will be the *two* square roots of the solution thus obtained.

EXAMPLE 1

Solve the equation $3x^2 - 27 = 0$.

Solution

We first transpose 27 and then solve for x^2; thus,

$$3x^2 = 27,$$
$$x^2 = 9.$$

Hence,

$$x = + \sqrt{9} = 3,$$

and also

$$x = - \sqrt{9} = -3.$$

NOTE: The last two statements are usually written in a shorter form by use of the double sign $\pm$. Using this notation, the two statements become

$$x = \pm \sqrt{9} = \pm 3.$$

EXAMPLE 2

Solve the equation $4x^2 + 16 = 0$.

Solution

$$4x^2 + 16 = 0,$$
$$4x^2 = -16, \qquad \text{(transposing 16)}$$
$$x^2 = -4, \qquad \text{(dividing by 4)}$$
$$x = \pm \sqrt{-4},$$
$$x = \pm \sqrt{(4)(-1)},$$
$$x = \pm 2\sqrt{-1}. \qquad \text{[by (1), Art. 50]}$$

NOTE: In mathematics, the letter i is used to denote $\sqrt{-1}$. Hence, $i^2 = -1$. In terms of this notation, the solutions of Example 2 are $x = \pm 2i$.

56. Solution of quadratic equations by factoring. The use of factoring in solving a quadratic equation depends upon the following principle:

The product of two or more factors is zero if any one of the factors is zero.

Thus, the equation $(x - 2)(x + 1) = 0$ is satisfied if either $x - 2 = 0$ or $x + 1 = 0$. Hence, the roots of the equation are $x = 2$ and $x = -1$.

This principle furnishes us with a very efficient method for solving quadratic equations and also for solving equations of higher order. However, we cannot use it unless the equation is equivalent to one in which the left member is a product of two or more factors and the right member is zero.

We solve a quadratic equation by use of the factoring method by performing the following steps:

1. *Transpose all terms in the equation to the left of the equality sign, thus making the right member zero.*

2. *Factor the left member into linear factors.*

3. *Set each factor equal to zero and solve the resulting two linear equations for x.*

Obviously, the process cannot be completed if, after performing Step 1, the left member of the resulting equation is not factorable.

EXAMPLE

Solve the equation $2x^2 = x + 6$ by use of factoring.

Solution

We show below Steps 1, 2, and 3 applied to this problem.

$$2x^2 = x + 6. \quad \text{(given equation)}$$

1. $\quad 2x^2 - x - 6 = 0.$ (transposing $x + 6$)

2. $\quad (2x + 3)(x - 2) = 0.$ (factoring $2x^2 - x - 6$)

3. $\qquad\qquad 2x + 3 = 0,$ (setting the first factor equal to zero and solving)

$$2x = -3,$$
$$x = -\tfrac{3}{2};$$

$\qquad\qquad x - 2 = 0,$ (setting the second factor equal to zero and solving)

$$x = 2.$$

Hence, the two solutions are $x = -\tfrac{3}{2}$ and $x = 2$.

NOTE: We wish to impress the reader with the fact that this method is applicable *only when the right member of the equation is zero.* If one of the factors of the left member is zero, their product is zero, regardless of the value of the other factor. However, if the right member of the equation is not zero, as in

$$(x - 1)(x + 2) = 6,$$

we cannot arbitrarily assign a value to either factor without at the same time fixing the value of the other. For example, if in the above example we let $x - 1 = 3$, then surely $x + 2 = 2$, if their product is 6. Obviously, these two conditions cannot be satisfied by the same value of x.

EXERCISE 32

Solve the pure quadratic equation in each of Problems 1 to 20.

1. $4x^2 - 9 = 0.$ 2. $25x^2 - 16 = 0.$ 3. $9x^2 - 49 = 0.$

4. $16x^2 - 81 = 0.$ 5. $6x^2 - 24 = 0.$ 6. $5x^2 - 45 = 0.$

7. $3x^2 - 75 = 0.$ 8. $7x^2 - 63 = 0.$ 9. $3x^2 - 16 = 0.$

10. $9x^2 - 24 = 0.$ 11. $5x^2 - 12 = 0.$ 12. $6x^2 - 27 = 0.$

13. $3x^2 + 12 = 0.$ 14. $5x^2 + 125 = 0.$ 15. $2x^2 + 18 = 0.$

16. $4x^2 + 16 = 0.$ **17.** $x^2 + 7 = 0.$ **18.** $3x^2 + 15 = 0.$
19. $2x^2 + 6 = 0.$ **20.** $5x^2 + 30 = 0.$

Solve the following equations by the factoring method.

21. $x^2 + 2x - 3 = 0.$ **22.** $x^2 - 4x - 5 = 0.$
23. $x^2 + 2x - 8 = 0.$ **24.** $x^2 + x - 6 = 0.$
25. $x^2 - 10 = 3x.$ **26.** $x^2 = x + 20.$
27. $x^2 + 2x = 15.$ **28.** $x^2 + 4x = 12.$
29. $2x^2 + x = 6.$ **30.** $3x^2 - 4 = 4x.$
31. $5x^2 = 2x + 3.$ **32.** $3x^2 + 7x + 4 = 0.$
33. $2x^2 - 5 = 3x.$ **34.** $7x^2 + 13x = 2.$
35. $5x^2 = 8x + 4.$ **36.** $3x^2 + 6 = 11x.$
37. $4x^2 + 8x = -3.$ **38.** $6x^2 = 7x + 5.$
39. $8x^2 + 3 = 10x.$ **40.** $9x^2 + 3x = 2.$
41. $6x^2 = x + 12.$ **42.** $8x^2 = 6x + 9.$
43. $6x^2 + 7x = 3.$ **44.** $5x^2 = 3x + 2.$
45. $12x^2 + 7x = 12.$ **46.** $8x^2 = 2x + 15.$
47. $15x^2 - x = 6.$ **48.** $14x^2 + 9x = 18.$
49. $13x = 21x^2 - 18.$ **50.** $10x^2 + 3x = 18.$
51. $43x = 20x^2 + 21.$ **52.** $24x^2 + 11x = 28.$
53. $13x = 42x^2 - 40.$ **54.** $36x^2 + 67x + 30 = 0.$
55. $54x^2 = 15x + 56.$ **56.** $48x^2 = 14x + 45.$
57. $27x^2 + 12x = 32.$ **58.** $12x + 32 = 35x^2.$
59. $20x^2 + 96x + 27 = 0.$ **60.** $13x = 22x^2 - 30.$
61. $2x^2 + 5mx + 3m^2 = 0.$ **62.** $3x^2 + 2rx = 8r^2.$
63. $2a^2x^2 = 5abx + 12b^2.$ **64.** $cdx = 6c^2x^2 - 12d^2.$
65. $x^2 = mx + nx - mn.$ **66.** $cx^2 - cdx - dx + d^2 = 0.$
67. $2x^2 - 4bx - ax + 2ab = 0.$
68. $2abx^2 + 4a^2x - 3b^2x - 6ab = 0.$

57. *Solution of quadratic equations by completing the square.*
If we square the binomial $x + a$, we get $x^2 + 2ax + a^2$. Thus, we
see that a trinomial with x^2 as the first term is a perfect square provided that (1) the second term contains the first power of x, and
(2) the last term is positive and equal to the square of one-half the
coefficient of x. Furthermore, the square root of such a trinomial
is the square roots of the first and last terms connected by the sign
of the second term.

EXAMPLES

1. The trinomial $x^2 - 6x + 9$ is a perfect square since the first term
is x^2, the second term contains only the first power of x, and the third

term, 9, is equal to the square of one-half the coefficient of x.   Furthermore, the square root of the trinomial is $x - 3$.

2. In the trinomial $x^2 + 5x + \frac{25}{4}$, the last term $\frac{25}{4}$ is equal to $(\frac{1}{2}$ of $5)^2$. Hence,

$$x^2 + 5x + \frac{25}{4} = (x + \frac{5}{2})^2.$$

The above facts constitute the basis for the process of solving an affected quadratic equation by the method of completing the square.   We shall illustrate the method by means of the following examples:

EXAMPLE 3

In order to solve

(1) $$x + 3 = 2x^2,$$

we first transpose and arrange our terms so that the first and second terms of the left member involve x^2 and x, respectively, and the constant term (or the term that does not involve x) appears in the right member; thus

$$-2x^2 + x = -3.$$

Now we divide both members by the coefficient of x^2 and get

(2) $$x^2 - \tfrac{1}{2}x = \tfrac{3}{2}.$$

Next we add to both members of (2) the square of one-half the coefficient of x, or $(\frac{1}{2}$ of $-\frac{1}{2})^2 = (-\frac{1}{4})^2 = \frac{1}{16}$, and obtain

(3) $$x^2 - \tfrac{1}{2}x + \tfrac{1}{16} = \tfrac{3}{2} + \tfrac{1}{16}.$$

We now express the left member of (3) as the square of the binomial $x - \frac{1}{4}$ and simplify the right member and get

$$(x - \tfrac{1}{4})^2 = \frac{24 + 1}{16}$$

or

(4) $$(x - \tfrac{1}{4})^2 = \tfrac{25}{16}.$$

Now, since corresponding square roots of equal numbers are equal and also since the square roots of $\frac{25}{16}$ are $\frac{5}{4}$ and $-\frac{5}{4}$, we have

(5) $$x - \tfrac{1}{4} = \tfrac{5}{4}$$

and

(6) $$x - \tfrac{1}{4} = -\tfrac{5}{4}.$$

Hence, from (5)

$$x = \tfrac{1}{4} + \tfrac{5}{4}$$
$$= \tfrac{6}{4}$$
$$= \tfrac{3}{2},$$

and from (6)

$$x = \tfrac{1}{4} - \tfrac{5}{4}$$
$$= -\tfrac{4}{4}$$
$$= -1.$$

Hence, the solutions of (1) are $x = \tfrac{3}{2}$ and $x = -1$.

NOTE 1: Usually Eqs. (5) and (6) are combined in the form

(7) $$x - \tfrac{1}{4} = \pm\tfrac{5}{4},$$

and the solution completed thus,

$$x = \tfrac{1}{4} \pm \tfrac{5}{4}$$
$$= \tfrac{6}{4} \text{ and } -\tfrac{4}{4}$$
$$= \tfrac{3}{2} \text{ and } -1.$$

NOTE 2: Frequently a student asks, "Why not use both the plus and minus signs on the left member also?" The answer is that so doing leads to no new solutions. If we use the double sign on the left member of (7) we have

$$\pm(x - \tfrac{1}{4}) = \pm\tfrac{5}{4};$$

then the use of the plus sign on the left leads to the above roots, and the use of the minus sign yields

$$-(x - \tfrac{1}{4}) = \pm\tfrac{5}{4}.$$

Then, dividing by -1, we have

$$x - \tfrac{1}{4} = \mp\tfrac{5}{4}$$

and when this is solved, we get the roots already obtained.

The process of solving a quadratic equation by completing the squares consists of five formal steps which we shall list below.

1. *Transpose and arrange the terms in the equation so that the terms involving x^2 and x appear as the first and second terms, respectively, in the left member, and the constant term appears as the right member.*

2. *Divide both members by the coefficient of x^2.*

3. *Add to both members the square of one-half the coefficient of x.*

4. *Equate the square roots of the two members of the equation obtained in Step 3, giving the square root of the constant term both the plus and minus signs. This step yields two linear equations.*

5. *Solve the two linear equations obtained in Step 4 for x.*

EXAMPLE 4

Solve the equation $4x^2 = 4x + 11$ by completing the square.

Solution

The numbers at the left in the discussion below indicate the steps in the solution that we are performing.

$$4x^2 = 4x + 11, \quad \text{(given equation)}$$

1. $\quad\quad 4x^2 - 4x = 11, \quad\quad\quad \text{(transposing } 4x)$

2. $\quad\quad\quad\quad x^2 - x = \frac{11}{4}, \quad\quad\quad \text{(dividing both members by 4)}$

3. $x^2 - x + (\frac{1}{2})^2 = \frac{11}{4} + (\frac{1}{2})^2 \quad [\text{adding } (\frac{1}{2} \text{ of 1})^2 \text{ to both sides}]$

$$= \frac{11}{4} + \frac{1}{4}$$

$$= \frac{12}{4},$$

$$(x - \tfrac{1}{2})^2 = 3,$$

4. $\quad\quad\quad\quad x - \tfrac{1}{2} = \pm \sqrt{3},$

5. $\quad\quad\quad\quad\quad\quad x = \tfrac{1}{2} \pm \sqrt{3}. \quad \text{(solving for } x)$

Since $\sqrt{3}$ is an irrational number, we can simplify the solution no further.

We may check the solution by substituting $\frac{1}{2} \pm \sqrt{3}$ for x in each member of the given equation. Thus, we get

$$4(\tfrac{1}{2} \pm \sqrt{3})^2 = 4[\tfrac{1}{4} \pm 2(\tfrac{1}{2}\sqrt{3}) + (\sqrt{3})^2] = 4(\tfrac{1}{4} \pm \sqrt{3} + 3)$$

$$= 13 \pm 4\sqrt{3}$$

for the left member and

$$4(\tfrac{1}{2} \pm \sqrt{3}) + 11 = 2 \pm 4\sqrt{3} + 11 = 13 \pm 4\sqrt{3}$$

for the right member. Since the two above values are equal, the solution checks.

If an approximate numerical value of x is desired, we may obtain the value of $\sqrt{3}$ to as many decimal places as we need and complete the solution. To three decimal places, $\sqrt{3} = 1.732$. Then

$$x = \tfrac{1}{2} \pm 1.732 = .5 \pm 1.732 = 2.232$$

and -1.232, correct to three decimal places.

EXAMPLE 5

Solve the equation $x^2 + 8 = 4x$ by completing the square.

Solution

	$x^2 + 8 = 4x,$	(given equation)
1.	$x^2 - 4x = -8,$	(transposing and arranging terms. Note that Step 2 is unnecessary.)
3.	$x^2 - 4x + (-2)^2 = -8 + (-2)^2,$	[adding ($\frac{1}{2}$ of -4)^2 to both sides]
	$(x - 2)^2 = -4,$	(simplifying)
4.	$x - 2 = \pm \sqrt{-4}$	
	$\quad\quad = \pm \sqrt{4(-1)}$	
	$\quad\quad = \pm 2 \sqrt{-1}$	
	$\quad\quad = \pm 2i,$	(see 2d Note, Art. 55)
5.	$x = 2 \pm 2i.$	

In order to check, we substitute $2 \pm 2i$ in each member of the given equation and obtain from the left member

$$
\begin{aligned}
(2 \pm 2i)^2 + 8 &= 4 \pm 8i + (2i)^2 + 8 \\
&= 4 \pm 8i + 4i^2 + 8 \\
&= 4 \pm 8i - 4 + 8 \quad (\text{since } i^2 = -1) \\
&= 8 \pm 8i;
\end{aligned}
$$

and from the right member we have

$$4(2 \pm 2i) = 8 \pm 8i.$$

Hence, the solution checks.

58. Complex numbers. The solution of Example 5 of the previous article introduces a type of number which we have not previously met. We shall describe such numbers in the following definition:

DEFINITION. *A number of the type* **a** + **b**i *where* **a** *and* **b** *are real and* i = $\sqrt{-1}$ *is called a* **complex number.**

If neither a nor b is zero, then $a + bi$ is called an *imaginary number*. If $a = 0$ and $b \neq 0$, then $a + bi$ is called a *pure imaginary number*. If $a \neq 0$ and $b = 0$, then $a + bi$ is a real number. Hence, the field of complex numbers includes all of the real numbers as special cases.

The imaginary numbers $2 + 3i$, $\frac{3}{4} - \frac{1}{4}i$, the pure imaginary number $2i$, and the real number 3 are examples of complex numbers.

Solve the following quadratic equations by the method of completing the squares.

1. $x^2 + 6x - 16 = 0$.
2. $x^2 + 2x - 15 = 0$.
3. $x^2 + 8x + 7 = 0$.
4. $x^2 + 4x - 12 = 0$.
5. $x^2 + 3x = 4$.
6. $x^2 + 4 = 5x$.
7. $x^2 = 7x - 6$.
8. $x^2 = 7x - 10$.
9. $4x^2 - 21 = 8x$.
10. $4x^2 + 12x = 7$.
11. $9x^2 - 18x = 16$.
12. $9x^2 + 11 = 36x$.
13. $5x + 12 = 2x^2$.
14. $2x^2 - 3x = 5$.
15. $3x^2 - 12 = 5x$.
16. $3x^2 + 7x + 2 = 0$.
17. $6x^2 = 5x - 1$.
18. $x + 1 = 6x^2$.
19. $8x^2 - 5x = 3$.
20. $10x^2 = 7x - 1$.
21. $18x - 9 = 8x^2$.
22. $15x = 6x^2 + 6$.
23. $8x^2 + 2 = 17x$.
24. $10x^2 + 11x = 6$.
25. $x^2 - 4x = 2$.
26. $2x = x^2 - 4$.
27. $x^2 = 6x - 6$.
28. $x^2 + 7 = 6x$.
29. $4x^2 + 8x = 1$.
30. $4x^2 - 12x + 7 = 0$.
31. $12x = 9x^2 - 1$.
32. $8x + 3 = 4x^2$.
33. $9x^2 - 6x = 1$.
34. $9x^2 + 12x + 2 = 0$.
35. $9x^2 = 3x + 1$.
36. $4x^2 = 2x + 1$.
37. $x^2 - 4x + 8 = 0$.
38. $x^2 + 2x + 5 = 0$.
39. $x^2 = 6x - 10$.
40. $x^2 + 18 = 6x$.
41. $2x^2 = 2x - 13$.
42. $4x^2 + 8x + 13 = 0$.
43. $9x^2 - 12x + 8 = 0$.
44. $4x^2 + 5 = 4x$.
45. $9x - 7 = 9x^2$.
46. $9x^2 - 18x + 11 = 0$.
47. $4x^2 - 8x + 9 = 0$.
48. $12x = 4x^2 + 11$.
49. $x^2 - bx = 2b^2$.
50. $x^2 + 4ax = 12a^2$.
51. $x^2 + (2a - b)x = 2ab$.
52. $x^2 + (a + 3b)x = ab + 4b^2$.
53. $a^2x^2 + abx = ab + a^2$.
54. $a^2bx^2 + (a + ab)x + 1 = 0$.
55. $4x^2 + (a + 2b)x = -ab + 2b^2$.
56. $(a + b)x^2 + (4a + 2b)x = 8b$.
57. $abx^2 + (a^2 + b^2)x + ab = 0$.
58. $3x^2 + (a + b)x = 2a^2 - ab$.
59. $ax^2 + (a + 1)x + 1 = 0$.
60. $(a + b)x^2 + 2abx = a^3 - a^2b - 4ab^2 + 4b^3$.

59. *The quadratic formula.* By transposing and arranging the terms, any quadratic equation can be placed in the form

(1) $$ax^2 + bx + c = 0.$$

For example, if we transpose and arrange the terms in

$$3 = 4x - 2x^2,$$

we get

(2) $$2x^2 - 4x + 3 = 0.$$

Hence, (2) is in form (1) with $a = 2$, $b = -4$, and $c = 3$.

If we solve (1) by completing the square, we obtain a formula which is useful and efficient for obtaining the roots of any quadratic equation. We shall first derive the formula by solving (1) and then we shall explain its use. The solution of (1) follows:

$$ax^2 + bx + c = 0,$$ (given equation)

$$ax^2 + bx = -c,$$ (transposing c)

$$x^2 + \frac{b}{a}x = \frac{-c}{a},$$ (dividing both members by a)

$$x^2 + \frac{b}{a}x + \left(\frac{b}{2a}\right)^2 = \frac{-c}{a} + \frac{b^2}{4a^2},$$ [adding $\left(\frac{1}{2} \text{ of } \frac{b}{a}\right)^2$ to both members]

$$\left(x + \frac{b}{2a}\right)^2 = \frac{b^2 - 4ac}{4a^2},$$ (simplifying)

$$x + \frac{b}{2a} = \pm \frac{\sqrt{b^2 - 4ac}}{2a},$$ (equating the square roots of the two members)

$$x = -\frac{b}{2a} \pm \frac{\sqrt{b^2 - 4ac}}{2a}.$$ (solving for x)

Now, since the two denominators in the right member of the last equation are the same, we have

(3) $$x = \frac{-b \pm \sqrt{b^2 - 4ac}}{2a}.$$

The formula (3) is known as the *quadratic formula* and we shall illustrate its use in the following examples:

EXAMPLE 1

In order to solve the equation $6x^2 = 12 + x$ by the use of (3), we first transpose and arrange the terms so that the term involving x^2 is first, the term involving x is second, the constant term is third, and the right member is zero. Thus, we obtain

$$6x^2 - x - 12 = 0.$$

Now, if we compare the coefficients in this equation with those in (1), we see that $a = 6$, $b = -1$, and $c = -12$. Then, if we substitute these values in (3), we get

$$x = \frac{-(-1) \pm \sqrt{(-1)^2 - 4(6)(-12)}}{2(6)}$$

$$= \frac{1 \pm \sqrt{1 + 288}}{12}$$

$$= \frac{1 \pm 17}{12}$$

$$= \tfrac{18}{12} \text{ and } -\tfrac{16}{12}$$

$$= \tfrac{3}{2} \text{ and } -\tfrac{4}{3}.$$

EXAMPLE 2

Solve $8x - 13 = 4x^2$ by use of the quadratic formula.

Solution

If we transpose and arrange terms, we get

$$-4x^2 + 8x - 13 = 0.$$

Hence, comparing with (1), we have $a = -4$, $b = 8$, and $c = -13$. Substituting these values in (3) we get

$$x = \frac{-8 \pm \sqrt{8^2 - 4(-4)(-13)}}{2(-4)}$$

$$= \frac{-8 \pm \sqrt{64 - 208}}{-8}$$

$$= \frac{-8 \pm \sqrt{-144}}{-8}$$

$$= \frac{-8 \pm 12\sqrt{-1}}{-8}$$

$$= \frac{-8 \pm 12i}{-8}$$

$$= \frac{2 - 3i}{2} \text{ and } \frac{2 + 3i}{2}.$$

Solve the following quadratic equations by use of the quadratic formula.

1. $x^2 + 2x - 8 = 0$.
2. $x^2 + 4x - 12 = 0$.
3. $x^2 + 6x + 5 = 0$.
4. $x^2 - 6x - 7 = 0$.
5. $2x^2 + 2 = 5x$.
6. $3x^2 + 4x = 4$.
7. $2x^2 + 3x = 5$.
8. $3x^2 + 2 = 5x$.'
9. $6x^2 + 7x = 3$.
10. $8x^2 + 6x = 5$.
11. $12x^2 + x = 6$.
12. $16x^2 + 3 = 16x$.
13. $28x^2 + 17x - 6 = 0$.
14. $42x^2 + 11x - 3 = 0$.
15. $54x^2 + 21x = 5$.
16. $30x^2 + 29x = 7$.
17. $x^2 = 4 - 2x$.
18. $x^2 + 6 = 6x$.
19. $x^2 + 4 = 8x$.
20. $x^2 = 8x - 8$.
21. $4x^2 + 5 = 10x$.
22. $9x^2 - 12x + 2 = 0$.
23. $4x^2 + 1 = 6x$.
24. $4x^2 + 12x = 3$.
25. $3x^2 + 4x - 1 = 0$.
26. $5x^2 - 10x = 3$.
27. $7x^2 + 14x = 9$.
28. $8x^2 = 12x - 3$.
29. $5x^2 + 9 = 15x$.
30. $7x^2 + 1 = 6x$.
31. $5x^2 + 4x = 4$.
32. $6x^2 - 2x = 1$.
33. $x^2 + 2x + 5 = 0$.
34. $x^2 = 6x - 25$.
35. $x^2 = 8x - 17$.
36. $x^2 = 8x - 25$.
37. $4x^2 = 8x - 5$.
38. $9x^2 + 17 = 6x$.
39. $4x^2 + 4x = -5$.
40. $4x^2 + 12x + 25 = 0$.
41. $3x^2 + 4x + 2 = 0$.
42. $5x^2 = 6x - 3$.
43. $7x^2 + 4x + 1 = 0$.
44. $3x^2 + 3 = 5x$.
45. $12x^2 + 4x = -1$.
46. $10x^2 + 4x = -3$.
47. $8x^2 + 3 = 4x$.
48. $6x = 9x^2 + 4$.
49. $x^2 + (m + n)x + mn = 0$.
50. $x^2 + (1 - rs)x = rs$.
51. $a^2x^2 + 3abx + 2b^2 = 0$.
52. $cdx^2 = (d^2 - c^2)x + cd$.
53. $x^2 + (m - n)x = 2m^2 + 5mn + 2n^2$.
54. $abx^2 + (2a^2 - 2b^2)x = 4ab$.
55. $2cdx^2 - (c^2d^2 + 4)x + 2cd = 0$.
56. $x^2 + 2rx + r^2 - s^2 = 0$.
57. $p^2x^2 + 2p^2x + p^2 - 1 = 0$.
58. $(m^2 - 1)x^2 - 2mx + 1 = 0$.
59. $(a^2 - b^2)x^2 = a^2 - 2abx$.
60. $(h^2 - 4)x^2 + 2h^2x + h^2 = 0$.

60. *Facts about the roots of quadratic equations.*[1] Formula (3), Art. 59, enables us to ascertain important information about the roots of a quadratic equation without solving the equation. In the

[1] Articles 60, 61, and 62 may be omitted without loss of continuity.

discussion that follows, we shall assume that a, b, and c in (1), Art. 59, are rational. Furthermore, we shall let r represent the value of the left member of (3), Art. 59, when the plus sign is used before the radical, and s represent the value when the minus sign is used. Then we have

(1) $$r = \frac{-b + \sqrt{b^2 - 4ac}}{2a}$$

and

(2) $$s = \frac{-b - \sqrt{b^2 - 4ac}}{2a}.$$

Now, if the expression $b^2 - 4ac$ under the radicals in (1) and (2) is zero, we have $r = s = \frac{-b}{2a}$. Hence, the roots are equal. Furthermore, since a and b are rational, r and s are rational.

If $b^2 - 4ac$ is negative, $\sqrt{b^2 - 4ac}$ is a pure imaginary number. Consequently, r and s are imaginary numbers.

If $b^2 - 4ac$ is positive, we have two possibilities. First, if it is a perfect square, then $\sqrt{b^2 - 4ac}$ is rational, and r and s are rational and unequal. Second, if $b^2 - 4ac$ is not a perfect square, then $\sqrt{b^2 - 4ac}$ is irrational, and, therefore, r and s are irrational and unequal.

The expression $b^2 - 4ac$ is called the *discriminant* of the equation and it is usually denoted by the letter D.

Using this notation, we may summarize the above information in the following table:[1]

D	Roots
Zero	Rational and equal
Positive and a perfect square	Rational and unequal
Positive and not a perfect square	Irrational and unequal
Negative	Imaginary

[1] If we assume that a, b, and c are real, but not necessarily rational, then the information we gain about r and s is less specific.   If

$D = 0$, r and s are real and equal (not necessarily rational);
$D > 0$, r and s are real and unequal;
$D < 0$, r and s are imaginary.

EXAMPLES

1. In the equation $4x^2 - 4x + 1 = 0$,

$$D = (-4)^2 - 4(4)(1) = 16 - 16 = 0.$$

Hence, the roots are rational and equal.

2. In $2x^2 - x - 1 = 0$, $D = (-1)^2 - 4(2)(-1) = 1 + 8 = 9$. Since 9 is a perfect square, the roots are rational and unequal.

3. In $3x^2 + 2x - 4 = 0$, $D = (2)^2 - 4(3)(-4) = 4 + 48 = 52$. Since 52 is positive but not a perfect square, the roots are irrational and unequal.

4. In $2x^2 + 2x + 1 = 0$, $D = (2)^2 - 4(2)(1) = 4 - 8 = -4$. Since D is negative, the roots are imaginary.

By use of (1) and (2), we can see that the sum and product of the two roots are simple combinations of the coefficients of the equation. For example, the sum of the two roots is

$$\left(\frac{-b}{2a} + \frac{\sqrt{b^2 - 4ac}}{2a}\right) + \left(\frac{-b}{2a} - \frac{\sqrt{b^2 - 4ac}}{2a}\right) = \frac{-2b}{2a} = -\frac{b}{a}.$$

Hence,

(3) $$r + s = -\frac{b}{a}.$$

Furthermore, the product is

$$\left(\frac{-b}{2a} + \frac{\sqrt{b^2 - 4ac}}{2a}\right)\left(\frac{-b}{2a} - \frac{\sqrt{b^2 - 4ac}}{2a}\right)$$

$$= \left(\frac{-b}{2a}\right)^2 - \left(\frac{\sqrt{b^2 - 4ac}}{2a}\right)^2$$

$$= \frac{b^2}{4a^2} - \frac{b^2 - 4ac}{4a^2}$$

$$= \frac{b^2 - b^2 + 4ac}{4a^2}$$

$$= \frac{4ac}{4a^2} = \frac{c}{a}.$$

Consequently,

(4) $$rs = \frac{c}{a}.$$

Hence, since r and s are the two roots of $ax^2 + bx + c = 0$, we see that *the sum of the two roots of a quadratic equation is equal to the negative of the quotient of the coefficients of x and x^2, and the product of the two roots is the quotient of the constant term and the coefficient of x^2.*

The two formulas (3) and (4) are useful as a rapid check on the roots of a quadratic equation. In Example 1, Art. 59, we found that the two roots of $6x^2 - x - 12 = 0$ were $\frac{3}{2}$ and $-\frac{4}{3}$. By (3) and (4), we see that the sum and product of the two roots should be $\frac{1}{6}$ and $-\frac{12}{6} = -2$, respectively.

In order to check the solution, we first add and then multiply the two roots and get $\frac{3}{2} + (-\frac{4}{3}) = \frac{9}{6} - \frac{8}{6} = \frac{1}{6}$ for the sum, and $(\frac{3}{2})(-\frac{4}{3}) = -\frac{12}{6} = -2$ for the product. Hence, the solution checks.

EXERCISE 35

Without solving, determine the nature of the roots of each of the following equations, and also find the sum and product of the roots.

1. $x^2 + 6x - 3 = 0$.
2. $x^2 + 3x - 2 = 0$.
3. $x^2 + 7x + 4 = 0$.
4. $x^2 + 9x + 17 = 0$.
5. $x^2 + 4x + 3 = 0$.
6. $x^2 - 3x + 2 = 0$.
7. $x^2 + 6x + 9 = 0$.
8. $x^2 - 8x + 7 = 0$.
9. $2x^2 + 5x + 2 = 0$.
10. $3x^2 + 8x - 3 = 0$.
11. $2x^2 + 3x + 1 = 0$.
12. $3x^2 - 5x + 1 = 0$.
13. $4x^2 + 3x + 2 = 0$.
14. $3x^2 + 5x + 4 = 0$.
15. $5x^2 - 7x + 3 = 0$.
16. $6x^2 - 6x + 5 = 0$.
17. $4x^2 + 7x - 2 = 0$.
18. $3x^2 + 7x + 2 = 0$.
19. $5x^2 + 4x - 1 = 0$.
20. $7x^2 + 2x - 5 = 0$.
21. $3x^2 + 5x - 3 = 0$.
22. $4x^2 + 6x + 1 = 0$.
23. $2x^2 - 5x - 2 = 0$.
24. $7x^2 - 9x - 3 = 0$.
25. $2x^2 - 7x + 7 = 0$.
26. $7x^2 + 5x + 6 = 0$.
27. $8x^2 - 9x + 6 = 0$.
28. $9x^2 - 2x + 7 = 0$.
29. $3x^2 - 10x + 2 = 0$.
30. $5x^2 - 13x - 4 = 0$.
31. $7x^2 + 12x + 8 = 0$.
32. $6x^2 + 11x - 5 = 0$.

61. Equations that involve radicals of the second order. Since the squares of two equal quantities are equal, we have the following principle:

Any root of a given equation will also be a root of an equation obtained by equating the squares of the two members of the given equation.

The converse of this statement is not true.   For example, if we equate the squares of the two members of

(1) $$\sqrt{2x^2 - 1} = x,$$

we get

(2) $$2x^2 - 1 = x^2.$$

Hence,

$$2x^2 - x^2 = 1, \qquad \text{(transposing)}$$
$$x^2 = 1,$$
$$x = \pm 1.$$

The value $x = 1$ satisfies Eq. (1).   However, when $x = -1$, the left member of (1) becomes $\sqrt{2(-1)^2 - 1} = \sqrt{1} = 1$, while the right member is -1.   Hence, -1 is a root of (2) but not of (1). The value $x = -1$ is called an *extraneous* root.

In order to solve an equation that involves radicals of the second order, we perform the following steps:

1. *Isolate one radical on one side of the equality sign by transposing all other terms.*

2. *Square both members of the resulting equation and equate the two squares.*

3. *If the equation thus obtained contains no radical, solve it for x.   If the equation contains one or more radicals, we repeat Steps 1 and 2 until we obtain an equation which is free of radicals.   We then solve the latter equation for x.*

4. *Substitute the values of x obtained in Step 3 in the original equation in order to determine those values of x that are and are not roots.*

The process of applying Steps 1 and 2 until an equation free of radicals is obtained is called *rationalizing the equation.*

EXAMPLE 1

Solve the equation

(3) $$\sqrt{2x^2 - 2x + 1} - 2x + 3 = 0.$$

Solution

In the following discussion, the number at the left denotes the step in the solving process that is being applied.

1. We first isolate the radical by transposing $-2x + 3$ and get

$$\sqrt{2x^2 - 2x + 1} = 2x - 3.$$

2. Next we equate the squares of both members of the above equation and get

$$2x^2 - 2x + 1 = 4x^2 - 12x + 9.$$

3. This equation does not involve a radical so we solve it for x.

$2x^2 - 4x^2 - 2x + 12x + 1 - 9 = 0,$ (transposing and arranging terms)

$-2x^2 + 10x - 8 = 0,$ (collecting terms)

$x^2 - 5x + 4 = 0,$ (dividing by -2)

$(x - 4)(x - 1) = 0,$ (factoring the left member)

$x - 4 = 0,$ (setting each factor equal to zero and solving)

$x = 4;$

$x - 1 = 0,$

$x = 1.$

Hence, the roots of the rationalized equation are $x = 4$ and $x = 1$.

4. Now we substitute $x = 4$ in the left member of (3) and get

$$\sqrt{2(4)^2 - 2(4) + 1} - 2(4) + 3 = \sqrt{32 - 8 + 1} - 8 + 3$$
$$= \sqrt{25} - 8 + 3$$
$$= 5 - 8 + 3$$
$$= 0.$$

Hence, $x = 4$ is a solution of (3).

However, when $x = 1$ is substituted in the left member of (3), we get

$$\sqrt{2(1)^2 - 2(1) + 1} - 2(1) + 3 = \sqrt{2 - 2 + 1} - 2 + 3$$
$$= 1 - 2 + 3$$
$$= 2.$$

Hence, $x = 1$ is not a solution of (3) since the right member is zero. Consequently, the only solution of (3) is $x = 4$.

EXAMPLE 2

Solve the equation

(4) $\sqrt{11x - 6} = \sqrt{4x + 5} - \sqrt{x - 1}.$

Solution

1. Since we have one radical isolated on the left of the equality sign, we proceed at once to Step 2.

2.
$$11x - 6 = 4x + 5 - 2\sqrt{(4x + 5)(x - 1)} + x - 1,$$

[equating the squares of the members of (4)]

$$2\sqrt{(4x + 5)(x - 1)} = -11x + 4x + x + 6 + 5 - 1,$$

(transposing terms so as to isolate the radical)

$$2\sqrt{4x^2 + x - 5} = -6x + 10,$$ (collecting terms)

$$\sqrt{4x^2 + x - 5} = -3x + 5,$$ (dividing by 2)

$$4x^2 + x - 5 = 9x^2 - 30x + 25,$$ (equating the squares of the two members)

$$-5x^2 + 31x - 30 = 0.$$ (transposing and collecting)

3. $x = \dfrac{-31 \pm \sqrt{(31)^2 - 4(-5)(-30)}}{2(-5)}$ (solving by the quadratic formula)

$$= \frac{-31 \pm \sqrt{961 - 600}}{-10}$$

$$= \frac{-31 \pm \sqrt{361}}{-10}$$

$$= \frac{-31 \pm 19}{-10}$$

$$= \tfrac{6}{5} \text{ and } 5.$$

4. Now we substitute $x = \frac{6}{5}$ in both members of (4) and get for the left member

$$\sqrt{11(\tfrac{6}{5}) - 6} = \sqrt{\frac{66}{5} - 6} = \sqrt{\frac{66 - 30}{5}} = \sqrt{\frac{36}{5}} = \frac{6}{\sqrt{5}}$$

and for the right member

$$\sqrt{4(\tfrac{6}{5}) + 5} - \sqrt{\frac{6}{5} - 1} = \sqrt{\frac{49}{5}} - \sqrt{\frac{1}{5}} = \frac{7}{\sqrt{5}} - \frac{1}{\sqrt{5}} = \frac{6}{\sqrt{5}}.$$

Hence, $x = \frac{6}{5}$ is a solution of (4). When we substitute $x = 5$ in (4), we get

$$\sqrt{11(5) - 6} = \sqrt{55 - 6} = \sqrt{49} = 7$$

for the left member and

$$\sqrt{4(5) + 5} - \sqrt{5 - 1} = \sqrt{25} - \sqrt{4} = 5 - 2 = 3$$

for the right member. Hence, since the right and left members of (4) are not equal when $x = 5$, this value of x is not a solution.

EXERCISE 36

Solve the following equations.

1. $\sqrt{4x + 1} = \sqrt{6x - 3}$.

2. $\sqrt{5x + 1} = \sqrt{4x + 4}$.

3. $\sqrt{4x - 3} = \sqrt{2x + 11}$.

4. $\sqrt{2x - 1} = \sqrt{3x - 6}$.

5. $\sqrt{4x + 3} = \sqrt{8x + 2}$.

6. $\sqrt{7x + 1} = \sqrt{23x + 2}$.

7. $\sqrt{x + 3} - \sqrt{3x - 9} = 0$.

8. $\sqrt{2x + 1} - \sqrt{3x - 3} = 0$.

9. $\sqrt{2x^2 + 3x + 1} = \sqrt{4x + 7}$.

10. $\sqrt{3x^2 + 2x - 7} = \sqrt{7x + 5}$.

11. $\sqrt{2x^2 + 6x - 7} = \sqrt{5x + 8}$.

12. $\sqrt{3x^2 + 12x + 7} = \sqrt{2x + 15}$.

13. $x - \sqrt{2x + 1} = 1$.

14. $3x = \sqrt{2x + 5} + 3$.

15. $4x = \sqrt{3x + 10} - 10$.

16. $2x + \sqrt{5x - 1} = 4$.

17. $2x - \sqrt{2x^2 + 3x - 2} = 1$.

18. $2 + \sqrt{2x^2 + 3x + 2} = 3x$.

19. $2x - \sqrt{x^2 + 2x + 1} = 3$.

20. $\sqrt{3x^2 + 4x + 2} - 1 = 2x$.

21. $\sqrt{2x + 3} - \sqrt{x + 1} = 1$.

22. $\sqrt{3x - 2} - \sqrt{2x - 3} = 1$.

23. $\sqrt{3x - 3} + \sqrt{x - 3} = 4$.

24. $\sqrt{5x - 1} + \sqrt{4x - 4} = 5$.

25. $\sqrt{3x + 3} - \sqrt{3x - 2} = \sqrt{2x - 3}$.

26. $\sqrt{2x + 5} - \sqrt{x + 2} = \sqrt{2x - 3}$.

27. $\sqrt{x + 7} - \sqrt{2x + 10} = \sqrt{2x + 6}$.

28. $\sqrt{2x + 1} + \sqrt{3x + 4} = \sqrt{12x + 1}$.

29. $\sqrt{3x + 1} - \sqrt{2x - 1} = \sqrt{x - 4}$.

30. $\sqrt{3x + 1} - \sqrt{2x + 2} = \sqrt{4x - 4}$.

31. $\sqrt{4x - 3} - \sqrt{2x - 2} = \sqrt{x - 2}$.

32. $\sqrt{2x + 5} + \sqrt{3x + 7} = \sqrt{x + 6}$.

33. $\sqrt{x^2 + 5x + 3} - \sqrt{x^2 + 3x} = 1$.

34. $\sqrt{x^2 + x - 1} + \sqrt{x^2 + 3x + 3} = 2$.

35. $\sqrt{x^2 - 2x + 4} + \sqrt{x^2 - 3x + 3} = 3$.

36. $\sqrt{x^2 + 3x + 1} + \sqrt{x^2 + 2x - 3} = 1$.

37. $\dfrac{\sqrt{2x + 3} + 1}{\sqrt{4x - 3} - 1} = 2$.

38. $\dfrac{\sqrt{3x - 2} - 1}{\sqrt{x - 2} + 1} = 1$.

39. $\dfrac{\sqrt{x+5}-1}{\sqrt{x+2}+1} = \dfrac{1}{2}.$

40. $\dfrac{\sqrt{2x-2}+1}{\sqrt{x+1}-1} = 3.$

41. $\sqrt{ax-a^2} + \sqrt{3ax+a^2} = 2a.$

42. $\sqrt{bx+2b^2} - \sqrt{bx-b^2} = b.$

43. $\sqrt{x+3c^2} = \sqrt{2x-c^2} + c.$

44. $\sqrt{2ax-3a^2} = \sqrt{ax+2a^2} - a.$

62. *Equations in quadratic form.* An equation of the type

$$(1) \qquad a[f(x)]^2 + b[f(x)] + c = 0$$

is said to be in *quadratic form*. The symbol $f(x)$ stands for an expression in x, and it should be noted that this expression appears in both brackets. For example, the equation

$$(2) \qquad 4(x^2 - x)^2 - 11(x^2 - x) + 6 = 0$$

is in quadratic form since $x^2 - x$ appears in both parentheses.

If the expression $f(x)$ in (1) is of degree one or two, we may solve the equation by the methods of this chapter. We shall illustrate the procedure in the following example:

EXAMPLE 1

In order to solve Eq. (2) for x, we first let $z = x^2 - x$. Then (2) becomes

$$(3) \qquad 4z^2 - 11z + 6 = 0,$$

which is a quadratic equation in the variable z, and, by use of the quadratic formula, we get the following values for z:

$$z = \frac{-(-11) \pm \sqrt{(-11)^2 - 4(4)(6)}}{2(4)}$$
$$= \frac{11 \pm \sqrt{121 - 96}}{8}$$
$$= \frac{11 \pm \sqrt{25}}{8}$$
$$= \frac{11 \pm 5}{8}$$
$$= 2 \text{ and } \tfrac{3}{4}.$$

Hence, we have

$$(4) \qquad z = 2,$$

and

$$(5) \qquad z = \tfrac{3}{4}.$$

We now replace z by $x^2 - x$ in each of these equations and solve for x. Thus, we obtain from (4)

$$x^2 - x = 2,$$
$$x^2 - x - 2 = 0, \quad \text{(transposing)}$$
$$(x - 2)(x + 1) = 0, \quad \text{(factoring the left member)}$$
$$x - 2 = 0, \quad \text{(setting each factor equal to zero and solving for } x\text{)}$$
$$x = 2;$$
$$x + 1 = 0,$$
$$x = -1.$$

Similarly, we get from (5)

$$x^2 - x = \tfrac{3}{4},$$

the solutions of which are $x = \tfrac{3}{2}$ and $x = -\tfrac{1}{2}$. Hence, the solutions of (2) are $x = 2, \tfrac{3}{2}, -\tfrac{1}{2}$, and -1.

EXAMPLE 2

In order to solve $3x^4 = 2x^2 + 1$, we let $z = x^2$, and get

$$3z^2 = 2z + 1.$$

The solutions of this equation by use of any one of the three methods for solving quadratics are $z = 1$ and $z = -\tfrac{1}{3}$. Now, since $z = x^2$, we have

$$x^2 = 1,$$
$$x = \pm 1$$

and

$$x^2 = -\tfrac{1}{3},$$
$$x = \pm \sqrt{-\tfrac{1}{3}}$$
$$= \pm \frac{1}{\sqrt{3}} i.$$

Hence, the solutions of the original equation are $x = 1, -1, \dfrac{1}{\sqrt{3}} i$, and

$$-\frac{1}{\sqrt{3}} i.$$

EXERCISE 37

Reduce the following equations to the quadratic form and solve for x.

1. $x^4 + 64 = 20x^2$.   2. $x^4 = 34x^2 - 225$.
3. $4x^4 - 37x^2 + 9 = 0$.   4. $9x^4 + 4 = 13x^2$.
5. $x^4 = 7x^2 - 12$.   6. $x^4 + 45 = 14x^2$.

7. $4x^4 - 17x^2 + 18 = 0$.

8. $22x^2 = 9x^4 + 8$.

9. $x^4 + 2x^2 = 8$.

10. $x^4 = 18 - 7x^2$.

11. $x^4 = 2x^2 + 3$.

12. $x^4 - 2x^2 = 24$.

13. $8x^4 = 10x^2 + 3$.

14. $6x^2 + 54 = 8x^4$.

15. $6x^4 - 6 = 5x^2$.

16. $2x^4 + 5x^2 = 3$.

17. $6x^{-2} = x^{-1} + 1$.

18. $2x^{-2} + 3x^{-1} = 2$.

19. $3x^{-2} + 1 = 4x^{-1}$.

20. $2x^{-2} = 6 - x^{-1}$.

21. $x^6 + 27 = 28x^3$.

22. $8x^6 = 19x^3 + 27$.

23. $x^8 + 81 = 82x^4$.

24. $27x^6 + 26x^3 = 1$.

25. $(x^2 - 1)^2 + 24 = 11(x^2 - 1)$.

26. $(2x^2 - 1)^2 = 8(2x^2 - 1) - 7$.

27. $(x^2 + 2)^2 + 66 = 17(x^2 + 2)$.

28. $(3x^2 - 7)^2 = (3x^2 - 7) + 20$.

29. $(x^2 + 2x)^2 - 4(x^2 + 2x) + 3 = 0$.

30. $(2x^2 + x)^2 + 6 = 7(2x^2 + x)$.

31. $(x^2 - 3x)^2 = 2(x^2 - 3x) + 8$.

32. $(3x^2 - 5x)^2 - 4 = 0$.   **33.** $(x^2 - 2x)^2 + 6 = 5(x^2 - 2x)$.

34. $(x^2 + 3x)^2 = 6(x^2 + 3x) - 8$.

35. $(2x^2 - x)^2 + 2 = 3(2x^2 - x)$.

36. $(2x^2 - 3x)^2 = 12(2x^2 - 3x) - 27$.

37. $\left(\dfrac{x}{x - 1}\right)^2 = \dfrac{x}{x - 1} + 6$.   **38.** $\left(\dfrac{x + 1}{x + 2}\right)^2 + 2\left(\dfrac{x + 1}{x + 2}\right) = 8$.

39. $\left(\dfrac{x - 1}{x + 3}\right)^2 + 4\left(\dfrac{x - 1}{x + 3}\right) + 3 = 0$.

40. $\left(\dfrac{2x - 1}{x - 2}\right)^2 + \dfrac{2x - 1}{x - 2} = 2$.

41. $\dfrac{x + 1}{2x - 1} + 3\left(\dfrac{2x - 1}{x + 1}\right) = 4$.   Hint: Let $z = \dfrac{x + 1}{2x - 1}$; then

$$\frac{1}{z} = \frac{2x - 1}{x + 1}.$$

42. $\dfrac{x - 2}{x + 3} = 2\left(\dfrac{x + 3}{x - 2}\right) + 1$.   **43.** $\dfrac{x + 3}{x + 2} - 2 = 3\left(\dfrac{x + 2}{x + 3}\right)$.

44. $\dfrac{2x - 1}{x + 3} + 2 = 3\left(\dfrac{x + 3}{2x - 1}\right)$.   **45.** $2 - 3\sqrt{3x + 2} + 3x + 2 = 0$.

46. $\sqrt{2x - 1} = 7 - 2x$.   Hint: Add -6 to each member of the equation; then let $z = \sqrt{2x - 1}$.

47. $2x + 1 = 3\sqrt{2x - 1}$.   **48.** $\dfrac{x + 2}{x - 1} + \sqrt{\dfrac{x + 2}{x - 1}} = 6$.

63. *Problems that lead to quadratic equations.* Many stated problems, especially those which deal with products or quotients involving the unknown, lead to quadratic equations. The method of obtaining the equation for solving such problems is the same as that in Art. 6, and the reader should review that article at this point. It should be noted here that often a problem which can be solved by the use of a quadratic equation has only one solution, while the equation has two solutions. In such cases, the root which does not satisfy the conditions of the problem is discarded.

EXAMPLE 1

A rectangular building whose depth is twice its frontage is divided into two parts by a partition that is 30 ft. from, and parallel to, the front wall. If the rear portion of the building contains 3500 sq. ft., find the dimensions of the building.

Solution

Let
$$x = \text{the frontage of the building in feet.}$$
Then
$$2x = \text{the depth.}$$
Also,
$$2x - 30 = \text{the length of the rear portion,}$$
and
$$x = \text{the width of the rear portion.}$$
Hence,
$$x(2x - 30) = \text{the area of the rear portion.}$$
Therefore,
$$x(2x - 30) = 3500.$$
Performing the indicated multiplication and transposing 3500, we have
$$2x^2 - 30x - 3500 = 0$$
or
$$(x - 50)(2x + 70) = 0.$$
Therefore, $x = 50$ and $x = -35$. However, since the dimensions cannot be negative, we have
$$x = 50 \text{ ft. (frontage),}$$
$$2x = 100 \text{ ft. (depth).}$$

EXAMPLE 2

The periods of time required by two painters to paint a square yard of floor differ by 1 min. Together, they can paint 27 sq. yd. in 1 hr. How long does it take each to paint 1 sq. yd.?

Solution

Let
$$x = \text{the number of minutes required by the faster painter to paint 1 sq. yd.}$$

Then
$$x + 1 = \text{the number of minutes required by the other.}$$

Consequently,
$$\frac{1}{x} = \text{the fraction of a square yard the first man paints in 1 min.,}$$

and
$$\frac{1}{x + 1} = \text{the fraction of a square yard the other paints in 1 min.}$$

Hence,
$$\frac{1}{x} + \frac{1}{x + 1} = \text{the fraction of a square yard painted by both men in 1 min.}$$

However, since together they painted 27 sq. yd. in 60 min., they covered $\frac{27}{60} = \frac{9}{20}$ of a square yard in 1 min. Therefore,

$$\frac{1}{x} + \frac{1}{x + 1} = \frac{9}{20}.$$

Solving this equation, we have

$20(x + 1) + 20x = 9x(x + 1),$ (clearing of fractions)

$20x + 20 + 20x = 9x^2 + 9x,$ (performing the indicated multiplication)

$-9x^2 + 31x + 20 = 0,$ (transposing)

$$x = \frac{-31 \pm \sqrt{(31)^2 - 4(-9)(20)}}{2(-9)}$$

$$= \frac{-31 \pm \sqrt{961 + 720}}{-18}$$

$$= \frac{-31 \pm \sqrt{1681}}{-18}$$

$$= \frac{-31 \pm 41}{-18}$$

$$= -\tfrac{5}{9} \text{ and } 4.$$

We discard $-\frac{5}{9}$, since a negative time has no meaning in this problem. Hence,

$$x = 4,$$

and

$$x + 1 = 5.$$

Thus, the painters require 4 and 5 min., respectively, to paint 1 sq. yd.

EXERCISE 38

1. The units digit of a certain number is 1 more than the tens digit. The sum of the squares of the two digits is 25. Find the number.

2. Find two consecutive integers whose product exceeds their sum by 71.

3. The difference between a positive number and its square is 8 more than the number. Find the number.

4. Find a negative number such that its square increased by 5 times the number is 14.

5. Find two numbers that differ by 6 and whose product is 112.

6. Find two numbers that differ by 10 and whose product is 119.

7. Divide 21 into two parts whose product is 90.

8. Divide 47 into two parts whose product is 312.

9. If the radius of a circle is increased by 6 units, the area is multiplied by 9. Find the original radius.

10. The product of a positive number and the reciprocal of the next larger number is $\frac{5}{2}$ less than their sum. Find the number.

11. The difference between a number and 8 times its reciprocal is 2. Find the number.

12. The product of 8 times an integer and the reciprocal of the next one is equal to 3 more than the number. Find the number.

13. Find the base and altitude of a triangle if the former exceeds the latter by 4 ft. and the area of the triangle is 30 sq. ft.

14. If 105 ft. of fencing is required to fence two adjacent sides of a rectangular lot whose area is 2250 sq. ft., find the dimensions of the lot.

15. It took 54 ft. of wallpaper 2 ft. wide to paper one wall of a room. If the wall contained no windows or doors, and if the width exceeded the height by 3 ft., find the dimensions.

16. The length of a rectangle is 6 ft. greater than the width. Find the dimensions if the area is 24 sq. yd.

17. The length of a rectangle exceeds the width by 10 ft. Find the dimensions if the diagonal is 50 ft. in length.

18. Find the length and width of a swimming pool if the perimeter is 100 ft. and the area of the surface of the water is 600 sq. ft.

19. A square cake and a rectangular cake were cut into slices 1 in. square, and the former yielded twice as many slices as the latter. If the length and width of the second cake were, respectively, 3 and 4 in. less than one side of the first, find the dimensions of each.

20. The hypotenuse of a right triangle is 10 in. long. Find the length of each of the legs if the perimeter is 24 in.

21. During a short vacation a student drove a car to his home 300 miles away and returned to the campus on a bus. The average speed of the car was 10 miles per hr. more than that of the bus, and the homeward trip required 1 hr. less time than the return. Find the average speed on the homeward journey.

22. Towns *A* and *B* are 360 miles apart. At 1 P.M. a car left *A* and traveled at a uniform speed toward *B*; 1 hr. later a second car left *B* for *A* and traveled 15 miles per hr. faster than the first. If the two cars met half way between the towns, find the speed of each.

23. A man made a round trip to a city 200 miles away in 9 hr. On his return trip he pulled a trailer that retarded his speed by 10 miles per hr. How fast did he travel each way?

24. A pilot flew 700 miles against the wind and back in 12 hr. Find the speed of the plane in still air if the wind velocity was 20 miles per hr. throughout the flight.

25. Two boys washed a car together in one hour. How long would it take each to do the job alone if one of them requires $1\frac{1}{2}$ hr. longer than the other?

26. A laboratory instructor can perform a certain experiment in $2\frac{1}{2}$ hr. less time than a student. Working together, they completed the experiment in 3 hr. How long would it take each of them to do the experiment alone?

27. The cost of the annual class banquet was divided equally among the students attending. On two consecutive years the banquet costs were $150 and $175, respectively, but the banquet tickets were 25 cents less the second year. How many attended each banquet if the attendance the second year was 25 more than that of the first?

28. Two boys each earned $480 during their summer vacation. Find the daily wage of each if one earned $2 per day more than the other and together they worked a total of 140 days.

29. A class of students chartered a bus for $80 to attend a track meet in a neighboring town and shared equally in the cost. A month later the class again chartered the bus for $80 but 10 members were unable to make the trip, and those going had to pay 40 cents more per ticket. How many students were in the class?

30. A swimming pool holds 2400 cu. ft. of water when full. It can be drained at the rate of 10 cu. ft. per min. faster than it can be filled.   If it takes 20 min. longer to fill it than to drain it, find the drainage rate.

31. During a certain period of time a landlady collected $270 in rentals from the smaller of two rooms and $320 from the larger.   The larger room rented for $10 per month more than the smaller, but it was vacant for 1 month during the period.   Find the monthly rental on each.

32. A family planned to spend $360 on their summer vacation trip. However, they found the daily expense to be $10 less than they expected, so they extended their vacation period by 3 days.   How long were they gone?

CHAPTER 9

SYSTEMS OF QUADRATIC EQUATIONS IN TWO VARIABLES

64. Introduction. The most general form of a quadratic equation in two variables consists of six terms as in the equation

$$3x^2 + 5xy + 2y^2 - 3x + 4y - 7 = 0.$$

However, in elementary mathematics, one seldom meets such an equation with all terms present. In this chapter, we shall discuss the graphs of certain special cases of quadratic equations in two variables and shall present methods for solving pairs of such equations that require only those processes that are explained in previous chapters.

65. Graphs of quadratic equations in two variables. It is proved in analytic geometry that the graph of a quadratic equation in two variables, if it exists, is either a circle, an ellipse, a hyperbola, or a parabola (see Fig. 10). In certain special cases, the graph may degenerate into a point or a pair of straight lines.

We shall discuss the graphs of the following special cases of the general quadratic:

(a) $x^2 + y^2 = r^2$.
(b) $ax^2 + by^2 = c$.   (a, b, and c positive)
(c) $ax^2 - by^2 = c$.   (a and b positive)
(d) $y = ax^2 + bx + c$.   ($a \neq 0$)
(e) $x = ay^2 + by + c$.   ($a \neq 0$)

As in Art. 36, the steps followed in constructing the graph are:

1. *Solve[1] the equation for y in terms of x.*

[1] If the equation is easier to solve for x than for y, we solve it for x. Then in reading the succeeding steps, we interchange x and y.

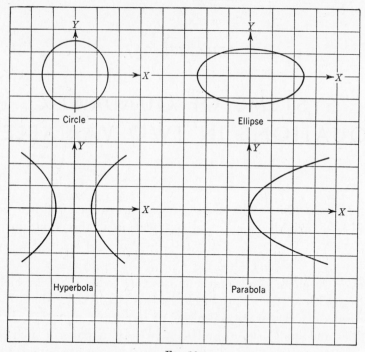

FIG. 10.

2. *Assign several values to x, compute each corresponding value of y, and arrange the associated pairs of values in tabular form.*

3. *Plot the points determined by the above pairs of values and then draw a smooth curve through them.*

Graphs of Equations of the Type $x^2 + y^2 = r^2$

EXAMPLE 1

As our first example, we shall consider the equation

(1) $$x^2 + y^2 = 25.$$

If we perform the operations suggested by the above steps, we have

1. $$y = \pm \sqrt{25 - x^2}.$$

2. Assign the integers from -5 to 5, inclusive, to x and compute each corresponding value of y. For example, if $x = -5$, then

$$y = \pm \sqrt{25 - (-5)^2} = \pm \sqrt{25 - 25} = 0.$$

Similarly, if $x = 2$,

$$y = \pm \sqrt{25 - (2)^2} = \pm \sqrt{25 - 4} = \pm \sqrt{21} = \pm 4.6.$$

When a similar computation is performed for each of the other values assigned to x and the results are arranged in tabular form, we have

x	-5	-4	-3	-2	-1	0	1	2	3	4	5
y	0	± 3	± 4	± 4.6	± 4.9	± 5	± 4.9	± 4.6	± 4	± 3	0

3. Note that in the above table we have two values of y for each x except $x = -5$ and $x = 5$. The pair of values $x = 3$, $y = \pm 4$ determines the two points $(3,4)$ and $(3,-4)$.

With this understanding, if we plot the points determined by the above table and join them by a smooth curve, we have the graph in Fig. 11.

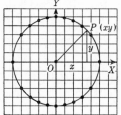

FIG. 11.

It may be seen readily that the curve is a circle, since the coordinates (x,y) of any point P on it satisfy (1); that is, the sum of their squares is 25. Furthermore, by looking at the figure, we see that the square of the distance OP of P from the center is $x^2 + y^2$. Hence, any point whose coordinates satisfy (1) is at a distance of 5 from the origin.

In general, by similar reasoning, we conclude that the graph of $x^2 + y^2 = r^2$ is a circle of radius r, and the graph of $ax^2 + ay^2 = c$ is a circle of radius $\sqrt{\dfrac{c}{a}}$ if a and c have the same sign.

Equations of the Type $ax^2 + by^2 = c$

EXAMPLE 2

As an example of the above type of equations, we shall construct the graph of

$$(2) \qquad\qquad 4x^2 + 9y^2 = 36.$$

Solution

1. Solving for y, we have

$$y = \pm \sqrt{\frac{36 - 4x^2}{9}}$$

$$= \pm\tfrac{2}{3} \sqrt{9 - x^2}.$$

2. We note here that if $x^2 > 9$, the radicand is negative and y is imaginary. Hence, the graph exists only for values of x from -3 to 3, inclusive. Therefore, we assign to x the integers 0, ± 1, ± 2, ± 3, compute each corresponding value of y, arrange the results in a table, and get

x	-3	-2	-1	0	1	2	3
y	0	± 1.5	± 1.9	± 2	± 1.9	± 1.5	0

When we construct the graph determined by this table, we get the curve in Fig. 12.

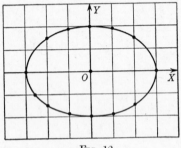

FIG. 12.

By referring to Fig. 10, we see that this curve is an ellipse. The proof that the equation

$$ax^2 + by^2 = c,$$

with a, b, and c positive, always defines an ellipse is beyond the scope of this book. However, the statement is true, and it is helpful to remember this fact when dealing with such an equation.

Equations of the Type $ax^2 - by^2 = c$

EXAMPLE 3

Here, we shall discuss the graph of the equation

(3) $$3x^2 - 4y^2 = 12.$$

Solution

Proceeding as before, we have

1. $$y = \pm \sqrt{\frac{3x^2 - 12}{4}}$$

$$= \pm \tfrac{1}{2} \sqrt{3(x^2 - 4)}.$$

2. In this case, we notice that if $x^2 < 4$, the radicand is negative and y is imaginary. Hence, the graph does not exist between $x = -2$ and $x = 2$. However, if x is either 2 or -2, y is zero. Thus, the curve must extend to the right from $(2,0)$ and to the left from $(-2,0)$. Hence, we assign the values ± 2, ± 3, ± 4, ± 5, ± 7, ± 9 to x, proceed as in the previous example, and get the following table:

x	-9	-7	-5	-4	-3	-2	2	3	4	5	7	9
y	±7.6	±5.8	±4	±3	±1.9	0	0	±1.9	±3	±4	±5.8	±7.6

3. When the above points are plotted and the graph is drawn, we obtain the curve in Fig. 13.

Again, by referring to Fig. 10, we see that this curve is a hyperbola.

This example illustrates the fact that an equation of the type

$$ax^2 - by^2 = c$$

defines a hyperbola. If c is positive, the curve is in the same general position as that in Fig. 13. However, if c is negative, the two branches

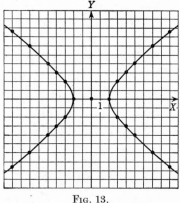

Fig. 13.

of the curve cross the y-axis instead of the x-axis and open upward and downward.

Equations of the Type $y = ax^2 + bx + c$ *or* $x = ay^2 + by + c$

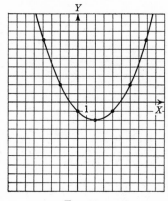

Fig. 14.

EXAMPLE 4

By solving the equation

$$(4) \qquad x^2 - 4x - 4y - 4 = 0$$

for y, we have

$$(5) \qquad y = \tfrac{1}{4}x^2 - x - 1,$$

and this is the first type mentioned above. We avoid fractions here if we substitute only even values for x. If we use the values $-4, -2, 0, 2, 4, 6, 8$ for x and proceed as before, we get the following table of corresponding values of x and y:

x	-4	-2	0	2	4	6	8
y	7	2	-1	-2	-1	2	7

Plotting the above points and drawing the graph, we get the curve in Fig. 14.

EXAMPLE 5

As a final example, we shall construct the graph of

(6) $$2y^2 + 1 = x + 4y.$$

Solution

Since this equation contains only one term in x, the algebra is easier if we solve for x in terms of y and get

(7) $$x = 2y^2 - 4y + 1.$$

Now we assign values to y and compute each corresponding value of x. The table below was obtained by using the values $-2, -1, 0, 1, 2, 3, 4$, for y.

x	17	7	1	-1	1	7	17
y	-2	-1	0	1	2	3	4

Now we plot the graph and obtain the curve in Fig. 15.

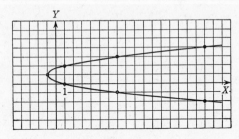

FIG. 15.

The curves in Fig. 14 and Fig. 15 are parabolas. It is proved in analytic geometry that an equation of the type

$$y = ax^2 + bx + c$$

defines a parabola opening upward if a is positive and a parabola opening downward if a is negative. Furthermore, an equation of the type

$$x = ay^2 + by + c$$

defines a parabola opening to the right if a is positive and a parabola opening to the left if a is negative.

Plot the graphs of the equations in Problems 1 to 20.

1. $y^2 = 4x$.
2. $y^2 = -6x$.
3. $x^2 = 2y$.
4. $x^2 = -8y$.
5. $x^2 + y^2 = 16$.
6. $x^2 + y^2 = 9$.
7. $x^2 + y^2 = 196$.
8. $x^2 + y^2 = 36$.
9. $4x^2 + y^2 = 100$.
10. $9x^2 + y^2 = 90$.
11. $4x^2 + 9y^2 = 36$.
12. $16x^2 + 9y^2 = 144$.
13. $4x^2 - y^2 = 4$.
14. $y^2 - 9x^2 = 9$.
15. $4x^2 - 9y^2 = 36$.
16. $9y^2 - 16x^2 = 144$.
17. $y^2 - 2x - 2y - 1 = 0$.
18. $x^2 + 6x - 4y + 13 = 0$.
19. $y^2 - 2y - 4x - 11 = 0$.
20. $x^2 - 4x - 6y - 20 = 0$.

Plot the graph of each member of each of the following pairs of equations on the same axes and estimate the coordinates of the points of intersection.

21. $y^2 = 9x$.
    $y = 3x$.
22. $x^2 = -2y$.
    $y = 2x + 1$.
23. $x^2 + y^2 = 16$.
    $y = x + 1$.
24. $x^2 + y^2 = 20$.
    $2x + 3y = 5$.
25. $x^2 + 4y^2 = 16$.
    $2x - y = 3$.
26. $9x^2 + y^2 = 225$.
    $4x + y = 4$.
27. $y^2 - 2x^2 = 7$.
    $2x - y = -2$.
28. $4x^2 - y^2 = 16$.
    $2x - 3y = 6$.
29. $x^2 + y^2 = 49$.
    $y = 2x$.
30. $x + y^2 = 3$.
    $x^2 = 3y$.
31. $x^2 + 4y = 4$.
    $y^2 = 4x$.
32. $9x + y^2 = 9$.
    $x^2 = 2y$.

66. Solution of pairs of equations involving quadratics in two variables. In the remainder of this chapter, we shall consider pairs of equations in two variables that consist either of a linear equation and a quadratic or of two quadratic equations. We obtain the solution of two such equations by first eliminating one of the variables and then solving the resulting equation for the unknown that remains. We then substitute this value into one of the original equations and solve for the other variable. If both equations are quadratic, the elimination of the first variable usually leads to an equation of the fourth degree, the solution of which is beyond the scope of this book. However, we shall present the method for solving several types of equation pairs which are completely solvable by the methods now available, and this will suffice until the student reaches more advanced fields.

67. Pairs of equations in two variables involving a linear and a quadratic equation. Since we can always solve a linear equation easily for one variable in terms of the other, the most logical method for solving a pair of equations in two variables in which one is linear and the other quadratic consists of the following steps:

1. *Solve the linear equation for one variable in terms of the other.*
2. *Substitute the solution in the quadratic equation, thus obtaining a quadratic equation in one variable.*
3. *Solve this equation for the variable involved.*
4. *Substitute each value obtained in Step 3 into the solution obtained in Step 1, thus obtaining the corresponding value of the second variable.*
5. *Pair[1] the solutions; thus,*

$$x = \underline{\quad}, \quad y = \underline{\quad};$$
$$x = \underline{\quad}, \quad y = \underline{\quad},$$

filling the blanks in each line with the value obtained in Step 3 and the corresponding value obtained by using it in Step 4.

EXAMPLE 1

As a first example of the above method, we shall solve

(1) $x^2 + 4y^2 = 25$
(2) $x - 2y = -1$

simultaneously. The number on the left in the solution indicates which of the above steps is being applied.

1. $x = 2y - 1.$ [solving (2) for x in terms of y]

2. $(2y - 1)^2 + 4y^2 = 25,$ [substituting $2y - 1$ for x in (1)]

          $4y^2 - 4y + 1 + 4y^2 = 25,$ (squaring $2y - 1$)
          $8y^2 - 4y - 24 = 0.$ (transposing and collecting)

---

[1] The graphs of a quadratic and a linear equation in two variables are one of the curves shown in Fig. 10 and a straight line. Since two such curves intersect at most in two points, we may, in general, expect two algebraic solutions for such a pair.

3. $2y^2 - y - 6 = 0,$ (dividing by 4)

$$y = \frac{-(-1) \pm \sqrt{(-1)^2 - 4(2)(-6)}}{2(2)}$$ (by the quadratic formula)

$$= \frac{1 \pm \sqrt{1 + 48}}{4}$$

$$= \frac{1 \pm \sqrt{49}}{4}$$

$$= \frac{1 \pm 7}{4}$$

$$= \tfrac{8}{4} \text{ and } -\tfrac{6}{4}$$

$$= 2 \text{ and } -1\tfrac{1}{2}.$$

Hence, $y = 2$ and $y = -1\tfrac{1}{2}$.

4. Substituting each of these values in the equation obtained in Step 1, we have when $y = 2$, $x = 2(2) - 1 = 4 - 1 = 3$, and when $y = -1\tfrac{1}{2}$, $x = 2(-1\tfrac{1}{2}) - 1 = -3 - 1 = -4$.

5. Hence, the solutions are

$$x = 3, \quad y = 2;$$
$$x = -4, \quad y = -1\tfrac{1}{2}.$$

These solutions may be checked by substituting in Eq. (1).

We shall next construct the graphs of the above equations and interpret the solutions geometrically. If we solve Eq. (1) for y, we get

(3) $$y = \pm\tfrac{1}{2}\sqrt{25 - x^2}.$$

Now we assign the values ±5, ±4, ±3, ±2, ±1, and 0 to x, calculate the corresponding values of y, arrange the associated pairs of numbers in tabular form, and get

x	-5	-4	-3	-2	-1	0	1	2	3	4	5
y	0	±1.5	±2	±2.3	±2.4	±2.5	±2.4	±2.3	±2	±1.5	0

When we construct the graph determined by the above table, we obtain the ellipse in Fig. 16.

If we assign the values -3, 0, and 3 to x in (2) and calculate the corresponding values of y, we obtain the following:

x	-3	0	3
y	-1	$\tfrac{1}{2}$	2

These pairs of values determine the straight line in Fig. 16.

The two graphs thus obtained intersect in the points whose coordinates are $(-4, -1\frac{1}{2})$ and $(3, 2)$. We should expect this result since we obtain algebraically two real solutions of the equations.

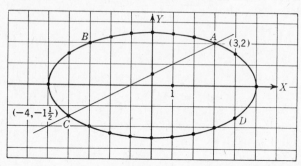

Fig. 16.

The graphical situation offers an explanation for our procedure in Step 4 of the algebraic solution. After we have found the values of one of the variables in Step 3, we could find the values of the other by substituting in either of the given equations. However, if we look at Fig. 16, we see that there are *two* points, A and B, on the ellipse whose y-coordinate is 2. Also there are two points, C and D, whose y-coordinate is $-1\frac{1}{2}$. Hence, if we had substituted in (1), we would have obtained four solutions, two of which would not be acceptable since they do not determine points on the line. We avoid this difficulty by substituting the values obtained in Step 3 in the linear equation instead of the quadratic. Some work is avoided if we use the solved form of the linear equation obtained in Step 1 for the substitution.

EXAMPLE 2

As a second example of a pair of equations consisting of a linear and a quadratic, we shall solve

(4) $x^2 - 2x + y - 1 = 0$
(5) $2x - 3y = -5$

simultaneously. Again, the numbers at the left below indicate the step in the process of the solution.

1. $y = \dfrac{2x + 5}{3}$.   [solving[1] (5) for y]

---

[1] Note that (4) contains only one term involving y and it is a first-degree term. Hence the algebra in Step 2 is simpler if (5) is solved for y instead of for x.

2. $x^2 - 2x + \dfrac{2x + 5}{3} - 1 = 0,$ [substituting in (4)]

$\qquad 3x^2 - 6x + 2x + 5 - 3 = 0,$ (multiplying by 3)

$\qquad\qquad 3x^2 - 4x + 2 = 0.$ (collecting terms)

3. $x = \dfrac{-(-4) \pm \sqrt{(-4)^2 - 4(3)(2)}}{2(3)}$ (by the quadratic formula)

$\quad = \dfrac{4 \pm \sqrt{16 - 24}}{6}$

$\quad = \dfrac{4 \pm \sqrt{-8}}{6}$

$\quad = \dfrac{4 \pm 2i\sqrt{2}}{6}$

$\quad = \dfrac{2 \pm i\sqrt{2}}{3}.$

Hence, $x = \dfrac{2 + i\sqrt{2}}{3}$ and $x = \dfrac{2 - i\sqrt{2}}{3}.$

4. Substituting each of these values for x in the equation in Step 1, we see that for $x = \dfrac{2 + i\sqrt{2}}{3},$ the value of y is

$$y = \dfrac{2\left(\dfrac{2 + i\sqrt{2}}{3}\right) + 5}{3}$$

$$= \dfrac{4 + 2i\sqrt{2} + 15}{9}$$

$$= \dfrac{19 + 2i\sqrt{2}}{9}.$$

Similarly, when

$$x = \dfrac{2 - i\sqrt{2}}{3},$$

we have

$$y = \dfrac{2\left(\dfrac{2 - i\sqrt{2}}{3}\right) + 5}{3}$$

$$= \dfrac{4 - 2i\sqrt{2} + 15}{9}$$

$$= \dfrac{19 - 2i\sqrt{2}}{9}.$$

5. Hence, the solutions are

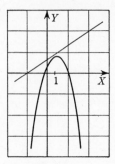

$$x = \frac{2 + i\sqrt{2}}{3}, \quad y = \frac{19 + 2i\sqrt{2}}{9}$$

and

$$x = \frac{2 - i\sqrt{2}}{3}, \quad y = \frac{19 - 2i\sqrt{2}}{9}.$$

We may check these solutions by substituting in (4).

If we apply the usual methods for obtaining the graphs of these equations, we get the parabola in Fig. 17 for Eq. (4) and the straight line for Eq. (5). It should be noted that the two graphs do not intersect each other—a situation that we should expect since the algebraic solutions of the two equations were imaginary.

Fig. 17.

EXERCISE 40

Solve the following pairs of equations simultaneously for x and y.

1. $x^2 + 3y = -2$
$2x + y = 1.$

2. $3x + y^2 = 6$
$-x + 2y = 7.$

3. $x + y^2 = 5$
$2x + y = 4.$

4. $x^2 - y = 5$
$x + 3y = -1.$

5. $x^2 + y^2 = 13$
$2x - y = 1.$

6. $x^2 + y^2 = 10$
$x + 2y = 1.$

7. $x^2 + y^2 = 25$
$3x + y = 15.$

8. $x^2 + y^2 = 13$
$2x - 3y = -5.$

9. $2x^2 + y^2 = 12$
$2x + y = 2.$

10. $2x^2 + y^2 = 11$
$2x - y = 5.$

11. $3x^2 + y^2 = 37$
$3x + y = 1.$

12. $x^2 + 5y^2 = 21$
$x - 3y = 1.$

13. $3x^2 - 2y^2 = 3$
$3x - 2y = 3.$

14. $x^2 - 3y^2 = 1$
$x + y = 3.$

15. $5x^2 - 7y^2 = 38$
$x - y = 2.$

16. $x^2 - 4y^2 = 25$
$x - 2y = 1.$

17. $x^2 + 2x - y = 3$
$3x + y = 3.$

18. $x^2 - 3x - 2y = 2$
$2x + 5y = 1.$

19. $x^2 - 2x + y^2 + y = 5$
$x + 3y = -3.$

20. $x^2 + 4x + y^2 - 5y = 1$
$3x + 4y = 1.$

21. $x^2 + 3x + 2y^2 - y = 7$
$2x + y = 1.$

22. $4x^2 - 5x + y^2 - 4y = 3$
$2x - y = 1.$

23. $x^2 - 4x - y^2 + 5y = -1$
$4x - 3y = 2.$

24. $2x^2 - 7x - y^2 - 2y = 1$
$6x + 5y = 2.$

25. $x^2 + ay = 2a^2$
$3x - y = 2a.$

26. $y^2 - 2ay - bx = b^2$
$x + 2y = 2a - 2b.$

27. $x^2 + y^2 = 10a^2$
$2x + y = -a.$

28. $x^2 + y^2 = 2a^2 + 2b^2$
$x + y = 2a.$

29. $x^2 + bxy = a^2 + b^2$
$bx - a^2y = 0.$

30. $ax^2 - by^2 = ab^2 - a^2b$
$ax - by = 0.$

31. $m^2x^2 + y^2 = b^2$ **32.** $y^2 - x^2 = a^2 + b^2$

    $y = mx + b.$ $by - ax = b^2.$

68. *Elimination by addition or subtraction.* If one of the unknowns occurs in only one term of each member of a pair of quadratic equations and if these two terms are of the same type, then they may be eliminated by addition or subtraction.

This method can always be applied to two equations of the type $ax^2 + by^2 = c$. As we pointed out in Art. 65, the graph of an equation of the type $ax^2 + by^2 = c$ is either a circle, an ellipse, or a hyperbola, and in each case the center[1] is at the origin. Except when there are points of tangency, two such curves, whether they are different in nature or are of the same kind, intersect either in four points or not at all. If two such curves are tangent to each other at one point, they are also tangent to each other at another point. Hence, we may expect four solutions when two such equations are solved simultaneously. Either all four solutions are real, or all of them are imaginary. If there are points of tangency, we have two pairs of equal solutions. We shall illustrate each case by means of an example.

EXAMPLE 1

Solve the equations

(1) $x^2 + 4y^2 = 36$

(2) $2x^2 - y^2 = 8$

simultaneously.

Solution

We can solve Eqs. (1) and (2) simultaneously by first eliminating either x^2 or y^2 by addition or subtraction. We shall eliminate y^2 and then complete the solution by the method below.

(1) $x^2 + 4y^2 = 36$

(3) $8x^2 - 4y^2 = 32$ [Eq. (2) $\times$ 4]

(4) $9x^2 \qquad = 68,$ [Eq. (1) + Eq. (3)]

                        $x^2 = \frac{68}{9},$ [solving (4) for x^2]

                       $x = \pm \sqrt{\frac{68}{9}}$

                         $= \pm \frac{2}{3} \sqrt{17}.$

---

[1] The center of an ellipse is the intersection of the longest and shortest chords that can be drawn in it. The center of a hyperbola is the mid-point of the shortest line that can be drawn from one branch of the curve to the other.

Hence, $x = \frac{2}{3}\sqrt{17}$ and $x = -\frac{2}{3}\sqrt{17}$. The square of each of these values is $\frac{68}{9}$. Thus, when we substitute either of them in (1), we get

(5) $$\frac{68}{9} + 4y^2 = 36.$$

Solving (5) for y, we get

$$68 + 36y^2 = 324, \qquad \text{(clearing of fractions)}$$
$$36y^2 = 324 - 68,$$
$$36y^2 = 256,$$
$$y^2 = \frac{256}{36}$$
$$= \frac{64}{9}.$$

Hence,

$$y = \pm\tfrac{8}{3}.$$

Thus, if x is either $\frac{2}{3}\sqrt{17}$ or $-\frac{2}{3}\sqrt{17}$, y is both $\frac{8}{3}$ and $-\frac{8}{3}$. Thus, the solutions of the given pair of equations are

$$x = \tfrac{2}{3}\sqrt{17}, \qquad y = \tfrac{8}{3};$$
$$x = \tfrac{2}{3}\sqrt{17}, \qquad y = -\tfrac{8}{3};$$
$$x = -\tfrac{2}{3}\sqrt{17}, \qquad y = \tfrac{8}{3};$$

and

$$x = -\tfrac{2}{3}\sqrt{17}, \qquad y = -\tfrac{8}{3}.$$

Since $\sqrt{17} = 4.12$ (to two decimal places), the approximate values of the above solutions to two decimal places are

$$x = 2.75, \qquad y = 2.67;$$
$$x = 2.75, \qquad y = -2.67;$$
$$x = -2.75, \qquad y = 2.67;$$
$$x = -2.75, \qquad y = -2.67.$$

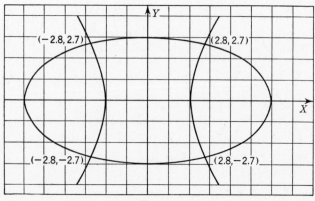

Fig. 18.

If we apply the usual method of graphing to Eqs. (1) and (2), we obtain Fig. 18, in which the ellipse is the graph of (1) and the hyperbola is the graph of (2).   These two curves intersect at four points whose coordinates are approximately $(2.8,2.7)$, $(2.8,-2.7)$, $(-2.8,2.7)$, $(-2.8,-2.7)$.   To one decimal place, these coordinates agree with the approximate solutions obtained above.

This method may also be applied to systems of equations that involve xy-terms or first-degree terms, or both, provided that one unknown is involved in only one term of each equation and that these two terms are of the same type.

EXAMPLE 2

Solve the equations

(6) $$x^2 + 2xy - 2x = 15$$
(7) $$xy - 3x = -3$$

simultaneously.

Solution

We shall eliminate the xy-term and complete the solution by performing the following steps:

(6)	$x^2 + 2xy - 2x = 15$	[rewriting Eq. (6)]
(8)	$2xy - 6x = -6$	[Eq. (7) × 2]
	$x^2 \qquad + 4x = 21,$	[Eq. (6) − Eq. (8)]
	$x^2 + 4x - 21 = 0,$	(transposing 21)
	$(x + 7)(x - 3) = 0,$	(factoring)
	$x = -7,$	(setting each factor equal to zero and solving for x)
	$x = 3.$	
	$(-7)y - 3(-7) = -3,$	[substituting $x = -7$ in (7)]
	$-7y + 21 = -3,$	
	$-7y = -3 - 21,$	
	$-7y = -24,$	
	$y = 3\tfrac{3}{7}.$	
	$(3)y - 3(3) = -3,$	[substituting $x = 3$ in (7)]
	$3y - 9 = -3,$	
	$3y = -3 + 9,$	
	$3y = 6,$	
	$y = 2.$	

Hence the solutions are

$$x = -7, \qquad y = 3\tfrac{3}{7};$$
$$x = 3, \qquad y = 2.$$

The graphs of Eqs. (6) and (7) and their points of intersection are shown in Fig. 19.

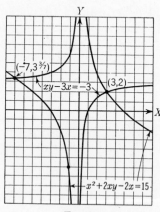

Fɪɢ. 19.

Solve the following pairs of equations simultaneously.

1. $x^2 + 3y^2 = 7$
$2x^2 + y^2 = 9.$

2. $2x^2 - 3y^2 = 6$
$x^2 + y^2 = 13.$

3. $4x^2 + 3y^2 = 7$
$2x^2 - 5y^2 = -3.$

4. $3x^2 - y^2 = 3$
$5x^2 - 2y^2 = 2.$

5. $x^2 + 3y^2 = 19$
$2x^2 - 7y^2 = 25.$

6. $3x^2 + 2y^2 = 14$
$2x^2 + 3y^2 = 11.$

7. $4x^2 + 3y^2 = 4$
$2x^2 - 5y^2 = 2.$

8. $5x^2 - 4y^2 = 4$
$3x^2 - y^2 = 8.$

9. $2x^2 + y^2 - 3x = 3$
$3x^2 + 2y^2 + x = 16.$

10. $2x^2 - y^2 + 2x = 8$
$3x^2 - 2y^2 + 3x = 14.$

11. $3x^2 + y^2 - 6x = 9$
$2x^2 + 2y^2 - 11x = 15.$

12. $3x^2 + 4y^2 - 3x = 4$
$4x^2 - 3y^2 - x = 0.$

13. $3x^2 - 2y^2 + 2x = 1$
$x^2 - y^2 + 3x = 2.$

14. $x^2 + 4y^2 - 2x = 1$
$3x^2 + 8y^2 - 6x = 2.$

15. $x^2 + 4y^2 + 2y = 11$
$x^2 - 4y^2 - 4y = 6.$

16. $2x^2 + y^2 + y = 4$
$3x^2 - y^2 + y = -3.$

17. $x^2 - 3y^2 + 2y = 3$
$2x^2 + 2y^2 - y = 9.$

18. $2x^2 - 3y^2 - 2y = 2$
$x^2 + 2y^2 - 7y = 3.$

19. $2x^2 + y^2 + 2y = 1$
$4x^2 - 3y^2 + y = 0.$

20. $3x^2 - 2y^2 + 3y = 3$
$2x^2 + 2y^2 - 7y = 5.$

21. $x^2 - xy - 3x = 0$
$x^2 + 2xy - 3x = 12.$

22. $x^2 + xy - x = 4$
$2x^2 + 3xy - 4x = 6.$

23. $2x^2 - 3xy + x = 3$
$3x^2 - 2xy - x = 2.$

24. $x^2 + 5xy + 7x = -2$
$x^2 - 3xy - 5x = 6.$

25. $3x^2 - 5xy + x = 4$
$2x^2 - 4xy + x = 2.$

26. $2x^2 - 2xy + 3x = 3$
$3x^2 - 3xy + 2x = -3.$

27. $y^2 + 3xy - 3y = -5$
$y^2 + 2xy - 2y = -2.$

28. $5y^2 - 4xy + y = 2$
$2y^2 - 3xy + 2y = 1.$

29. $2y^2 - 2xy - y = 4$
$3y^2 - 5xy + 2y = -4.$

30. $4y^2 + 2xy - 4y = 1$
$8y^2 + 3xy - 2y = 4.$

31. $4y^2 + 6xy - 6y = 7$
$2y^2 + 4xy - 5y = 4.$

32. $5y^2 + 7xy + y = 4$
$3y^2 + 4xy + 3y = -2.$

69. Two equations of the type $ax^2 + bxy + cy^2 = d$. The solution of two equations of the type $ax^2 + bxy + cy^2 = d$ may be obtained by performing the following steps:

1. *Eliminate the constant terms by addition or subtraction and obtain an equation of the type* $Ax^2 + Bxy + Cy^2 = 0.$

2. *Solve[1] the latter equation for* y *in terms of* x *by use of one of the methods of Chap. 8. Two[2] solutions of the form* $y = Kx$ *and* $y = Gx$, *where* K *and* G *are constants, will be obtained by this process.*

3. *Substitute each value of* y *obtained in Step 2 in one of the original equations, thus obtaining two equations that involve* x *only.*

4. *Solve each of these equations for* x, *obtaining two solutions for each equation.*

5. *Substitute each solution of the equation obtained by use of* $y = Kx$ *for* x *in* $y = Kx$, *thus obtaining each corresponding value of* y. *Similarly, substitute each solution of the equation obtained by use of* $y = Gx$ *for* x *in* $y = Gx$.

6. *Arrange solutions in the form*

$$x = \underline{\quad}, \qquad y = \underline{\quad};$$
$$x = \underline{\quad}, \qquad y = \underline{\quad};$$
$$x = \underline{\quad}, \qquad y = \underline{\quad};$$
$$x = \underline{\quad}, \qquad y = \underline{\quad},$$

filling the blanks with the corresponding values of x *and* y.

[1] The computation is sometimes easier if this equation is solved for x in terms of y. If this is done, then x and y should be interchanged in reading Steps 3, 4, and 5.

[2] If $(Bx)^2 - 4ACx^2 = 0$, these two values of y will be equal. The constants K and G may involve radicals.

EXAMPLE 1

Solve the equations

$$(1) \qquad\qquad 3x^2 + 4xy + y^2 = -8$$
$$(2) \qquad\qquad 7x^2 + 2xy - y^2 = -28$$

simultaneously.

Solution

Step 1

$$(3) \qquad 21x^2 + 28xy + 7y^2 = -56 \qquad \text{[Eq. (1) $\times$ 7]}$$
$$(4) \qquad \underline{14x^2 + 4xy - 2y^2 = -56} \qquad \text{[Eq. (2) $\times$ 2]}$$
$$(5) \qquad 7x^2 + 24xy + 9y^2 = 0. \qquad \text{[Eq. (3) $-$ Eq. (4)]}$$

Step 2

[solving (5) for y by the quadratic formula with $a = 9$, $b = 24x$, and $c = 7x^2$]

$$y = \frac{-24x \pm \sqrt{576x^2 - 252x^2}}{18}$$

$$= \frac{-24x \pm \sqrt{324x^2}}{18}$$

$$= \frac{-24x \pm 18x}{18}$$

$$= -\frac{x}{3} \text{ and } -\frac{7x}{3}.$$

Hence,

$$(6) \qquad y = -\frac{x}{3},$$

and

$$(7) \qquad\qquad y = -\frac{7x}{3}.$$

Steps 3, 4, and 5

$$3x^2 + 4x\left(-\frac{x}{3}\right) + \left(-\frac{x}{3}\right)^2 = -8, \qquad \text{[substituting (6) in (1)]}$$

$$3x^2 - \frac{4x^2}{3} + \frac{x^2}{9} = -8, \qquad \text{(performing the indicated operations)}$$

$$27x^2 - 12x^2 + x^2 = -72, \qquad \text{(clearing of fractions)}$$

$$16x^2 = -72,$$

$$x^2 = -\tfrac{72}{16} = -\tfrac{18}{4},$$

$$x = \pm \sqrt{-\frac{18}{4}} = \pm \frac{3\sqrt{2}}{2} i.$$

$$y = -\frac{1}{3}\left(\pm \frac{3\sqrt{2}}{2} i\right) = \mp \frac{\sqrt{2}}{2} i. \qquad \left[\text{substituting} \atop \pm \frac{3\sqrt{2}}{2} i \text{ for } x \text{ in (6)}\right]$$

Hence, two solutions are

$$x = \pm \frac{3\sqrt{2}}{2} i, \qquad y = \mp \frac{\sqrt{2}}{2} i.$$

$$3x^2 + 4x\left(-\frac{7x}{3}\right) + \left(-\frac{7x}{3}\right)^2 = -8, \qquad \begin{array}{l}[\text{substituting (7)} \\ \text{in (1)}]\end{array}$$

$$3x^2 - \frac{28x^2}{3} + \frac{49x^2}{9} = -8, \qquad \begin{array}{l}\text{(performing the} \\ \text{indicated opera-} \\ \text{tions)}\end{array}$$

$$27x^2 - 84x^2 + 49x^2 = -72,$$
$$-8x^2 = -72,$$
$$x^2 = 9,$$
$$x = \pm 3.$$
$$y = -\tfrac{7}{3}(\pm 3) = \mp 7. \qquad \begin{array}{l}[\text{substituting} \ \pm 3 \\ \text{for } x \text{ in (7)}].\end{array}$$

Therefore, two additional solutions are

$$x = \pm 3, \qquad y = \mp 7.$$

Step **6**

Hence the four solutions are

$$x = \frac{3\sqrt{2}}{2} i, \qquad y = -\frac{\sqrt{2}}{2} i;$$

$$x = -\frac{3\sqrt{2}}{2} i, \qquad y = \frac{\sqrt{2}}{2} i;$$

$$x = 3, \qquad y = -7;$$
$$x = -3, \qquad y = 7.$$

If one of the equations in a given system contains no constant term, as in the pair

$$3x^2 - 2xy - y^2 = 0$$
$$2x^2 + xy - 2y^2 = 9,$$

then Step 1 is unnecessary. We apply Step 2 to the first of these equations and then proceed with the other steps.

Solve the following pairs of equations simultaneously.

1. $x^2 + 3xy + 4y^2 = 8$
$x^2 + xy - 2y^2 = 0.$

2. $x^2 - 5xy + 10y^2 = 16$
$x^2 - 2xy - 3y^2 = 0.$

3. $x^2 + 4xy - 17y^2 = -20$
$x^2 + xy - 6y^2 = 0.$

4. $x^2 - 10xy + 25y^2 = 36$
$x^2 - xy - 6y^2 = 0.$

5. $3x^2 + 6xy + 4y^2 = 4$
$2x^2 + 3xy + 2y^2 = 4.$

6. $11x^2 - 23xy - 19y^2 = 11$
$9x^2 - 13xy - 9y^2 = 33.$

7. $x^2 + 4xy - y^2 = 5$
$x^2 - 2xy + y^2 = 1.$

8. $x^2 - 2xy + y^2 = 1$
$2x^2 - xy - 2y^2 = 4.$

9. $2x^2 - xy + y^2 = 1$
$4x^2 + 16xy - 4y^2 = 5.$

10. $28x^2 + 114xy - 28y^2 = 9$
$36x^2 - 12xy + y^2 = 1.$

11. $12x^2 + 29xy - 12y^2 = -4$
$108x^2 - 27xy - 4y^2 = -4.$

12. $4x^2 - 4xy + y^2 = 1$
$18x^2 + 17xy - 18y^2 = 12.$

13. $4x^2 + 6xy - y^2 = 1$
$3x^2 + 4xy - 2y^2 = -3.$

14. $2x^2 + xy - 2y^2 = -2$
$3x^2 + 2xy - 2y^2 = 3.$

15. $x^2 + xy - y^2 = -1$
$x^2 + 2xy + y^2 = 9.$

16. $x^2 - 3xy - 9y^2 = 1$
$x^2 - 6xy + 9y^2 = 1.$

17. $5x^2 + 2xy - 4y^2 = 5$
$3x^2 + 4xy - 8y^2 = 3.$

18. $3x^2 + 3xy + 9y^2 = 1$
$x^2 + 6xy + 9y^2 = 1.$

19. $x^2 + 3xy + y^2 = -5$
$x^2 - xy - 3y^2 = 3.$

20. $2x^2 + 4xy + y^2 = -17$
$x^2 + xy - y^2 = -11.$

21. $2x^2 - 4xy - 3y^2 = 3$
$x^2 - 2xy - 2y^2 = 2.$

22. $3x^2 + 4xy - 2y^2 = -3$
$2x^2 + 2xy - y^2 = -2.$

23. $3x^2 + 5xy - 7y^2 = -1$
$2x^2 - 5xy - 3y^2 = 6.$

24. $2x^2 - 4xy - 3y^2 = 3$
$x^2 - 2xy + 3y^2 = -3.$

25. $x^2 + xy + 3y^2 = -5$
$3x^2 + 3xy - 5y^2 = -1.$

26. $6x^2 - 4xy + y^2 = 9$
$3x^2 + 7xy - y^2 = 45.$

27. $3x^2 - 2xy + y^2 = 22$
$2x^2 + 9xy - y^2 = 44.$

28. $2x^2 + 4xy + y^2 = 5$
$x^2 + 3xy + y^2 = -5.$

29. $2x^2 + 4xy - 3y^2 = 3$
$x^2 + xy - 2y^2 = 4.$

30. $2x^2 - 3xy + y^2 = 3$
$x^2 - 5xy + 3y^2 = -3.$

31. $4x^2 + 8xy - y^2 = -1$
$2x^2 + xy + 4y^2 = 1.$

32. $x^2 + 2xy + 2y^2 = -5$
$2x^2 + 5xy - 2y^2 = -1.$

70. *Pairs of quadratic equations solvable by substitution.* The method of substitution is advisable for solving a pair of equations if one of them is readily solvable for one of the variables in terms of the other, or if, after eliminating one or more terms from the equations by addition or subtraction, we obtain an equation that can be easily solved for one variable in terms of the other. The method for solving each of these cases is illustrated in Examples 1 and 2, respectively.

EXAMPLE 1

In order to solve the equations

(1)
$$xy = 6$$
(2)
$$x^2 + y^2 = 13$$

simultaneously, we first solve (1) for y in terms of x and obtain

(3)
$$y = \frac{6}{x}.$$

Now we substitute (3) in (2) and get

$$x^2 + \frac{36}{x^2} = 13.$$

If we clear this equation of fractions, we have

$$x^4 + 36 = 13x^2,$$

which is a fourth-degree equation in quadratic form, and we can solve it as follows:

$$x^4 - 13x^2 + 36 = 0, \quad \text{(transposing } 13x^2\text{)}$$
$$(x^2 - 9)(x^2 - 4) = 0,$$
$$x^2 - 9 = 0,$$
$$x = \pm 3;$$
$$x^2 - 4 = 0,$$
$$x = \pm 2.$$

We now substitute $x = \pm 3$ in (3) and get $y = \dfrac{6}{\pm 3} = \pm 2.$ Similarly, if $x = \pm 2, y = \pm 3.$

Hence, the solutions are

$$x = 3, \qquad y = 2;$$
$$x = -3, \qquad y = -2;$$
$$x = 2, \qquad y = 3;$$
$$x = -2, \qquad y = -3.$$

EXAMPLE 2

If in the equations

(4)
$$x^2 + y^2 + \ x - 2y = 9$$
(5)
$$x^2 + y^2 - 2x \qquad = 1$$

we subtract (5) from (4), we get

(6) $$3x - 2y = 8.$$

This is a linear equation, and if we solve it for x in terms of y, we get

(7) $$x = \frac{2y + 8}{3}.$$

Now, we substitute this value for x in (5) and obtain

(8) $$\left(\frac{2y + 8}{3}\right)^2 + y^2 - 2\left(\frac{2y + 8}{3}\right) = 1,$$

and we can complete the solution by performing the following operations:

$$\frac{4y^2 + 32y + 64}{9} + y^2 - \frac{4y + 16}{3} = 1,$$ [performing the indicated operations in (8)]

$$4y^2 + 32y + 64 + 9y^2 - 12y - 48 = 9,$$ (clearing of fractions)

$$13y^2 + 20y + 7 = 0,$$ (transposing and collecting terms)

$$y = \frac{-20 \pm \sqrt{400 - 364}}{26}$$ (solving for y by the quadratic formula)

$$= \frac{-20 \pm \sqrt{36}}{26}$$

$$= \frac{-20 \pm 6}{26}$$

$$= -1 \text{ and } -\tfrac{7}{13}.$$

Substituting these values in (7), we have

$$x = \frac{-2 + 8}{3} = \frac{6}{3}$$

$$= 2 \qquad \text{(when } y = -1)$$

and

$$x = \frac{-\frac{14}{13} + 8}{3}$$

$$= \frac{-14 + 104}{39} = \frac{90}{39}$$

$$= \tfrac{30}{13}. \qquad \text{(when } y = -\tfrac{7}{13})$$

Hence, the solutions are

$$x = 2, \qquad y = -1;$$
$$x = \tfrac{30}{13}, \qquad y = -\tfrac{7}{13}.$$

71. *Symmetric equations.* An equation is symmetric in two variables if the equation is not altered when the two variables are interchanged. For example, if in equation

$$x^2 + y^2 + 2xy + x + y = 2$$

we change x to y and y to x, we obtain the same equation. The solution of two such equations is simplified by first substituting $u + v$ for x and $u - v$ for y, and then solving the resulting equations for u and v. We then add v to u to get x, and subtract v from u to get y. The method is illustrated in the following example:

EXAMPLE

Solve the equations

(1) $$x^2 + y^2 + 3xy + x + y = -4$$
(2) $$4xy + x + y = -23$$

simultaneously.

Solution

We first let

(3) $$x = u + v,$$
(4) $$y = u - v;$$

then substitute these values in (1) and get

$$u^2 + 2uv + v^2 + u^2 - 2uv + v^2 + 3u^2 - 3v^2 + u + v + u - v = -4.$$

Collecting terms, we have

$$5u^2 - v^2 + 2u = -4.$$

Similarly, from (2), we obtain

$$4u^2 - 4v^2 + u + v + u - v = -23$$

or

$$4u^2 - 4v^2 + 2u = -23.$$

Hence, we have the two following equations in u and v.

(5) $$5u^2 - v^2 + 2u = -4,$$
(6) $$4u^2 - 4v^2 + 2u = -23.$$

Each of these equations involves v in only one term, and these terms can be eliminated by addition. Then the solution can be completed. The remainder of the solution follows.

(7) $20u^2 - 4v^2 + 8u = -16$ [Eq. (5) $\times$ 4]
(6) $4u^2 - 4v^2 + 2u = -23$ [Eq. (6) recopied]

$\qquad 16u^2 + 6u = 7,$ [Eq. (7) $-$ Eq. (6)]

$\qquad 16u^2 + 6u - 7 = 0,$ (transposing 7)

$$u = \frac{-6 \pm \sqrt{36 + 448}}{32},\qquad \text{(by the quadratic formula)}$$

$$u = \frac{-6 \pm 22}{32} = \frac{16}{32} \text{ and } -\frac{28}{32}.$$

Hence, $u = \frac{1}{2}$, and $u = -\frac{7}{8}$.

Now we substitute $\frac{1}{2}$ for u in (6) and get

$$4(\tfrac{1}{4}) - 4v^2 + 2(\tfrac{1}{2}) = -23$$

or

$$1 - 4v^2 + 1 = -23,$$
$$-4v^2 = -25,$$
$$v^2 = \tfrac{25}{4},$$
$$v = \pm\tfrac{5}{2}.$$

Hence, two solutions of (5) and (6) are

$$u = \tfrac{1}{2}, \qquad v = \tfrac{5}{2};$$
$$u = \tfrac{1}{2}, \qquad v = -\tfrac{5}{2}.$$

For the first pair of values of u and v, we have, by use of (3) and (4),

$$x = \tfrac{1}{2} + \tfrac{5}{2} = 3, \qquad y = \tfrac{1}{2} - \tfrac{5}{2} = -2,$$

and, for the second pair, we get

$$x = \tfrac{1}{2} - \tfrac{5}{2} = -2, \qquad y = \tfrac{1}{2} + \tfrac{5}{2} = 3.$$

Next, we substitute $u = -\frac{7}{8}$ in (6) and get

$$4(\tfrac{49}{64}) - 4v^2 + 2(-\tfrac{7}{8}) = -23.$$

Performing the indicated multiplication and clearing of fractions, we have

$$196 - 256v^2 - 112 = -1472.$$

Transposing and collecting, we obtain

$$-256v^2 = -1556.$$

Hence,

$$v^2 = \tfrac{1556}{256} = \tfrac{389}{64},$$
$$v = \pm\frac{\sqrt{389}}{8}.$$

Hence, two additional solutions of (5) and (6) are

$$u = -\frac{7}{8}, \quad v = \frac{\sqrt{389}}{8};$$

$$u = -\frac{7}{8}, \quad v = -\frac{\sqrt{389}}{8}.$$

When these values are substituted successively in (3) and (4), we obtain

$$x = -\frac{7}{8} + \frac{\sqrt{389}}{8}, \quad y = -\frac{7}{8} - \frac{\sqrt{389}}{8},$$

and

$$x = -\frac{7}{8} - \frac{\sqrt{389}}{8}, \quad y = -\frac{7}{8} + \frac{\sqrt{389}}{8}.$$

Hence, the four simultaneous solutions of (1) and (2) are

$$x = 3, \qquad y = -2;$$
$$x = -2, \qquad y = 3;$$
$$x = \tfrac{1}{8}(-7 + \sqrt{389}), \qquad y = \tfrac{1}{8}(-7 - \sqrt{389});$$
$$x = \tfrac{1}{8}(-7 - \sqrt{389}), \qquad y = \tfrac{1}{8}(-7 + \sqrt{389}).$$

EXERCISE 43

Solve each of the following pairs of equations simultaneously.

1. $x^2 + y = 5$
   $2x^2 + y^2 = 9.$

2. $x^2 - y = 11$
   $x^2 - y^2 = 5.$

3. $x - 2y^2 = -1$
   $x^2 - 16y^2 = -15.$

4. $x + 3y^2 = 1$
   $x^2 - 39y^2 = -35.$

5. $x^2 - y = 8$
   $x^2 - y^2 = 8.$

6. $x^2 + y = -1$
   $2x^2 - y^2 = -17.$

7. $x + y^2 = 6$
   $x^2 + x + y^2 = 15.$

8. $x - y^2 = 1$
   $x^2 - x + y^2 = 3.$

9. $xy = 3$
   $x^2 + y^2 = 10.$

10. $xy = -2$
    $4x^2 + 9y^2 = 40.$

11. $xy = 4$
    $x^2 + 2y^2 = 12.$

12. $xy = -20$
    $2x^2 - 3y^2 = 2.$

13. $2x - 3y + xy = 6$
    $3x - 2y + xy = 11.$

14. $2x - 5y + xy = 1$
    $3x - 7y + xy = 1.$

15. $3x + 2y + 2xy = 3$
    $2x - 3y + 3xy = 2.$

16. $3x - 4y + 5xy = 4$
    $5x - 2y + 3xy = 2.$

17. $x^2 + y^2 - x + y = 4$
    $x^2 + y^2 + x - y = 6.$

18. $x^2 + y^2 + 2x + y = 6$
    $x^2 + y^2 + 3x + 2y = 1.$

19. $x^2 + y^2 + 5x - 3y = -2$
$x^2 + y^2 + 3x - 5y = -4.$

20. $x^2 + y^2 + 2x - 4y = -3$
$x^2 + y^2 + 3x - y = 4.$

21. $x^2 + xy + y^2 = 3$
$2x^2 + 3xy + 2y^2 = 4.$

22. $x^2 - xy + y^2 = 1$
$2xy - x^2 - y^2 = 0.$

23. $x^2 - xy + y^2 = 3$
$xy + x^2 + y^2 = 7.$

24. $x^2 - 2xy + y^2 = 1$
$xy - x^2 - y^2 = -7.$

25. $x^2 + y^2 = 13$
$x^2 + xy + y^2 = 19.$

26. $x^2 + y^2 = 2$
$x^2 - xy + y^2 = 1.$

27. $x^2 + y^2 = 5$
$x^2 - xy + y^2 = 7.$

28. $x^2 + y^2 = 13$
$x^2 + 2xy + y^2 = 1.$

29. $x^2 + y^2 + x + y = 14$
$x + y + xy = -5.$

30. $x^2 + y^2 - x - y = 2$
$xy + x + y = -1.$

31. $x^2 + y^2 - 3x - 3y = 8$
$x + y + 2xy = -5.$

32. $x^2 + y^2 + 2x + 2y = 11$
$xy - 3x - 3y = -3.$

EXERCISE 44

1. Find two numbers whose sum is 23 and whose product is 126.

2. Find two numbers whose product is 108 and whose quotient is 3.

3. Find two numbers whose sum is 15 and the sum of whose squares is 113.

4. Two numbers differ by 2, and their squares differ by 32. Find the numbers.

5. The area of a rectangular flower bed is 105 sq. ft. Find its dimensions if its length is 8 ft. more than its width.

6. Find the dimensions of a rectangle if its diagonal is 15 ft. and its area is 108 sq. ft.

7. Find the length of the legs of a right triangle whose area is 30 sq. ft. and whose hypotenuse is 13 ft. long.

8. Find the base and altitude of an isosceles triangle if its area is 12 sq. in. and its altitude is $\frac{2}{3}$ of the base.

9. Find two numbers such that their product is 2 and the sum of their reciprocals is $\frac{19}{6}$.

10. The sum of the squares of the digits in a two-digit number is 25. Find the number if interchanging the digits increases it by 9.

11. If the digits in a two-digit number are interchanged, the number is decreased by 18. Find the number if the product of the digits is 15.

12. Determine c such that the sum of the squares of the roots of $x^2 - 6x + c = 0$ is 20.

13. A rectangular garden with an area of 1500 sq. ft. has a 2-ft. walk around it. Find the dimensions of the garden if the area of the walk is 336 sq. ft.

14. A box was made from a rectangular sheet of metal of area 221 sq. in. by cutting $1\frac{1}{2}$-in. squares from each corner and then turning up the edges.

Find the original dimensions of the sheet if the volume of the box is 210 cu. in.

15. A rectangle is constructed in a right triangle by selecting a point on the hypotenuse and drawing perpendiculars to the legs. Find the dimensions of the rectangle if its area is 24 sq. in. and the legs of the triangle are 9 and 12 in. in length, respectively.

16. A rectangular bin with a square base and no top was built at a cost of $42.80. The material for the base cost 14 cents per square foot, and that for the sides, 9 cents per square foot. Find the dimensions of the bin if the combined area of the base and sides was 420 sq. ft.

17. Two circles, the sum of whose radii is 7 in., are tangent internally. Find the length of the radius of each if the area between the circles is 66 sq. in. (Use $\frac{22}{7}$ for π.)

18. A Norman window in the shape of a rectangle surmounted by a semicircle has an area of $\frac{400}{7}$ sq. ft. and a perimeter of $\frac{200}{7}$ ft. Find the dimensions of the rectangle. (Use $\frac{22}{7}$ for π.)

19. The sum of the circumferences of two circles is 44 cm., and the sum of their areas is $\frac{550}{7}$ sq. cm. Find the radius of each. (Use $\frac{22}{7}$ for π.)

20. The sum of the circumference of a circle and the perimeter of a square is $\frac{100}{7}$ in., and the sum of the areas of the two figures is $\frac{50}{7}$. Find the radius of the circle and the side of the square.

21. A man made two investments of which the first was $720 more than the second. If, during the first year, the second investment earned 1 per cent more than the first and the income from each was $144, find the amount of the first investment and the rate it earned.

22. A farmer who operated two farms sold his cotton crop at the end of a certain year for $10,800. The first farm produced 10 bales less than the second, but the price of this cotton was $10 more per bale than that produced on the second. If the crop from the first sold for $4800, find the number of bales produced on each farm and the price per bale of each lot.

23. Two boys rowed 6 miles up a river, then walked 3 miles to a cave, and found that the trip required 5 hr. After lunch they returned to their starting point in $2\frac{1}{2}$ hr. Their rate of walking from the canoe to the cave was $\frac{1}{2}$ mile per hr. less than that of the return trip. If the rate of the current in the river was 2 miles per hr., find their rowing rate in still water and their walking rate to the cave.

24. A truck left A at 6 A.M. on a trip to B, 200 miles away. At 7 A.M. a car left A, overtook the truck at C, delivered a message and returned to A. Find the speed of the truck and the distance from A to C if the car traveled at 60 miles per hr. and reached A at the same time that the truck reached B.

CHAPTER 10

RATIO, PROPORTION, AND VARIATION

72. Ratio. The ratio of any number a to a second number b is the quotient obtained by dividing a by b. Thus, the *ratio* of **a** to b is $\dfrac{a}{b}$, or, as it is often written, $a:b$, where the colon indicates division. Hence, the ratio of 10 to 2 feet is $\frac{10}{2} = 5$, and the ratio of 6 to 15 pounds is $\frac{6}{15} = \frac{2}{5}$.

If a and b are magnitudes of the same kind, then they must be expressed in the same unit if $\dfrac{a}{b}$ is to have a meaning. Thus, in order to find the ratio of 3 inches to 2 feet, we reduce 2 feet to 24 inches; then the desired ratio is $\frac{3}{24} = \frac{1}{8}$. In such cases, the ratio $\dfrac{a}{b}$ represents an abstract number and is the answer to the question "The number a is what multiple of b, or what fractional part of b?"

Although we ordinarily think of a ratio as an operation that involves quantities of the same kind, we frequently see a ratio expressed between magnitudes that are entirely different in their nature. For example, in physics the velocity v of a body is expressed thus:

$$v = \frac{s}{t}.$$

The value of the ratio is the number of feet, or the part of s, that a body moves in 1 second. Also, the price P per acre of a farm is equal to the ratio of the total cost C to the number of acres n, or

$$P = \frac{C}{n}.$$

214

Again, the value of the ratio is the portion of C that corresponds to 1 acre.

Thus if a and b do not represent magnitudes of the same kind, the ratio $a:b$ represents the portion of a that corresponds to one unit of b.

73. Proportion. One of the most frequent applications of the ratio relation occurs in situations involving numbers that can be separated into pairs in which the ratios of the members are equal. For example, if a car is traveling at a speed that is double that of another, it will cover twice as great a distance in a given time. In fact, if S and s are the average speeds of the two cars and D and d are the respective distances covered in a given time, we have

$$\frac{S}{s} = \frac{D}{d}.$$

We call an equation of the above type a *proportion*, and it is an illustration of the following definition:

DEFINITION. *A **proportion** is a statement that two ratios are equal.*

Proportions are written in two[1] ways;

(1)
$$\frac{a}{b} = \frac{c}{d}$$

or

(2)
$$a:b = c:d.$$

In either (1) or (2), the terms b and c are called the *means* and a and d the *extremes*. Also, a and c are called the *antecedents* and b and d the *consequents*.

Many important relationships in mathematics and in the other sciences are stated as proportions, and hence some familiarity with them will be helpful to one entering a technical field. We shall present below several properties that are useful in dealing with proportions.

If we multiply each member of (1) by bd, we obtain

$$\frac{abd}{b} = \frac{cbd}{d}.$$

Now, dividing each member of the fraction on the left by b and

---

[1] In older algebras and arithmetics, proportions were usually written $a:b::c:d$.

each member on the right by d, we have

(3) $ad = cb.$

Hence, we have the important property stated below.

PROPERTY I.   *In any proportion, the product of the means is equal to the product of the extremes.*

EXAMPLE 1

Find x if $3:4 = x:12.$

Solution

Applying Property I, we have

$$4x = 36.$$

Hence,

$$x = 9.$$

If we divide each member of (3) by cd, we get

$$\frac{ad}{cd} = \frac{cb}{cd}$$

or

$$\frac{a}{c} = \frac{b}{d}.$$

Furthermore, by dividing each member of (3) by ac, we obtain

$$\frac{ad}{ac} = \frac{cb}{ac}$$

or

$$\frac{d}{c} = \frac{b}{a}.$$

Hence, we have

PROPERTY II.   *If $\dfrac{a}{b} = \dfrac{c}{d}$ then $\dfrac{a}{c} = \dfrac{b}{d}$ and also $\dfrac{b}{a} = \dfrac{d}{c}.$*

The second proportion is said to be derived from the first by *alternation*, and the third is derived from the first by *inversion*.

EXAMPLE 2

If $\dfrac{a}{b} = \dfrac{c}{d}$ and $\dfrac{n}{d} = \dfrac{m}{c}$, show that $\dfrac{a}{b} = \dfrac{m}{n}.$

Solution

Since $\dfrac{n}{d} = \dfrac{m}{c}$, we have first by alternation

$$\frac{n}{m} = \frac{d}{c},$$

and then by inversion,

$$\frac{m}{n} = \frac{c}{d}.$$

Hence,

$$\frac{a}{b} = \frac{m}{n}.$$

We may derive two other proportions from (1) by first adding 1 to each member of (1) and simplifying, and then by adding -1 to each member of (1) and simplifying. In the first case, we get

$$\frac{a}{b} + 1 = \frac{c}{d} + 1.$$

Hence,

(4)
$$\frac{a + b}{b} = \frac{c + d}{d}.$$

In the second, we have

$$\frac{a}{b} - 1 = \frac{c}{d} - 1.$$

Simplifying, we get

(5)
$$\frac{a - b}{b} = \frac{c - d}{d}.$$

Now, dividing corresponding members of (4) and (5), we obtain

$$\frac{a + b}{a - b} = \frac{c + d}{c - d}.$$

Consequently, we have

PROPERTY III. *If* $\dfrac{a}{b} = \dfrac{c}{d}$, *then* $\dfrac{a + b}{b} = \dfrac{c + d}{d}$, $\dfrac{a - b}{b} = \dfrac{c - d}{d}$,

and $\dfrac{a + b}{a - b} = \dfrac{c + d}{c - d}$.

In Property III, the second and third proportions are said to be derived from the first by addition and subtraction, respectively. The fourth is said to be derived from the first by addition and subtraction.

EXAMPLE 3

If $\dfrac{a}{b} = \dfrac{c}{d}$, $a + b = 60$, $c = 3$, and $d = 2$, find a and b.

Solution

If $\dfrac{a}{b} = \dfrac{c}{d}$, we have by addition,

$$\frac{a + b}{b} = \frac{c + d}{d}.$$

Hence, when we substitute the given values for $a + b$, c and d, we have

$$\frac{60}{b} = \frac{3 + 2}{2}$$

or

$$\frac{60}{b} = \frac{5}{2}.$$

Hence, by Property I,
$$5b = 120,$$
$$b = 24.$$

Furthermore, since
$$a + b = 60,$$
it follows that
$$a = 36.$$

If, in any proportion, the two means are equal, we have a *mean proportion*. Thus, in (1), if $c = b$, we have $\dfrac{a}{b} = \dfrac{b}{d}$ or $a:b = b:d$. Then b is called the *mean proportional* to (or between) a and d, and d is called the *third proportional* to a and b. However, if $b \neq c$ in (1), d is called the *fourth proportional* to a, b, and c.

EXAMPLE 4

Find the mean proportional between 12 and 3.

Solution

If we let x represent the desired mean proportional, we have

$$12:x = x:3.$$

Hence,

$$x^2 = 36, \qquad \text{(by Property I)}$$

and

$$x = \pm 6.$$

EXAMPLE 5

Find the third proportional to 16 and 12.

Solution

If we let x represent the third proportional, we have

$$16:12 = 12:x.$$

Hence,

$$16x = 144, \qquad \text{(by Property I)}$$

and

$$x = 9.$$

EXAMPLE 6

Find x if 7 is the fourth proportional to 35, 28, and x.

Solution

By definition we have

$$35:28 = x:7.$$

Hence,

$$28x = 245, \qquad \text{(by Property I)}$$

and

$$x = \frac{245}{28} = \frac{35}{4}.$$

A symbolic statement resembling a proportion is frequently used to indicate that three ratios are equal. For example,

$$(6) \qquad\qquad a:b:c = x:y:z$$

is a short way of stating that

$$(7) \qquad a:b = x:y, \qquad a:c = x:z, \qquad b:c = y:z,$$

or that

$$(8) \qquad\qquad \frac{a}{x} = \frac{b}{y} = \frac{c}{z}.$$

If in (8) each of the ratios is equal to a constant k, we have

(9) $\qquad a = kx, \qquad b = ky, \qquad$ and $c = kz.$

From (9), it follows at once that

$$a + b + c = k(x + y + z).$$

Hence,

$$\frac{a + b + c}{x + y + z} = k$$

or

(10) $\qquad \dfrac{a + b + c}{x + y + z} = \dfrac{a}{x} = \dfrac{b}{y} = \dfrac{c}{z}.$

EXAMPLE 7

If the sides of two triangles are A, B, C and a, b, c, respectively, and if $\dfrac{A}{a} = \dfrac{B}{b} = \dfrac{C}{c}$, find A, B, and C if the perimeter of the first triangle is 176 and if $a = 5$, $b = 18$, and $c = 21$.

Solution

It is given that

$$\frac{A}{a} = \frac{B}{b} = \frac{C}{c}.$$

Hence, by (10),

$$\frac{A + B + C}{a + b + c} = \frac{A}{a}.$$

Now, if we substitute the value of the perimeter for $A + B + C$ and the given values for a, b, and c, we have

$$\frac{176}{5 + 18 + 21} = \frac{A}{5},$$

or

$$\frac{176}{44} = \frac{A}{5}.$$

Hence, by Property I,

$$44A = 880,$$
$$A = 20.$$

Then, since

$$\frac{A}{a} = \frac{B}{b},$$

we have

$$\frac{20}{5} = \frac{B}{18},$$
$$5B = 360,$$

and

$$B = 72.$$

Finally, since

$$A + B + C = 176,$$
$$C = 176 - (A + B)$$
$$= 176 - 92$$
$$= 84.$$

EXERCISE 45

In each of Problems 1 to 12 express the indicated ratio as a fraction and simplify.

1. 4 ft. to 9 in.

2. 3 yd. to 2 ft.

3. $2\frac{1}{2}$ yd. to 4 in.

4. $7\frac{3}{4}$ ft. to 3 in.

5. 3 weeks to 6 days.

6. 1 day to 9 hr.

7. $2\frac{1}{3}$ hr. to 15 min.

8. $4\frac{1}{5}$ hr. to 12 min.

9. $a^2b^3 : ab$.

10. $a^2x^5 : ax^4$.

11. $(c^2 - cd) : (c^2 - d^2)$.

12. $(x^2 + xy - 2y^2) : (x^2 + 3xy + 2y^2)$.

Find the value of the ratio in each of Problems 13 to 16 and interpret the result.

13. 540 mi. to 12 hr.

14. \$3 to 4 lb.

15. \$6300 to 12 months.

16. \$1600 to 8 men.

By use of Property I, find the value of x in Problems 17 to 24.

17. $x : 3 = 8 : 24$.

18. $2 : x = 12 : 6$.

19. $3 : 5 = x : 10$.

20. $4 : 7 = 10 : x$.

21. $(x + 1) : 2 = 5 : 10$.

22. $3 : (2x + 1) = 6 : 14$.

23. $3 : 7 = (2x - 3) : 14$.

24. $7 : 9 = 14 : (2x + 1)$.

Find the mean proportionals to the pair of numbers or expressions in each of Problems 25 to 32.

25. 2, 8.

26. 3, 27.

27. 1, 4.

28. 5, 45.

29. x^2, x^4.

30. x^2, y^{-6}.

31. $\dfrac{y^2 + y - 2}{y + 3}, \dfrac{y^2 + 2y - 3}{y + 2}$.

32. $\dfrac{y^2 + 2y - 8}{y + 1}, \dfrac{y^2 + 5y + 4}{y - 2}$.

Find the third proportional to each pair of numbers in Problems 33 to 36.

33. 3, 6.

34. 2, 8.

35. 3, 5.

36. 2, 7.

Find the fourth proportional to each set of numbers in Problems 37 to 40.

37. 2, 3, 6.   **38.** 3, 5, 6.   **39.** 5, 2, 2.5.   **40.** 4, 3, 6.

41. If $x:y = 3:4$ and $x + y = 14$, find x and y.

42. If $x:y = 1:5$ and $x + y = 12$, find x and y.

43. If $x:7 = y:3$ and $x - y = 8$, find x and y.

44. If $x:8 = y:3$ and $x - y = 5$, find x and y.

45. Divide 40 into two parts which are in the ratio $3:2$.

46. Find the acute angles of a right triangle if they are in the ratio $13:5$.

47. The sum of $14,700 was divided between two partners in the ratio $3:4$. How much did each partner receive?

48. Find two numbers whose sum is 96 and whose ratio is $3:5$.

49. Divide 84 into two parts such that if 5 is added to the smaller and subtracted from the larger, the numbers thus obtained are in the ratio $8:13$.

50. If a man 6 ft. tall is standing 21 ft. from a street light and casts a shadow 9 ft. in length, find the height of the light.

51. Find the three angles of a triangle if they are in the ratio $2:3:4$.

52. The sides of a triangle are 5, 7, and 11 in., respectively, in length. Find the length of the sides of a similar triangle whose perimeter is 46 in.

53. The pitch of a roof is the distance the roof rises per unit of horizontal distance covered. Find the pitch of a roof if a rafter is 13 ft. in length and one of its ends is 5 ft. higher than the other.

54. The grade of a highway is the distance it rises per unit of length along the surface. Find the average grade of a highway that rises 264 ft. in a mile.

55. The specific gravity of a body is the ratio of the weight of the body to the weight of an equal body of water. If a cubic foot of water weighs 62.5 lb. and a cubic foot of iron weighs 487.5 lb., what is the specific gravity of iron?

56. The density of a body is defined as the ratio of the mass of the body to its volume. If the mass of 120 cc. of aluminum is 224 g., find its density.

74. Variation. We are continually dealing with situations involving two quantities which vary in such a way that their ratio does not change. For example, if the price of cotton does not change during one day, then at any time during this day the ratio of the amount paid for one bale of a certain grade of cotton to the weight of the bale always has the same value, and this value is the price per pound.

In such cases, the first quantity is said to vary as the second, or, stated more precisely, to vary directly as the second. Thus, if a

varies directly as b, then the ratio $\frac{a}{b}$ is equal to a constant. If k represents this constant, we have $\frac{a}{b} = k$ or $a = kb$.

Many scientific laws that deal with relations between physical quantities use the above terminology. We shall state below two such laws and show how the laws are translated into equations.

Charles's law states that if the pressure is constant the volume of a given mass of gas varies as the absolute temperature. If we let V represent the volume and t the temperature, then the law states that $V = kt$, where k is a constant.

Boyle's law states that if the temperature is constant the volume of a mass of gas varies *inversely* as the pressure to which it is subjected. Hence, if V is the volume and p is the pressure, then V varies inversely as p. This means that V is at all times the product of a constant k and $\frac{1}{p}$ or $V = k\left(\frac{1}{p}\right)$.

The above examples illustrate two of the three types of variation defined below.

DIRECT VARIATION. *If one quantity* **varies directly** *as another, then the first quantity is equal to a constant times the second.*

INVERSE VARIATION. *If one quantity* **varies inversely** *as another, then the first quantity is equal to a constant times the reciprocal of the second.*

JOINT VARIATION. *If one quantity* **varies jointly** *as two or more others, then the first is equal to a constant times the product of the remaining quantities.*

In each of the above definitions, the constant is known as the *constant of variation*.

Frequently situations involve relations that are combinations of the above types. For example, Newton's law of gravitation states that the gravitational attraction between two bodies varies directly as the product of their masses and inversely as the square of the distance between their centers of gravity. If we let G, M, m, and d, respectively, represent the gravitational attraction, the two masses, and the distance, then the law states that

$$G = k\left(\frac{Mm}{d^2}\right).$$

EXAMPLE 1

The pressure on the bottom of a swimming pool varies directly as the depth. If the pressure is 624,000 lb. when the water is 2 ft. deep, find the pressure when it is $4\frac{1}{2}$ ft. deep.

Solution

If we let P represent the pressure and d the depth, then P varies directly as d. Hence,

$$P = kd.$$

Now, when $P = 624,000$ lb., $d = 2$ ft., then

$$624,000 = 2k.$$

Hence,

$$k = \frac{624,000}{2}$$
$$= 312,000.$$

Thus,

$$P = (312,000)d.$$

Consequently, if $d = 4\frac{1}{2}$ ft., then

$$P = (312,000)4\frac{1}{2}$$
$$= 1,404,000 \text{ lb.}$$

EXAMPLE 2

The amount of coal used by a steamship traveling at a uniform speed varies jointly as the distance traveled and the square of the speed. If a steamship uses 45 tons of coal traveling 80 miles at 15 miles per hr., how many tons will it use if it travels 120 miles at 20 miles per hr.?

Solution

We shall let

T = the number of tons used,
s = the distance in miles,

and

v = the speed in miles per hour;

then

(1) $T = k(sv^2)$.   (by the definition of joint variation)

Hence, when $T = 45$, $s = 80$, and $v = 15$, we have

$$45 = k(80)(15^2).$$

Therefore,

$$k = \frac{45}{(80)(225)}$$

$$= \tfrac{1}{400}.$$

If we substitute this value for k in (1), we have

$$T = \tfrac{1}{400}(sv^2).$$

Now, when $s = 120$ and $v = 20$, it follows that

$$T = \tfrac{1}{400}(120)(20^2)$$

$$= \frac{48{,}000}{400} = 120 \text{ tons.}$$

EXAMPLE 3

If the volume of a mass of gas at a given temperature is 56 cu. in. when the pressure is 18 lb., use Boyle's law to find the volume when the pressure is 16 lb.

Solution

Boyle's law states that the volume varies inversely as the pressure. Hence, if we let

$$V = \text{the volume}$$

and

$$p = \text{the pressure,}$$

we have

(2) $V = k\left(\dfrac{1}{p}\right).$ (by the definition of inverse variation)

Thus, if $V = 56$ when p is 18, we have

$$56 = k(\tfrac{1}{18}).$$

Therefore,

$$k = (56)(18)$$

$$= 1008.$$

Now we substitute this value for k in (2) and get

$$V = 1008\left(\frac{1}{p}\right).$$

Hence, when $p = 16$, we have

$$V = 1008(\tfrac{1}{16}) = 63 \text{ cu. in.}$$

EXAMPLE 4

The safe load for a horizontal beam supported at both ends varies jointly as the width and the square of the depth, and inversely as the distance between the supports. If a 4- by 6-in. beam 15 ft. long supports 1470 lb. when standing on edge, what is the safe load if the beam is turned on its side?

Solution

If we let

$$L = \text{the load,}$$
$$w = \text{the width,}$$
$$d = \text{the depth,}$$

and

$$l = \text{the distance between supports,}$$

we have

(3) $$L = k\left(\frac{wd^2}{l}\right).$$

When the beam is on its edge, $w = 4$, $d = 6$, $l = 15$, and $L = 1470$. After substituting these values in (3), we have

$$1470 = k\left[\frac{(4)(6^2)}{15}\right].$$

Hence,

$$22{,}050 = 144k$$

and

$$k = \frac{22{,}050}{144}$$
$$= \frac{1225}{8}.$$

Now, if the beam is turned on its side, $w = 6$, $d = 4$, and $l = 15$. If we substitute these values and the value of k in (3), we have

$$L = \left[\frac{1225}{8}\right]\left[\frac{(6)(4^2)}{15}\right]$$
$$= \left[\frac{1225}{8}\right]\left[\frac{(6)(16)}{15}\right]$$
$$= 980 \text{ lb.}$$

Problems that can be solved by the methods illustrated in the above examples consist of three parts. First, we have a statement of the law that operates in the problem from which we can write the equation of variation. Second, we have a set of data that enables us to find the value of the constant of variation. Third, we have another set of data in which all but one of the quantities in the problem are given. Using the information contained in the first two parts, we can find the unknown quantity in the third.

The following example illustrates a situation that involves variation, but the problem is to compare, or find the ratio of two variables, instead of obtaining a numerical value for either.

EXAMPLE 5

The volume of a right circular cone of a given height varies as the square of the radius of the base. Compare the volumes of two such cones of the same height if the radii of their bases are 3 and 6 in., respectively.

Solution

If we represent the volume of the cone by V and the radius of the base by r, the equation of variation is

$$V = kr^2.$$

Now, if we let the volumes of the two cones be V_1 and V_2, respectively, and substitute each of these symbols and the corresponding value of the radius in the above equation, we have

$$V_1 = k3^2 = 9k$$

and

$$V_2 = k6^2 = 36k.$$

Hence,

$$\frac{V_1}{V_2} = \frac{9k}{36k} = \frac{1}{4}.$$

EXERCISE 46

Express the statements in Problems 1 to 4 as equations.

1. (a) y varies directly as x. (b) s varies inversely as t. (c) m varies jointly as p and q.

2. (a) v varies directly as the cube of e. (b) I varies jointly as the rate r and the time t. (c) y varies inversely as z^2.

3. (a) The force F varies inversely as the square of the distance s. (b) The intensity I varies as the strength s of the source. (c) The force F varies jointly as the masses m_1 and m_2.

4. (*a*) The cost *c* varies as the number *n* of articles purchased. (*b*) The number *n* of articles purchased varies inversely as the price *p* per article. (*c*) The cost *c* varies jointly as the price *p* per article and the number *n* of articles purchased.

5. If y varies directly as x and is 12 when $x = 4$, find the constant of variation and the value of y when $x = 7$.

6. If y varies as w and is 21 when $w = 1\frac{1}{2}$, find the constant of variation and the value of y when $w = 4$.

7. If w varies inversely as v and is 3 when $v = 12$, find the constant of variation and the value of w when $v = 6$.

8. If y varies jointly as x and z and is 36 when $x = 3$ and $z = 6$, find the constant of variation and the value of y when $x = 9$ and $z = 3$.

9. The simple interest earned in a given time varies jointly as the principal and the rate. If $500 earned $50 at 4 per cent, find the interest earned by $800 at $3\frac{1}{2}$ per cent for the same length of time.

10. The circumference of a circle varies directly as the radius. Compare the circumferences of two circles of radii 6 and 9, respectively.

11. The mass of a rectangular iron sheet varies jointly as the length, the width, and the thickness. If the mass of a rectangular sheet of iron whose dimensions are 18 by 24 by 1 in. is 122.4 lb., find the mass of a similar sheet 12 in. long, 6 in. wide, and 2 in. thick.

12. The mass of a triangular sheet of metal of a given thickness varies jointly as the base and altitude. If a triangular sheet of aluminum 1 in. thick weighs 2.79 lb. and has a base and altitude 12 and 5 in., respectively, in length, find the weight of a triangular sheet of the same thickness whose base and altitude are 6 and 21 in., respectively.

13. The lateral surface of a right circular cylinder varies jointly as the radius of the base and the altitude. Compare the surfaces of two cylinders if the radius of the base and the altitude of the first are 6 and 8 in., respectively, and of the second, 9 and 6 in., respectively.

14. The weight of a body above the surface of the earth varies inversely as the square of its distance from the center of the earth. If a man weighs 200 lb. on the surface, how much would he weigh if he were 100 miles above the surface? (Assume the radius of the earth to be 4000 miles.)

15. The intensity of light varies inversely as the square of the distance from the source. If the intensity of illumination on a screen 10 ft. from a light is .8 foot candle, find the intensity on a screen 4 ft. from the light.

16. The surface of a cube varies as the square of a side. Compare the surfaces of two cubes whose sides are 2 and 5 in., respectively.

17. The kinetic energy E of a moving body varies jointly as the mass and the square of the velocity. If the kinetic energy of a 30-lb. body moving 10 ft. per sec. is 1500 ft.-lb., find the kinetic energy of a 100-lb. body moving 40 ft. per sec.

18. The period of one complete vibration of a pendulum varies as the square root of the length. If the period of a 16-in. pendulum is .36 sec., find the period of a 25-in. pendulum.

19. The weight of a clothesline varies jointly as the length and the square of the diameter. If the weight of a 40-ft. line $\frac{1}{8}$ in. in diameter is 1.7 lb., find the weight of a 30-ft. line $\frac{3}{16}$ in. in diameter.

20. The amount of paint needed to paint a spherical ball varies as the square of the diameter. Compare the amount of paint needed for a ball 14 in. in diameter to that needed for one 10 in. in diameter.

21. The time necessary to make an enlargement from a photographic negative varies directly as the area. If 6 sec. is required for an enlargement that is 4 by 5 in., how many seconds are required for an enlargement that is 8 by 10 in. from the same negative?

22. The exposure time necessary to obtain a good negative varies directly as the square of the F-numbers on the camera shutter. If $\frac{1}{25}$ of a second is required when the shutter is set at F-16 (usually written $F/16$), what exposure is required under the same conditions if the shutter is set at F-8?

23. On the ocean, the square of the distance in miles to the horizon varies as the height in feet that the observer is above the surface of the water. If a 6-ft. man on a surfboard can see 3 miles, how far can one see if he is in a plane that is 1000 ft. above the water?

24. The kinetic energy of a body varies as the square of its velocity. Compare the kinetic energy of a car traveling 10 miles per hr. with that of the same car traveling 50 miles per hr.

25. The power available in a jet of water varies jointly as the cube of the water's velocity and the cross-sectional area of the jet. Compare the power of a jet with that of another that is moving twice as fast through an opening that is half as large.

26. The volume of water in a horizontal tank whose cross section is a trapezoid varies jointly as the length, the depth, and the sum of the widths at the top and bottom. Compare the volume of water in a tank 12 ft. long, 18 in. deep, and whose top and bottom widths are 16 and 12 in., respectively, to that of another tank whose corresponding dimensions are 18 ft., 20 in., 12 in., and 9 in.

27. The power required to propel a ship varies as the cube of the speed. If a speed of 14 knots requires a horsepower of 9800, find the power required for 7 knots.

28. The horsepower required to operate a fan varies as the cube of the speed. If .75 horsepower will drive a fan at 300 revolutions per minute, find the speed derived from 1.5 horsepower.

29. The maximum horsepower of a boiler that can be served by a chimney of a given cross-sectional area varies as the square root of the height of the chimney. If a chimney 25 ft. high serves a boiler with 500 horsepower, how high must a chimney with the same cross-sectional area be built to serve 600 horsepower?

30. The force of a wind on a plane surface perpendicular to the direction of the wind varies as the square of the wind velocity. If the force of a 25-mile-per-hr. wind on a signboard is 3 lb. per sq. ft., find the force of a 60-mile-per-hour wind.

31. One of Kepler's laws states that the square of the time required by a planet to make one revolution about the sun varies directly as the cube of the average distance of the planet from the sun. If Mars is $1\frac{1}{2}$ times as far from the sun, on the average, as the earth, find the approximate length of time required for it to make one revolution about the sun.

32. The strength of a rectangular horizontal beam that is supported at the ends varies jointly as the width w and the square of the depth d and inversely as the length L. Compare the strengths of two beams if one of them is 20 ft. long, 4 in. wide, and 6 in. deep and the other is 10 ft. long, 2 in. wide, and 4 in. deep.

33. The current I varies directly as the electromotive force E and inversely as the resistance R. If in a certain system a current of 20 amp. flows through a resistance of 5 ohms with an electromotive force of 100 volts, find the current that 160 volts will send through the system.

34. The force of attraction between two bodies varies jointly as their masses and inversely as the square of the distance between them. Compare the attractive force between two bodies whose masses are m and M, respectively, and that are separated by a distance of d with that between two others whose masses are $2m$ and $2M$, respectively, that are $2d$ units apart.

35. The pitch of a vibrating string of a given cross-sectional area varies as the square root of the tension and inversely as the length. Compare the pitches of two strings if the first is twice as long as the second and is under twice the tension.

36. The pitch of a string of given length varies directly as the square root of the tension and inversely as the square root of the mass. If a string that weighs 12 oz. and is under a tension of 192 lb. has a pitch of 256, find the pitch of a string of the same length that weighs 9 oz. and is under a tension of 225 lb.

CHAPTER 11

LOGARITHMS

75. *Introduction.* In the statement

(1) $$2^3 = 8,$$

we use the term *exponent* to indicate the relationship that exists between 3 and 2. However, 3 is also related to 8 in (1) and we indicate this relationship by the term *logarithm*. In other words, in (1), 3 is the exponent of 2 and also the logarithm of 8, or, more precisely, the logarithm to the base 2 of 8. Hence, this chapter will be a continuation of the discussion of exponents. In particular, we shall show how exponents, or logarithms, may be used to simplify numerical computation and to solve certain types of equations that are not solvable by more elementary methods. Since we shall employ the definitions and laws of Chap. 7, the reader is advised to review that chapter before proceeding further.

As a basis for our subsequent discussion, we shall next present the following definition:

DEFINITION I. *The **logarithm** to a given base of any number is the exponent that indicates the power to which the base must be raised in order to obtain the number.*

The abbreviated form of the statement "the logarithm to the base b of N is L" is $\log_b N = L$. If we use this notation we may express definition I in symbolic form as

(2) $$\log_b N = L \qquad implies \qquad b^L = N.$$

Note that the abbreviation "log" appears without a period and that the symbol for the base appears as a subscript.

EXAMPLES

1. $\log_8 64 = 2$ since $8^2 = 64$.
2. $\log_4 64 = 3$ since $4^3 = 64$.
3. $\log_{81} 9 = \frac{1}{2}$ since $81^{\frac{1}{2}} = 9$.
4. $\log_a 1 = 0$ since $a^0 = 1$.

In many cases, if two of the three letters in (2) are known, the third can be found by inspection.

EXAMPLE 5

Find the value of N if $\log_7 N = 2$.

Solution

If we convert the above logarithmic statement to the exponential form, we have

$$7^2 = N,$$

and then it is obvious that $N = 49$.

EXAMPLE 6

If $\log_b 125 = 3$, find the value of b.

Solution

By use of (2), we have
$$b^3 = 125.$$
Hence,
$$b = \sqrt[3]{125} = 5.$$

EXAMPLE 7

Find a if $\log_{27} 3 = a$.

Solution

Again, using (2), we have
$$27^a = 3.$$

Hence, since $27^{\frac{1}{3}} = 3$, it follows that

$$a = \tfrac{1}{3}.$$

EXERCISE 47

Express the statements in Problems 1 to 16 in exponential form.

1. $\log_6 36 = 2$.   2. $\log_2 16 = 4$.   3. $\log_4 64 = 3$.
4. $\log_3 81 = 4$.   5. $\log_2 \frac{1}{4} = -2$.   6. $\log_3 \frac{1}{27} = -3$.

7. $\log_8 \frac{1}{64} = -2.$ **8.** $\log_5 \frac{1}{125} = -3.$ **9.** $\log_9 27 = \frac{3}{2}.$
10. $\log_4 32 = \frac{5}{2}.$ **11.** $\log_{25} 125 = \frac{3}{2}.$ **12.** $\log_8 32 = \frac{5}{3}.$
13. $\log_a a^2 = 2.$ **14.** $\log_{a^2} a^6 = 3.$ **15.** $\log_{a^3} a^6 = 2.$
16. $\log_{a^9} a^3 = \frac{1}{3}.$

Express the statements in Problems 17 to 32 in logarithmic form.
17. $5^2 = 25.$ **18.** $6^3 = 216.$ **19.** $2^5 = 32.$
20. $3^4 = 81.$ **21.** $2^{-1} = \frac{1}{2}.$ **22.** $3^{-2} = \frac{1}{9}.$
23. $(\frac{1}{2})^{-2} = 4.$ **24.** $(\frac{1}{3})^{-3} = 27.$ **25.** $8^{\frac{1}{3}} = 2.$
26. $64^{\frac{1}{6}} = 2.$ **27.** $27^{-\frac{1}{3}} = \frac{1}{3}.$ **28.** $64^{-\frac{1}{2}} = \frac{1}{8}.$
29. $8^{\frac{2}{3}} = 4.$ **30.** $32^{\frac{3}{5}} = 8.$ **31.** $64^{-\frac{5}{6}} = \frac{1}{32}.$
32. $81^{-\frac{3}{4}} = \frac{1}{27}.$

Find the value of the logarithms in Problems 33 to 56.
33. $\log_8 64.$ **34.** $\log_5 125.$ **35.** $\log_2 8.$
36. $\log_{16} 256.$ **37.** $\log_7 343.$ **38.** $\log_2 32.$
39. $\log_9 729.$ **40.** $\log_6 216.$ **41.** $\log_{64} 8.$
42. $\log_{27} 3.$ **43.** $\log_{32} 2.$ **44.** $\log_8 2.$
45. $\log_2 \frac{1}{4}.$ **46.** $\log_3 \frac{1}{27}.$ **47.** $\log_4 \frac{1}{16}.$
48. $\log_5 \frac{1}{125}.$ **49.** $\log_8 4.$ **50.** $\log_{64} 16.$
51. $\log_9 27.$ **52.** $\log_{32} 64.$ **53.** $\log_a a^3.$
54. $\log_{a^2} a^3.$ **55.** $\log_{b^{\frac{1}{2}}} b^2.$ **56.** $\log_{b^5} b^2.$

Find the value of the unknown letter in each of Problems 57 to 68.
57. $\log_4 16 = L.$ **58.** $\log_3 27 = L.$ **59.** $\log_8 2 = L.$
60. $\log_5 \frac{1}{25} = L.$ **61.** $\log_2 N = 3.$ **62.** $\log_3 N = 3.$
63. $\log_{27} N = \frac{1}{3}.$ **64.** $\log_{64} N = \frac{2}{3}.$ **65.** $\log_b 81 = 2.$
66. $\log_b 64 = 6.$ **67.** $\log_b 2 = \frac{1}{4}.$ **68.** $\log_b \frac{1}{81} = -4.$

76. Common, or Briggs, logarithms. Examples 1, 2, 3, 4, and 7 of the previous article are illustrations of situations in which the logarithm of a number can be determined by inspection. In general, this is not possible. For example, we cannot determine the value of L by elementary methods in $\log_{10} 32.71 = L$. However, since $10 < 32.71 < 10^2$, we know that the value of L is between 1 and 2. Tables have been prepared from which the logarithm of any number to the base 10 can be obtained. Furthermore, these tables may be used to find a number if its logarithm to the base 10 is known. The method for using these tables will be explained in the next three articles.

If the base is 10, the logarithm of a number is called the *common*, or *Briggs*, logarithm. It is customary to omit the symbol for the base when dealing with common logarithms.   Hence, hereafter, in the statement log $N = L$, it is understood that the base is 10.

77. The characteristic and mantissa.   As we stated in the previous article, log 32.71 is between 1 and 2.   Actually, this logarithm is irrational and cannot be expressed exactly in decimal form, but to four decimal places its value is 1.5146.   Thus,

$$\log 32.71 = 1.5146,$$

and therefore, by (2) of Art. 75, $32.71 = 10^{1.5146}$.   Obviously,

$$3271 = 32.71(10)^2 = (10^{1.5146})(10^2) = 10^{1.5146+2} = 10^{3.5146}.$$

Hence, log $3271 = 3.5146$.   Similarly,

$$3.271 = \frac{32.71}{10} = \frac{10^{1.5146}}{10} = 10^{0.5146}$$

and

$$.03271 = \frac{32.71}{10^3} = \frac{10^{1.5146}}{10^3} = 10^{1.5146-3} = 10^{-2+.5146}.$$

Hence,
$$\log 3.271 = 0.5146,$$

and
$$\log .03271 = -2 + .5146.\,^{1}$$

The above examples illustrate the following definition:

DEFINITION.   *The common logarithm of any number can be expressed approximately as an integer, either positive, zero, or negative, plus a positive decimal fraction.   When the logarithm is in this form, the integer is called the* **characteristic** *and the positive fraction is called the* **mantissa.**

The mantissa of a logarithm is obtained from a table by use of a method explained in Art. 79.

If the characteristic of a logarithm is positive, then the characteristic and the mantissa are written as a single number as in log $32.71 = 1.5146$.   However, when the characteristic is negative, as in the case of log $.03271 = -2 + .5146$, the characteristic and mantissa cannot be expressed as a single positive number, since the former is negative and the latter is positive and the former

---

[1] The reason for using this notation instead of the equivalent negative number -1.4854 will be explained later.

is greater than the latter.   Since it is desirable to keep the fractional part of a logarithm positive, it is customary to write a logarithm such as $-2 + .5146$ in the form $8.5146 - 10$.[1]   In general, if the characteristic of a logarithm is $-c$, it is customary to express $-c$ in the form $n - 10$, and then to write the mantissa preceded by a decimal point at the right of n.

If the decimal point in a number is shifted to the right or to the left, the number is multiplied by a positive or negative integral power of ten.   Thus, the logarithm is either increased or decreased by an integer.   Such an operation affects the characteristic only. Thus, the characteristic of the logarithm of any number depends upon the position of the decimal point and the mantissa depends upon the digits and their arrangement in the number.

The decimal point in a number that is between 1 and 10 is located at the right of the first digit in it.   Since such a number is between 10^0 and 10^1, the characteristic of its common logarithm is zero.   If the decimal point is shifted n places to the right, the number is multiplied by 10^n, and hence the characteristic of its logarithm is $0 + n$.   Similarly, if the decimal point is shifted n places to the left, the characteristic of the logarithm is $0 - n = -n$.

We shall now define the *reference position for the decimal point in a number as the position immediately to the right of the first nonzero digit in the number*.   For example, the reference position in 6234 is between 6 and 2, and the reference position in .003621 is between 3 and 6.   Using this terminology, we are now in position to state the following rule for obtaining the characteristic of the common logarithm of any number:

RULE.   *The characteristic of the common logarithm of a number is numerically equal to the number of digits between the reference position and the decimal point.   It is positive or negative according as the decimal point is to the right or the left of the reference position.*

EXAMPLES

1. The reference position in 236.78 is between 2 and 3.   Hence, there are two digits, 3 and 6, between the reference position and the decimal point.   Furthermore, the decimal point is to the right of the reference position.   Hence, the characteristic of the logarithm of 236.78 is 2.

---

[1] A logarithm of the type $-2 + .5146$ is sometimes written $\bar{2}.5146$.   However, we shall not employ this notation.

2. The characteristic of the logarithm of 3.124 is zero, since the decimal point is in the reference position.

3. The decimal point in .003271 is three places to the left of the reference position. Hence, the characteristic of the logarithm of .003271 is −3. As we stated earlier in this article, it is customary to write the characteristic, −3, as 7 − 10.

78. *Rounding off a number.* The tables in this book enable us to obtain the mantissa of a logarithm to four places only. By use of these tables, we can obtain results that are correct to only four places. Hence, we shall frequently resort to the practice of *rounding off a number*, or, stated more precisely, rounding off a number to n places. This practice consists of the following steps:

1. We replace all digits after the nth by zeros. If the number is a decimal fraction, we do not count the zeros between the decimal point and the first nonzero digit.

2. We consider the decimal fraction made by placing a decimal point before the number made up of the digits replaced. If this number is greater than .5, we increase the nth digit by 1. If the fraction is less than .5, we leave the nth digit unchanged.

3. If the above fraction is exactly .5 and the nth digit is odd, we increase it by 1. If the nth digit is even, we leave it unchanged. In other words, in this case, the "rounded-off" number should always be even.

EXAMPLES

1. 63276 rounded off to three places is 63300 since .76 > .5.

2. 8142183 rounded off to four places is 8,142,000 since .183 < .5.

3. 10.365 rounded off to four places is 10.36 since the fourth digit 6 is even; and 3.275 rounded off to three places is 3.28 since the third digit 7 is odd.

4. .006258461 rounded off to two places is .0063 since .58461 > .5.

79. *Use of the table to obtain the mantissa.* In this article, we shall explain the method of finding the mantissa of a logarithm by use of the table on page 300. We shall first discuss numbers of only three digits[1] and as a specific example shall consider 3.27. As we stated in the preceding article, the mantissa of the logarithm of a number is not affected by the position of the decimal point in the number. Hence, for the present, we shall disregard the decimal point. We now turn to the table on page 300 and look in the col-

---

[1] In this article, when we count the number of digits in a decimal fraction, we start with the first nonzero digit.

umn headed by N on the left side of the page for the first two digits 32 of the number 327. Then in line with this and across the page in the column headed by the third digit 7 we find the entry 5145. Except for the decimal point[1] before it, this is the desired mantissa. Since the decimal point in 3.27 is in the reference position, the characteristic of the logarithm is zero. Hence, log 3.27 = 0.5145.

As a second example, we shall consider .00634. Again, we temporarily disregard the decimal point and find 63 in the column headed by N. In line with this and in the column headed by 4, we find the entry 8021. By the rule in Art. 77, the characteristic of the logarithm of .00634 is −3, which we write as 7 − 10. Hence, log .00634 = 7.8021 − 10.

If a number is composed of less than three digits, we mentally annex one or two zeros at the right and proceed as before. For example, to get the mantissa of the logarithm of 72, we look up 720, and to get the mantissa of the logarithm of 3, we look up 300.

If all of the digits in a number after the third are zeros, we disregard them in the process of getting the mantissa.

In the discussion that follows, it will be necessary to use the expression "the mantissa of the logarithm of N" frequently. For the sake of brevity, we shall abbreviate the expression to ml N.

If a number is composed of four digits, we obtain the mantissa by a method known as *linear interpolation*. We shall explain and illustrate the method by employing it in two examples.

EXAMPLE 1

As a first example, we shall use the interpolation method to find ml 412.8. Since 412.8 is between 412 and 413, ml 412.8 is between ml 412 and ml 413. Furthermore, 413 differs from 412 by 1, and 412.8 differs from 412 by .8. Hence, 412.8 differs from 412 by .8 of the difference between 412 and 413. We now assume that ml 412.8 differs from ml 412 by .8 of the difference between ml 412 and ml 413. We now turn to the table and find that ml 413 = .6160 and ml 412 = .6149. Hence, since .6160 − .6149 = .0011, ml 412.8 differs from ml 412 by .8 × .0011 = .00088 = .0009 (to one digit). Therefore,

$$ml\ 412.8 = .6149 + .0009 = .6158.$$

[1] No decimal points are printed in the table of mantissas. Hence, when a mantissa is obtained from the table, a decimal point must be placed to the left of it.

The above procedure can be condensed into the following form in which the calculations can be easily performed:

$$1\left[\begin{array}{l} \text{ml } 413 \quad = .6160 \\ .8\left[\begin{array}{l} \text{ml } 412.8 = \\ \text{ml } 412 \quad = .6149 \end{array}\right].0011 \end{array}\right]$$

$$.8 \times .0011 = .00088 = .0009 \quad \text{(to one digit)}$$
$$\text{ml } 412.8 = .6149 + .0009 = .6158.$$

Hence, since the decimal point in 412.8 is two places to the right of the reference position, we have log 412.8 = 2.6158.

EXAMPLE 2

As a second example in interpolation, we shall find ml .006324. Since the position of the decimal point has no effect on the mantissa, it follows that ml .006324 = ml 632.4. Then the process of obtaining the latter mantissa is the same as in Example 1. We note that 632.4 is between 632 and 633. Hence, we have

$$1\left[\begin{array}{l} \text{ml } 633 \quad = .8014 \\ .4\left[\begin{array}{l} \text{ml } 632.4 = \\ \text{ml } 632 \quad = .8007 \end{array}\right].0007 \end{array}\right]$$

$$.4 \times .0007 = .00028 = .0003 \quad \text{(to one digit)}$$

Consequently,

$$\text{ml } 632.4 = .8007 + .0003 = .8010.$$

Since the decimal point in .006324 is three places to the left of the reference position, we have log .006324 = 7.8010 − 10.

The interpolation process consists of simple operations which, after some practice, can be performed mentally, thus saving considerable time. We suggest the following steps that can be carried forward rapidly:

1. Temporarily place the decimal point between the third and fourth digits of the given number.

2. Subtract the mantissas of the logarithms of the two numbers between which the above number lies.

3. Multiply this difference by the fourth digit of the given number considered as a decimal fraction.

4. Add the above product to the smaller of the mantissas in Step 2.

If a number contains more than four digits, we round it off to four places and proceed as before. For example, to get ml 17.6352, we find ml 17.64.

002   ,.0025 = -3.

EXERCISE 48

Find the characteristics of the logarithms of the numbers in Problems 1 to 16.

1. 2.4.	**2.** 3.76.	**3.** 5.814.
4. 7.2356.	**5.** 58.	**6.** 78.7.
7. 5814.	**8.** 682.91.	**9.** .25.
10. 1.39.	**11.** .19206.	**12.** .3473.
13. .02.	**14.** .003,	**15.** .0025.
16. .00058.		

Find the common logarithm of each number given below. Interpolate when necessary.

17. 2.34.	**18.** 5.79.	**19.** 4.59.	**20.** 8.41.
21. 58.3.	**22.** 82.4.	**23.** 754.	**24.** 9430.
25. 371.	**26.** 85.2.	**27.** 611.	**28.** 7700.
29. .325.	**30.** .702.	**31.** .320.	**32.** .673.
33. .0157.	**34.** .0025.	**35.** .030.	**36.** .0005.
37. 2580.	**38.** 2500.	**39.** 5700.	**40.** 2870.
41. 3.236.	**42.** 5.713.	**43.** 2.917.	**44.** 4.832.
45. 98.23.	**46.** 72.37.	**47.** 641.4.	**48.** 593.4.
49. 6714.	**50.** 3285.	**51.** 5823.	**52.** 1776.
53. .3257.	**54.** .7803.	**55.** .98241.	**56.** .71732.
57. .02051.	**58.** 683.57.	**59.** 1.2346.	**60.** 80.428.

80. *Use of the tables to find N when* log *N is given.* The next problem in the use of the tables is the process of finding a number when its logarithm is given. We shall illustrate the process in several examples and shall explain each step as we proceed.

EXAMPLE 1

In this example, we shall find N when $\log N = 1.6191$. The first step is to find the mantissa, .6191, in the body of the tables. Hence, we look through the tables until we find the mantissas starting with 61, and then we look through these until we locate 6191. We see that it is in line with 41 (in the column headed by N) and in the column headed by 6. Thus, N is made up of the digits 416, and the next step is to place the decimal point. Since the characteristic of $\log N$ is 1, the decimal point is one place to the right of the reference position, and hence is between 1 and 6. Therefore, $N = 41.6$.

If ml N is not listed in the tables, we must resort to interpolation. By the use of a four-place table, we cannot obtain accurately more than the first four digits in N. We shall show in the following discussion that the first three digits are obtained from the table and the fourth is determined by interpolation. If the characteristic of log N indicates that N contains more than four digits, then zeros are added after the fourth.

EXAMPLE 2

We shall illustrate the process by obtaining N when log $N = 5.4978$. We shall let T represent the number composed of the first four digits in N and shall determine T. Finally, we shall place the decimal point by considering the characteristic, and thus get N. The mantissa .4978 is not listed in the table, but the two nearest to it are .4969 and .4983. These two mantissas are ml 3140 and ml 3150, respectively. (We add the zero in each case in order to obtain four places for use in interpolation.) Furthermore, since $4983 - 4969 = 14$ and $4978 - 4969 = 9$, it follows that 4978 is $\frac{9}{14}$ of the way from 4969 to 4983. Hence, T is approximately $\frac{9}{14}$ of the way from 3140 to 3150. Furthermore,

$$\tfrac{9}{14} \times 10 = \tfrac{90}{14} = 6.4 = 6 \text{ (to one digit)},$$

and $3140 + 6 = 3146$. Hence, $T = 3146$. Since the characteristic of log N is 5, the decimal point in N is 5 places to the right of the reference position. Hence, $N = 314,600$.

The steps in the above process are shown in the condensed form given below.

$$\log N = 5.4978$$

$$14\left[\begin{array}{c} 4983 = \text{ml } 3150 \\ 9\left[\begin{array}{c} 4978 = \text{ml } T \\ 4969 = \text{ml } 3140 \end{array}\right] \end{array}\right]10$$

$$\tfrac{9}{14} \times 10 = 6.4 = 6 \quad \text{(to one digit)}$$

$$3140 + 6 = 3146 = T.$$

Hence,

$$N = 314,600,$$

since the characteristic of log N is 5.

EXAMPLE 3

As a third example, we shall determine N if log $N = 8.6736 - 10$. We shall again let T represent the number composed of the first four digits in N. The two entries in the table that are nearest to 6736 are $6730 = \text{ml } 4710$ and $6739 = \text{ml } 4720$. Using these in the interpolation process, we have

$$9 \begin{bmatrix} 6739 = \text{ml } 4720 \\ 6 \begin{bmatrix} 6736 = \text{ml } T \\ 6730 = \text{ml } 4710 \end{bmatrix} \end{bmatrix} 10$$

$\frac{6}{9} \times 10 = 6.7 = 7.$ (to the nearest integer)

Hence,

$$4710 + 7 = 4717 = T.$$

Therefore,

$$N = .04717,$$

since the characteristic of log N is $8 - 10 = -2$.

EXERCISE 49

Find the value of N if log N has the value indicated in each of Problems 1 to 20.

1. 1.1492.	**2.** 0.1732.	**3.** 2.1959.	**4.** 0.3181.
5. 2.4099.	**6.** 1.5441.	**7.** 3.6599.	**8.** 1.6928.
9. 0.6201.	**10.** 2.3747.	**11.** 3.3892.	**12.** 1.4440.
13. 9.8768 − 10.	**14.** 8.9015 − 10.	**15.** 7.9385 − 10.	
16. 8.9499 − 10.	**17.** 9.9996 − 10.	**18.** 8.2923 − 10.	
19. 7.2148 − 10.	**20.** 6.8136 − 10.		

Find the value of N to the nearest three digits if log N has the value indicated in Problems 21 to 40.

21. 1.0457.	**22.** 0.9887.	**23.** 2.2130.	**24.** 3.9860.
25. 1.3080.	**26.** 1.9677.	**27.** 3.4221.	**28.** 2.9402.
29. 1.5273.	**30.** 2.9120.	**31.** 0.5777.	**32.** 2.8947.
33. 9.6278 − 10.	**34.** 8.8671 − 10.	**35.** 7.6888 − 10.	
36. 7.8340 − 10.	**37.** 8.7231 − 10.	**38.** 9.8043 − 10.	
39. 6.7425 − 10.	**40.** 7.7777 − 10.		

By use of interpolation, find the value of N to four digits if log N has the value indicated in each of the following problems.

41. 0.2763.	**42.** 1.4823.	**43.** 2.3057.	**44.** 1.4141.
45. 2.5878.	**46.** 0.6892.	**47.** 3.7728.	**48.** 0.9662.
49. 1.2123.	**50.** 2.1776.	**51.** 3.1607.	**52.** 3.1891.
53. 9.1902 − 10.	**54.** 8.1914 − 10.	**55.** 7.3942 − 10.	
56. 8.6262 − 10.	**57.** 9.4053 − 10.	**58.** 8.7173 − 10.	
59. 6.6666 − 10.	**60.** 7.5437 − 10.		

81. Properties of logarithms. In this article, we shall employ the laws of exponents (see Chap. 7) and the definition of a logarithm to derive three important properties of logarithms. In the next article, we shall show how to use these properties in numerical computation.

We shall first show how to find the logarithm of a product of two numbers in terms of the logarithms of the two numbers.

If we are given

(1) $$\log_b M = m \quad \text{and} \quad \log_b N = n,$$

then, by (2) of Art. 75, we have

(2) $$M = b^m \quad \text{and} \quad N = b^n.$$

Hence,

$$MN = (b^m)(b^n)$$
$$= b^{m+n}, \qquad \text{[by (3) of Art. 45]}$$

and

$$\log_b MN = m + n \qquad \text{[by (2) of Art. 75]}$$
$$= \log_b M + \log_b N. \qquad \text{[by (1) of this article]}$$

Consequently, we have

PROPERTY I.   *The logarithm of the product of two numbers is equal to the sum of the logarithms of the numbers.*

$$\log 6 = \log (3 \times 2)$$
$$= \log 3 + \log 2$$
$$= .4771 + .3010$$
$$= .7781.$$

Property I can be extended to three or more numbers by the following process:

$$\log_b MNP = \log_b (MN)(P)$$
$$= \log_b M + \log_b N + \log_b P.$$

Again, using relations (2) of this article, we have

$$\frac{M}{N} = \frac{b^m}{b^n}$$
$$= b^{m-n}. \qquad \text{[by (4) of Art. 45]}$$

Hence,

$$\log_b \frac{M}{N} = m - n \qquad \text{[by (2) of Art. 75]}$$
$$= \log_b M - \log_b N. \qquad \text{[by (1) of this article]}$$

Therefore, we have

PROPERTY II. *The logarithm of the quotient of two numbers is equal to the logarithm of the dividend minus the logarithm of the divisor.*

EXAMPLE 2

$$\log 1.5 = \log \tfrac{3}{2}$$
$$= \log 3 - \log 2$$
$$= .4771 - .3010$$
$$= .1761.$$

Finally, if we raise both members of $M = b^m$ to the kth power, we have

$$M^k = (b^m)^k$$
$$= b^{km}. \qquad \text{[by (5), Art. 45]}$$

Therefore,

$$\log_b M^k = km \qquad \text{[by (2), Art. 75]}$$
$$= k \log_b M \qquad \text{[by (1) of this article]}$$

Thus, we have

PROPERTY III. *The logarithm of a power of a number is equal to the product of the exponent of the power and the logarithm of the number.*

EXAMPLE 3

$$\log 3^2 = 2 \log 3$$
$$= 2(.4771)$$
$$= .9542.$$

NOTE: Since a root of a number can be expressed as a fractional power, Property III can be used to find the logarithm of a root of a number. Thus,

$$\log_b \sqrt[r]{M} = \log (M)^{\frac{1}{r}} = \frac{1}{r} \log M.$$

EXAMPLE 4

$$\log \sqrt[3]{2} = \log 2^{\frac{1}{3}}$$
$$= \tfrac{1}{3} \log 2$$
$$= \tfrac{1}{3}(.3010)$$
$$= .1003.$$

For the convenience of the reader, we shall restate the above properties in symbolic form.

I. $\log_b MN = \log_b M + \log_b N,$

II. $\log_b \dfrac{M}{N} = \log_b M - \log_b N,$

III. $\log_b M^k = k \log_b M.$

82. Logarithmic computation.   As we stated previously, one of the most useful applications of logarithms is in the field of numerical computation.   We shall explain presently the methods involved by means of several examples.   However, before considering special problems, we wish to call attention again to the fact that results obtained by the use of four-place tables are correct at most to four places.   If the numbers in any computation problem contain only three places, the result is dependable to only three places.   If a problem contains a mixture of three-place and four-place numbers, we cannot expect more than three places of the result to be correct, so we round it off to three places.   Hence, in the problems that follow, we shall not obtain any answer to more than four nonzero places, and sometimes not that far.[1]   Tables exist from which logarithms may be obtained to five, six, seven, and even more places.   If results that are correct to more than four places are desired, longer tables should be used.   The methods which we have presented may be applied to a table of any length.

We shall now present examples with explanations that illustrate the methods for using logarithms to obtain (1) products and quotients, (2) powers and roots, (3) miscellaneous computation problems.

In all computation problems, we use the properties of logarithms in Art. 81 to find the logarithm of the result.   Then the value of the result can be obtained from the table.

1. Products and Quotients

EXAMPLE 1

As our first example, we shall show how logarithms may be used to find the value of R if $R = (8.56)(3.47)(198)$.

Since R is equal to the product of three numbers, by Property I, Art. 81, $\log R$ is equal to the sum of the logarithms of the three factors. Hence, we shall obtain the logarithm of each of the factors, add them

---

[1] The above remarks are based on the theory of significant figures.   A discussion of this theory is found in most trigonometries.   For example, "Plane Trigonometry," by Sparks and Rees, 3d ed., Prentice-Hall, Inc., New York, 1952, p. 20.

together, and thus have log R. Then we may use the table to get R.
Before we turn to the table, it is advisable to make an outline leaving
blanks in which to enter the logarithms as they are found. It is also
advisable to arrange the outline so that the logarithms to be added are
in a column. We suggest the following plan:

$$\begin{aligned} \log 8.56 &= \underline{\hspace{1.5cm}} \\ \log 3.47 &= \underline{\hspace{1.5cm}} \\ \log 198 &= \underline{\hspace{1.5cm}} \\ \hline \log R &= \underline{\hspace{1.5cm}} \\ & \text{(enter sum here)} \\ R &= \underline{\hspace{1.5cm}}. \end{aligned}$$

Next we enter the characteristics in each of the blanks and have

$$\begin{aligned} \log 8.56 &= 0.\underline{\hspace{1cm}} \\ \log 3.47 &= 0.\underline{\hspace{1cm}} \\ \log 198 &= 2.\underline{\hspace{1cm}} \\ \hline \log R &= \underline{\hspace{1.5cm}} \\ R &= \underline{\hspace{1.5cm}}. \end{aligned}$$

Now we turn to the tables, get the mantissas, and, as each is found,
enter it in the proper place in the outline. Then we perform the addition and, finally, determine R by the method of Art. 80. The completed
solution then appears as

$$\begin{aligned} \log 8.56 &= 0.9325 \\ \log 3.47 &= 0.5403 \\ \log 198 &= 2.2967 \\ \hline \log R &= 3.7695 \\ R &= 5880. \end{aligned}$$

NOTE: Each of the numbers in the problem contains only three digits.
Hence, we can determine only three digits in R. Since the mantissa
7695 is between the two entries 7694 and 7701 and nearer the former
than the latter, the first three digits in R are 588, the number corresponding to the mantissa .7694. The characteristic of log R is 3. Hence,
the decimal point is three places to the right of the reference position.
Therefore, we add one zero and place the decimal point.

We have written the outline of the solution three times in order to
show how the outline appears at the conclusion of each step. In practice, it is necessary to write the outline only once, since each operation
requires the filling of separate blanks.

EXAMPLE 2

As our second example, we shall use logarithms to find R where

$$R = \frac{(337)(2.68)}{(521)(.763)}.$$

In this problem, R is a quotient in which the dividend and divisor are each the product of two numbers. Hence, we shall add the logarithms of the two numbers in the dividend and also add the logarithms of the two in the divisor, subtract the latter sum from the former, thus obtaining $\log R$. We suggest the following outline for the solution:

$$\log 337 = \underline{\hspace{1cm}}$$
$$\log 2.68 = \underline{\hspace{1cm}}$$
$$\log \text{ dividend} = \underline{\hspace{1cm}}$$

(enter sum here)

$$\log 521 = \underline{\hspace{1cm}}$$
$$\log .763 = \underline{\hspace{1cm}}$$
$$\log \text{ divisor} = \underline{\hspace{1cm}}$$

(enter sum here)

$$\log R = \underline{\hspace{1cm}}$$

(enter the difference of the two sums here)

$$R = \underline{\hspace{1cm}}.$$

After the characteristics are entered and the mantissas are found and listed in the proper places, the problem can be completed as follows:

$$\log 337 = 2.5276$$
$$\log 2.68 = 0.4281$$
$$\log \text{ dividend} = \qquad 2.9557$$
$$\log 521 = 2.7168$$
$$\log .763 = 9.8825 - 10$$
$$\log \text{ divisor} = \qquad \cancel{1}2.5993 - \cancel{10}$$
$$\log R = \qquad 0.3564$$
$$R = 2.27.$$

NOTE: The logarithm of the divisor turned out to be $12.5993 - 10$. Hence, the characteristic is 2. Therefore, in the above outline, we cancel the 10 and the first digit in 12 before completing the solution.

EXAMPLE 3

If we use logarithms to evaluate $R = \dfrac{2.68}{33.2}$, we have

$$\begin{array}{l} \log 2.68 = 0.4281 \\ \underline{\log 33.2 = 1.5211} \\ \log R = \underline{\hspace{2cm}}, \end{array}$$

where $\log R$ is obtained by subtracting the second logarithm from the first. If we perform this subtraction, we get $\log R = -1.0930$. This is a correct value of $\log R$, but, since the fractional part .0930 is negative, it is not a mantissa, and the value of R cannot be obtained from the table. We avoid this type of difficulty by adding $10 - 10$ to $\log 2.68$ before performing the subtraction. Then we have

$$\begin{array}{l} \log 2.68 = 10.4281 - 10 \\ \underline{\log 33.2 = 1.5211} \\ \log R = 8.9070 - 10 \\ R = .0807. \end{array}$$

We use the device shown in Example 3 whenever a necessary subtraction of one logarithm from another leads to a negative remainder. Thus, in order to subtract $9.2368 - 10$ from 2.6841, we add $10 - 10$ to the latter and have

$$\begin{array}{l} 12.6841 - 10 \\ \underline{9.2368 - 10} \\ 3.4473. \end{array}$$

Similarly, in performing the indicated subtraction in $(7.3264 - 10) - (9.4631 - 10)$, we would again obtain a negative number, -2.1367. Hence, we add $10 - 10$ to $7.3264 - 10$ and proceed with the subtraction as below

$$\begin{array}{l} 17.3264 - 20 \\ \underline{9.4631 - 10} \\ 7.8633 - 10. \end{array}$$

2. *Powers and Roots*

EXAMPLE 4

In order to obtain the value of $R = (3.74)^5$ by use of logarithms, we use Property III, Art. 81, and have

$$\begin{aligned} \log R &= \log (3.74)^5 \\ &= 5(\log 3.74) \\ &= 5(0.5729) \\ &= 2.8645. \end{aligned}$$

Hence,

$$R = 732.$$

We may also use Property III to obtain the root of a number by means of logarithms. The method is illustrated in the following example:

EXAMPLE 5

If $R = \sqrt[3]{62.3}$, we rewrite the problem in the exponential form and get

$$R = (62.3)^{\frac{1}{3}}.$$

Hence,

$$\begin{aligned} \log R &= \tfrac{1}{3} \log 62.3 \\ &= \tfrac{1}{3}(1.7945) \\ &= 0.5982. \end{aligned}$$

Therefore,

$$R = 3.96.$$

In the application of Property III to the problem of extracting a root of a decimal fraction, we employ a device similar to that described in Example 3 in order to avoid a troublesome situation.

EXAMPLE 6

If $R = \sqrt[6]{.0628}$, we have

$$\begin{aligned} \log R &= \tfrac{1}{6} \log .0628 \\ &= \frac{8.7980 - 10}{6}. \end{aligned}$$

If we perform the division indicated above, we get

$$\begin{aligned} \log R &= 1.4663 - 1.6667 \\ &= -.2004. \end{aligned}$$

Thus, we have a negative logarithm and cannot obtain R from the table. We avoid a situation of this sort by adding $50 - 50$ to $\log .0628$, obtaining $\log .0628 = 58.7980 - 60$. Now we have

$$\log R = \frac{58.7980 - 60}{6}$$
$$= 9.7997 - 10.$$

The last logarithm is in the customary form, and, by referring to the table, we find that

$$R = .631.$$

3. *Miscellaneous Problems*

Many computation problems require a combination of the processes of multiplication, division, raising to powers and the extraction of roots. We shall illustrate the general procedure for solving such problems by an example.

EXAMPLE 7

Use logarithms to find R if

$$R = \sqrt[5]{\frac{\sqrt{2.689}(3.478)}{(52.18)^2(51.67)}}.$$

Solution

Since all of the numbers in this problem contain four digits, we must obtain the value of R to four places. Furthermore, we must use interpolation to obtain the mantissas. The steps in the solution are indicated in the following suggested outline:

$\log \sqrt{2.689} = \frac{1}{2} \log 2.689 = \frac{1}{2}(\_\_\_\_) = \_\_\_\_$
$\log 3.478 \hspace{5.5cm} = \_\_\_\_$

$\hspace{3cm} \log \text{dividend} = \hspace{3cm} \underline{\hspace{2cm}}$
$\hspace{7cm} \text{(sum here)}$

$\log (52.18)^2 = 2 \log 52.18 = 2(\_\_\_\_) = \_\_\_\_$
$\log 51.67 \hspace{5.5cm} = \_\_\_\_$

$\hspace{3cm} \log \text{divisor} = \hspace{3cm} \underline{\hspace{2cm}}$
$\hspace{7cm} \text{(sum here)}$
$\hspace{6.5cm} 5 \,\big|\, \underline{\hspace{2.5cm}}$
$\hspace{7cm} \text{(difference)}$

$\hspace{3.5cm} \log R = \_\_\_\_$
$\hspace{3.5cm} R = \_\_\_\_.$

We now enter the characteristics in the proper places, then turn to the table, get the mantissas and enter each in the space left for it, and complete the solution. Then the outline appears as below.

$\log \sqrt{2.689} = \frac{1}{2} \log 2.689 = \frac{1}{2}(0.4296) = 0.2148$

$\log 3.478 \qquad\qquad\qquad\qquad\qquad = 0.5413$

$\qquad\qquad\qquad\qquad \text{log dividend} = \;.7561$ 　　　　10.7561* − 10

$\log (52.18)^2 = 2 \log 52.18 = 2(1.7175) = 3.4350$

$\log 51.67 \qquad\qquad\qquad\qquad\qquad = 1.7132$

$\qquad\qquad\qquad\qquad\quad \text{log divisor} = $ 　　　　　　5.1482

　　　　　　　　　　　　　　　　　　　　5 | 45.6079 − 50†

$\qquad\qquad\qquad\qquad\quad \log R = $ 　　　　　　9.1216 − 10

$\qquad\qquad\qquad\qquad\quad R = .1323.$

EXERCISE 50

Use logarithms to perform the computation indicated in the following problems. In Problems 1 to 28 obtain the answers to three digits. In the others, obtain the answers to four digits.

1. $(3.47)(5.93)$.　　　**2.** $(76.3)(.148)$.　　　**3.** $(.129)(56.4)$.

4. $(80.3)(2.52)$.　　　**5.** $\dfrac{20.3}{5.87}$.　　　**6.** $\dfrac{165}{.149}$.

7. $\dfrac{381}{57.7}$.　　　**8.** $\dfrac{.207}{.0814}$.　　　**9.** $\dfrac{(2.43)(58.1)}{79.6}$.

10. $\dfrac{(5.14)(7.66)}{27.9}$.　　**11.** $\dfrac{80.8}{(12.2)(2.12)}$.　　**12.** $\dfrac{984}{(237)(3.16)}$.

13. $(57.7)^2(.325)^3$.　　**14.** $(29.1)^3(.173)^2$.　　**15.** $\dfrac{8.06^2}{3.17^3}$.

16. $\dfrac{11.4^3}{32.2^2}$.　　**17.** $\sqrt{(57.2)(.303)}$.　　**18.** $\sqrt[3]{(627)(.0457)}$.

19. $\sqrt[3]{\dfrac{68.2}{59.3}}$.　　**20.** $\sqrt{\dfrac{.837}{.0956}}$.　　**21.** $\dfrac{(.579)(3.62)}{3.71}$.

22. $\dfrac{(818)(.0472)}{51.4}$.　　**23.** $\dfrac{.271}{(3.62)(.914)}$.　　**24.** $\dfrac{.0359}{(5.87)(.0814)}$.

25. $\sqrt[3]{.713}$.　　**26.** $\sqrt[7]{.0498}$.　　**27.** $\sqrt[4]{(4.19)(.0127)}$.

28. $\sqrt[6]{\dfrac{21.4}{86.3}}$.　　**29.** $(147.2)(.02346)$.　　**30.** $(5.261)(.8042)$.

31. $(2.581)(47.33)$.　　**32.** $(.9832)(.3144)$.　　**33.** $\dfrac{5.783}{.1949}$.

34. $\dfrac{.5302}{.09763}$.　　**35.** $\dfrac{1.744}{1.447}$.　　**36.** $\dfrac{.8057}{.7236}$.

---

* Note that we add $10 - 10$ here so we can subtract 5.1482.

† We add $40 - 40$ here so that we can divide by 5.

37. $\dfrac{(5.719)(34.18)}{167.3}$.

38. $\dfrac{(.2572)(.03465)}{.006154}$.

39. $\dfrac{7.236}{(5.418)(.9774)}$.

40. $\dfrac{.5323}{(4.856)(.09612)}$.

41. $\sqrt[3]{8.723}$.

42. $\sqrt{58.66}$.

43. $\sqrt[5]{91.38}$.

44. $\sqrt[7]{2468}$.

45. $\dfrac{.5327}{8.123}$.

46. $\sqrt{\dfrac{43.51}{214.4}}$.

47. $\sqrt[3]{\dfrac{(27.33)(.4514)}{16.72}}$.

48. $\sqrt{\dfrac{8.537}{(2.144)(5.763)}}$.

49. $\dfrac{\sqrt[3]{.7688}}{4.971}$.

50. $\dfrac{8.472}{\sqrt{93.46}}$.

51. $\dfrac{\sqrt{3.729}}{\sqrt[3]{61.36}}$.

52. $\dfrac{\sqrt[4]{57.87}}{\sqrt[5]{196.6}}$.

83. *Logarithms to bases other than* 10. As we implied in the first article of this chapter, many real numbers can be used as a base for a system of logarithms. However, there are only two in general use, the common, or Briggs, system, and the natural, or Napierian, system. The former is the system more convenient for numerical computation, and the latter is very important in more advanced mathematics and its applications. The base for the Napierian system is the irrational number $e = 2.718 \cdots$ to three decimal places. Tables of Napierian logarithms may be found in most technical handbooks and manuals of mathematical tables. However, the logarithm of a number to any base can be expressed in terms of the logarithm of the number to another base. In particular, the logarithm of a number to any base can be obtained by use of a table of common logarithms, and it is the purpose of the present article to explain how this can be done.

THEOREM. *If **a** and **b** are any two bases, then*

(1)
$$\log_a N = \frac{\log_b N}{\log_b a}.$$

Proof. We shall let
$$N = a^y;$$
then
$$\log_a N = \log_a a^y$$
$$= y.$$

Furthermore,

$$\log_b N = \log_b a^y$$
$$= y \log_b a \qquad \text{(by Property III of Art. 81)}$$
$$= \log_a N \log_b a. \qquad \text{(since } y = \log_a N)$$

Now, solving this equation for $\log_a N$, we have

$$\log_a N = \frac{\log_b N}{\log_b a}.$$

COROLLARY. *The relation between $\log_{10} N$ and $\log_e N$ is given by*

$$(2) \qquad \log_e N = \frac{\log_{10} N}{\log_{10} e}.$$

Proof. If, in (1), we let $a = e$ and $b = 10$, we have the equation as stated in the corollary.

Since $\log_{10} e = .4343$ and $\dfrac{1}{.4343} = 2.3026$, (2) can be expressed in the form

$$(3) \qquad \log_e N = 2.3026 \log_{10} N.$$

EXAMPLE

By means of (1), find the value of $\log_7 236$.

Solution

If we substitute in (1), we get

$$\log_7 236 = \frac{\log_{10} 236}{\log_{10} 7}$$
$$= \frac{2.3729}{.8451} = 2.808.$$

84. Exponential and logarithmic equations. *An **exponential equation** is an equation in which the unknown occurs in one or more exponents. A **logarithmic equation** is an equation which involves the logarithm of a function of the unknown.*

EXAMPLES

In the examples below, (1) and (2) are exponential equations, and (3) is a logarithmic equation.

(1) $$3^x = 7,$$
(2) $$3^{x+1} = 5^{x-2},$$
(3) $$\log x + \log (x - 1) = 2.$$

In general, exponential and logarithmic equations cannot be solved by the methods heretofore discussed, but many such equations can be solved by use of the properties of logarithms. The following examples illustrate the procedure.

EXAMPLE 4

Solve the equation

$$3^{x+4} = 5^{x+2}.$$

Solution

If we take the common logarithm of each member of the above equation we have, by Property III, Art. 81,

$$(x + 4) \log 3 = (x + 2) \log 5,$$

and we complete the solution as follows:

$$x \log 3 + 4 \log 3 = x \log 5 + 2 \log 5,$$

$$x(\log 3 - \log 5) = 2 \log 5 - 4 \log 3 \quad \text{(transposing and collecting)}$$
$$= \log 25 - \log 81, \quad \text{(by III, Art. 81)}$$
$$x = \frac{\log 25 - \log 81}{\log 3 - \log 5} \quad \text{(solving for } x\text{)}$$
$$= \frac{1.3979 - 1.9085}{.4771 - .6990}$$
$$= \frac{-.5106}{-.2219}$$
$$= 2,301.$$

EXAMPLE 5

Solve

$$\log_6 (x + 3) + \log_6 (x - 2) = 1.$$

Solution

By applying I, Art. 81, to the left member of the given equation, we have

$$\log_6 (x + 3)(x - 2) = 1.$$

Hence,

$$(x + 3)(x - 2) = 6^1, \qquad \text{[by (2), Art. 75]}$$
$$x^2 + x - 6 = 6, \qquad \text{(performing the indicated operations)}$$
$$x^2 + x - 12 = 0, \qquad \text{(transposing and collecting terms)}$$
$$(x + 4)(x - 3) = 0.$$

Solving this equation, we get

$$x = -4, \qquad \text{and} \qquad x = 3.$$

EXAMPLE 6

Solve

(1)
$$5^{x-2y} = 100$$

and

(2)
$$3^{2x-y} = 10$$

for x and y.

Solution

If we take the logarithm of each member of (1) and of (2), we get

(3) $\qquad\qquad (x - 2y) \log 5 = 2,$
(4) $\qquad\qquad (2x - y) \log 3 = 1.$

Therefore,

(3′)
$$x - 2y = \frac{2}{\log 5},$$

and

(4′)
$$2x - y = \frac{1}{\log 3}.$$

If we perform the computation indicated in the right member, we have

(3″) $\qquad\qquad x - 2y = 2.861,$
(4″) $\qquad\qquad 2x - y = 2.096.$

Multiplying each member of (4″) by 2 and subtracting from the corresponding member of (3″), we obtain

$$-3x = -1.331,$$
$$x = .4437.$$

Substituting this value for x in $(3'')$ and solving for y, we get

$$-2y = 2.861 - .4437$$
$$= 2.4173.$$

Therefore,

$$y = -1.209.$$

Therefore the solution of the system is $x = .4437$ and $y = -1.209$.

EXERCISE 51

By use of a table of common logarithms, find to four digits the value of the logarithm in each of Problems 1 to 20.

1. $\log_e 58.5$.   **2.** $\log_e 7.53$.   **3.** $\log_e .803$.
4. $\log_e 1.64$.   **5.** $\log_5 31.2$.   **6.** $\log_2 8.23$.
7. $\log_3 1.68$.   **8.** $\log_7 362$.   **9.** $\log_2 .513$.
10. $\log_9 90.1$.   **11.** $\log_{17} 425$.   **12.** $\log_5 138$.
13. $\log_7 33.3$.   **14.** $\log_{11} 100$.   **15.** $\log_6 257$.
16. $\log_2 14.7$.   **17.** $\log_7 1066$.   **18.** $\log_5 1492$.
19. $\log_6 1607$.   **20.** $\log_7 1776$.

In Problems 21 to 40, find the value of x to four digits.

21. $2^{x+1} = 3^{x-1}$.   **22.** $2^{3x-4} = 3^{x+2}$.   **23.** $3^{2x+1} = 5^{x+1}$.
24. $3^{3x+1} = 7^{x+1}$.   **25.** $2^{2x-1} = 5^{x+1}$.   **26.** $3^{2x+1} = 5^{x+2}$.
27. $11^{x+1} = 3^{3x+1}$.   **28.** $7^{2x-1} = 13^{x+1}$.
29. $\log_6 (x + 2) + \log_6 (x + 3) = 1$.
30. $\log_6 (x + 1) + \log_6 (x + 2) = 1$.
31. $\log_3 (x + 1) + \log_3 (x + 3) = 1$.
32. $\log_3 (x + 4) + \log_3 (x + 6) = 1$.
33. $\log_2 (2x + 1) - \log_2 (2x + 4) = 2$.
34. $\log_2 (3x + 2) - \log_2 (3x + 5) = 2$.
35. $\log_2 (5x - 6) - \log_2 (5x + 1) = 3$.
36. $\log_2 (4x + 4) - \log_2 (x - 1) = 3$.
37. $\log_4 (x^2 - x - 2) - \log_4 (x - 2) = 1$.
38. $\log_5 (x^2 + 2x - 3) - \log_5 (x - 1) = 2$.
39. $\log_5 (x^2 + 21x - 10) - \log_5 (5x - 1) = 1$.
40. $\log_3 (2x^2 + 3x + 7) - \log_3 1 = 3$.

Solve the following pairs of equations simultaneously.

41. $5^{x+y} = 10$ **42.** $3^{2x+y} = 100$ **43.** $6^{x+y} = 1000$
$5^{x+3y} = 100$. $3^{x-y} = 10$. $6^{x-y} = 100$.
44. $7^{2x-y} = 1000$ **45.** $2^{x+y} = 7$ **46.** $5^{2x-3y} = 17$
$7^{x+y} = 100$. $3^{x-y} = 2$. $2^{3x-y} = 9$.
47. $7^{2x-y} = 50$ **48.** $6^{x-y} = 40$
$3^{x+2y} = 27$. $5^{x+y} = 71$.

CHAPTER 12

THE PROGRESSIONS

85. Introduction. Frequently in mathematics we have occasion to deal with a sequence of numbers each of which can be obtained from the preceding by the operation of some law. Sequences of this type are called progressions and are illustrated in the following examples:

EXAMPLE 1

The distances in feet that a body falls from rest during each of the first 5 sec. are

$$(1) \qquad 16.1, \quad 48.3, \quad 80.5, \quad 112.7, \quad 144.9.$$

If we add 32.2 to any number in this sequence, we obtain the next number.

EXAMPLE 2

Each person has two parents, four grandparents, eight great-grandparents, and so on. Hence, if there are no duplications, we may list the number of ancestors that any person has in each of the five generations that precede him in the sequence

$$(2) \qquad 2, \quad 4, \quad 8, \quad 16, \quad 32.$$

Here, each term after the first is double the preceding.

The two above examples are illustrations of arithmetic progressions and geometric progressions. These two progressions are met frequently in mathematics and in applied fields, and we shall devote the remainder of this chapter to a discussion of them.

86. Arithmetic progressions. DEFINITION. *An arithmetic progression is a sequence of numbers so related that each term after the first can be obtained from the preceding by adding a fixed quantity called the* **common difference.**

256

1. If the first term is 2 and the common difference is 5, then the first eight terms of an arithmetic progression are

$$2, \quad 7, \quad 12, \quad 17, \quad 22, \quad 27, \quad 32, \quad 37.$$

2. In the sequence

$$16, \quad 14\tfrac{1}{2}, \quad 13, \quad 11\tfrac{1}{2}, \quad 10, \quad 8\tfrac{1}{2}$$

each term after the first is $1\tfrac{1}{2}$ less than the preceding. Hence, this is an arithmetic progression with the common difference equal to $-1\tfrac{1}{2}$.

Most problems in arithmetic progressions deal with three or more of the following five quantities: the first term, the last term, the number of terms, the common difference, and the sum of all the terms. Hence, we shall derive formulas which enable us to determine any one of these five quantities if we know the values of three of the others.

We shall let[1]

$a =$ the first term in the progression,
$l =$ the last term,
$d =$ the common difference,
$n =$ the number of terms,

and

$s =$ the sum of all the terms.

87. The last term of an arithmetic progression. In terms of the above notation, the first four terms of an arithmetic progression are

$$a, \quad a + d, \quad a + 2d, \quad \text{and} \quad a + 3d.$$

We notice that d enters with the coefficient one in the second term and that this coefficient increases by one as we move from one term to the next. Hence, the coefficient of d in any term is one less than the number of that term in the progression. Therefore, the sixth term is $a + 5d$, the ninth is $a + 8d$, and finally the last, or nth, term is $a + (n - 1)d$. Hence, we have the formula

$$(1) \qquad l = a + (n - 1)d.$$

---

[1] Note that these symbols can be arranged so that they spell the word "lands."

EXAMPLE 1

If the first three terms of an arithmetic progression are 2, 6, and 10, find the eighth term.

Solution

Since the first and second terms, as well as the second and third, differ by 4, it follows that $d = 4$. Furthermore, $a = 2$ and $n = 8$. Hence, if we substitute these values in (1), we have

$$l = 2 + (8 - 1)4$$
$$= 2 + 28$$
$$= 30.$$

EXAMPLE 2

If the first term of an arithmetic progression is -3 and the eighth term is 11, find d and write the eight terms of the progression.

Solution

In this problem, $a = -3$, $n = 8$, and $l = 11$. If these values are substituted in (1), we have

$$11 = -3 + (8 - 1)d,$$

or

$$11 = -3 + 7d.$$

Hence,

$$-7d = -14,$$

and

$$d = 2.$$

Therefore, since $a = -3$, the first eight terms of the desired progression are $-3, -1, 1, 3, 5, 7, 9, 11$.

88. The sum of an arithmetic progression. In order to obtain the formula for the sum s of the n terms of an arithmetic progression in which the first term is a and the common difference is d, we note that the terms in the progression are a, $a + d$, $a + 2d$, and so on until we reach the last term which by (1), Art. 87, is $l = a + (n - 1)d$. Hence

(1) $\quad s = a + (a + d) + (a + 2d) + \cdots + [a + (n - 1)d].$

Since there are n terms in (1) and each term contains a, we may rearrange the terms and write s as

(2) $$s = na + [d + 2d + \cdots + (n - 1)d].$$

Now, if we reverse the order of the terms in the progression by writing l as the first term, then the second term is $l - d$, the third $l - 2d$, and so on to the nth term, which by (1), Art. 87, is $l + (n - 1)(-d)$. Hence, we can write the sum as

$$s = l + (l - d) + (l - 2d) + \cdots + [l + (n - 1)(-d)].$$

Next, combining the l's and the d's, we get

(3) $$s = nl - [d + 2d + \cdots + (n - 1)d].$$

Finally, if we add the corresponding members of (2) and (3), we see that the terms containing d cancel, and we have

$$2s = na + nl$$
$$= n(a + l).$$

Hence, dividing by 2, we obtain the formula

(4) $$s = \frac{n}{2}(a + 1).$$

EXAMPLE 1

Find the sum of all the even integers from 2 to 1000 inclusive.

Solution

Since the even integers, 2, 4, 6, etc., taken in order form an arithmetic progression with $d = 2$, we may use (4) with $a = 2$, $n = 500$, and $l = 1000$ to obtain the desired sum. The substitution of these values in (4) yields

$$s = \frac{500}{2}(2 + 1000)$$
$$= 250(1002) = 250,500.$$

EXAMPLE 2

A man buys a used car for $600 and agrees to pay $100 down and $100 per month plus interest at 6 per cent on the outstanding indebtedness until the car is paid for. How much will the car cost him?

Solution

The rate of 6 per cent per year is .5 per cent per month. Hence, when he makes his first payment, he will owe 1 month's interest on $500, or $(.005)(\$500) = \$2.50$. Since he pays $100 on the principal, his interest from month to month is reduced by .5 per cent of $100 or by $.50 per month. The final payment will be $100 plus interest on $100 for 1 month, which is $100.50. Hence his payments constitute an arithmetic progression with $a = \$102.50$, $l = \$100.50$, and $n = 5$. Therefore, by (4), the sum of his payments is

$$s = \tfrac{5}{2}(\$102.50 + \$100.50)$$
$$= \tfrac{5}{2}(\$203) = \$507.50.$$

Thus, the total cost of the car will be $607.50.

89. Simultaneous use of the formulas for l and s.

If any three of the quantities l, a, n, d, and s are known, the other two can be found by use of formulas (1) of Art. 87 and (4) of Art. 88. If all three known quantities appear in either of the two formulas, the two unknowns can be found by use of the formulas separately. However, if only two of the three known quantities appear in each of the formulas, we get the other two by solving (1), Art. 87, and (4), Art. 88, simultaneously.

EXAMPLE 1

If $a = 4$, $n = 10$, and $l = 49$, find d and s.

Solution

Since each of (1), Art. 87, and (4), Art. 88, contain a, n, and l, we may find d and s by using the formulas separately. If we substitute the given values for a, n, and l in (1), Art. 87, we get

$$49 = 4 + (10 - 1)d,$$

or

$$49 = 4 + 9d.$$

Hence,

$$9d = 45,$$

and

$$d = 5.$$

Similarly, substituting in (4), Art. 88, we have

$$s = \tfrac{10}{2}(4 + 49)$$
$$= 5(53)$$
$$= 265.$$

EXAMPLE 2

If $l = 23$, $d = 3$, and $s = 98$, find a and n.

Solution

If we substitute these values in (1), Art. 87, and (4), Art. 88, we obtain

(1) $$23 = a + (n - 1)3$$

from the former and

(2) $$98 = \frac{n}{2}(a + 23)$$

from the latter. Each of these equations contains the two desired unknowns a and n. Hence, we may complete the solution by solving (1) and (2) simultaneously. If we solve (1) for a we get

$$a = 23 - (n - 1)3,$$

or

(3) $$a = 26 - 3n.$$

Substituting the above value for a in (2), we obtain

$$98 = \frac{n}{2}(26 - 3n + 23),$$

which we may solve for n as follows:

$$196 = n(49 - 3n), \quad \text{(clearing of fractions and combining)}$$

$$196 = 49n - 3n^2, \quad \text{(performing the indicated operations)}$$

$$3n^2 - 49n + 196 = 0, \quad \text{(transposing)}$$

$$n = \frac{49 \pm \sqrt{(49)^2 - (4)(3)(196)}}{6} \quad \text{(by the quadratic formula)}$$

$$= \frac{49 \pm \sqrt{2401 - 2352}}{6}$$

$$= \frac{49 \pm \sqrt{49}}{6}$$

$$= \frac{49 \pm 7}{6}$$

$$= 9\tfrac{1}{3} \text{ and } 7.$$

Since n cannot be a fraction, we discard $9\frac{1}{3}$ and have

$$n = 7.$$

If we substitute 7 for n in (3), we obtain

$$a = 26 - 3(7)$$
$$= 5.$$

Hence, the progression consists of the seven terms 5, 8, 11, 14, 17, 20, and 23.

90. Arithmetic means. The terms between the first and last terms of an arithmetic progression are called *arithmetic means*. If the progression contains only three terms, the middle term is called *the arithmetic mean* of the first and last term. We may obtain the arithmetic means between two numbers by first using (1), Art. 87, to find d, and then the means can be computed. If the progression consists of the three terms a, m, and l, then by (1), Art. 87,

$$l = a + (3 - 1)d = a + 2d.$$

Hence,

$$d = \frac{l - a}{2},$$

and

$$m = a + \frac{l - a}{2} = \frac{a + l}{2}.$$

Therefore, *the arithmetic mean of two numbers is equal to one-half their sum.*

EXAMPLE 1

Insert five arithmetic means between 6 and -10.

Solution

Since we are to find five means between 6 and -10, we shall have seven terms in all. Hence, $n = 7$, $a = 6$, and $l = -10$. Thus, by (1), Art. 87, we have

$$-10 = 6 + (7 - 1)d.$$

Hence,

$$6d = -16,$$
$$d = -\frac{16}{6} = -\frac{8}{3},$$

and the progression consists of the terms 6, $\frac{10}{3}$, $\frac{2}{3}$, $-\frac{6}{3}$, $-\frac{14}{3}$, $-\frac{22}{3}$, $-\frac{30}{3}$.

Determine which of the sequences in Problems 1 to 8 are arithmetic progressions. State the value of d for each arithmetic progression.

1. $2, 6, 10, 14, 18.$
2. $1, 4, 7, 10, 13.$
3. $7, 5, 2, -2, -7.$
4. $8, 5, 2, -1, -4.$
5. $a, a + 2, a + 4.$
6. $b, 2b + 1, 3b + 2.$
7. $x, 2x^2, 3x^3, 4x^4.$
8. $3s + 4t, 2s + 2t, s, -2t.$

Write the n terms of the arithmetic progression that has the elements given in each of Problems 9 to 20.

9. $a = 7, d = 2, n = 5.$
10. $a = 1, d = 3, n = 6.$
11. $a = 8, d = -3, n = 7.$
12. $a = 11, d = -2, n = 4.$
13. First term, 3; second term, 5; $n = 6.$
14. First term, 8; second term, 7; $n = 6.$
15. First term, 4; third term, 6; $n = 5.$
16. First term, 11; fourth term, 5; $n = 8.$
17. Second term, -10; fourth term, -4; $n = 5.$
18. Third term, 9; sixth term, 3; $n = 8.$
19. Third term, 5; seventh term, -3; $n = 9.$
20. Second term, 0; fifth term, 6; $n = 6.$

Determine the value of x so that the sequence in each of Problems 21 to 28 is an arithmetic progression.

21. $1, 5, 3x.$
22. $1, 2x, 11.$
23. $x - 1, x + 1, 3.$
24. $2x - 1, 2x + 1, 3x + 1.$
25. $3, 5x, 2x^2 + 5x.$
26. $2, 2x, x^2 + x.$
27. $3, 2x, x^2 + 8x.$
28. $1, x, 2x^2 - x.$

Find the values of the two of the five letters l, a, n, d, and s that are missing in each of Problems 29 to 44.

29. $a = 2, n = 7, d = 2.$
30. $a = 3, n = 8, d = 1.$
31. $l = 16, n = 5, d = 3.$
32. $l = 9, n = 9, d = 1.$
33. $l = -1, a = 7, n = 5.$
34. $s = 33, a = -2, n = 6.$
35. $l = 3, a = -11, d = 2.$
36. $l = -7, a = -1, d = -1.$
37. $a = 2, l = 14, s = 56.$
38. $n = 8, l = 10, s = 52.$
39. $n = 5, d = 3, s = 50.$
40. $n = 9, d = 1, s = 45.$
41. $l = -1, d = -2, s = 15.$
42. $l = 13, d = 3, s = 33.$
43. $a = -11, d = 2, s = -32.$
44. $a = -1, d = -1, s = -28.$
45. Insert three arithmetic means between 4 and 16.
46. Insert three arithmetic means between -1 and 7.
47. Insert four arithmetic means between -2 and 13.
48. Insert six arithmetic means between 2 and 16.
49. Insert five arithmetic means between -7 and -1.
50. Insert six arithmetic means between 3 and -11.

51. Insert seven arithmetic means between 2 and 26.

52. Insert seven arithmetic means between −4 and 12.

53. Find the sum of all even integers from 6 to 22, inclusive.

54. Find the sum of all odd integers from 7 to 45, inclusive.

55. Find the sum of all multiples of 3 between 2 and 52.

56. Find the sum of all multiples of 7 between 2 and 52.

57. In order to raise money for a charitable fund 100 members of a club conducted a raffle with a turkey as the prize. Tickets were numbered with consecutive multiples of 5 from 5 to 500. Each member drew a ticket and agreed to pay in cents the amount indicated by the number on it. Find the amount realized from the raffle.

58. A college graduate accepted a position for $4000 a year and, during a 10-year period, he received an increase of $400 at the beginning of each year after the first. Find the salary he received during the tenth year and the total amount earned during the 10 years.

59. A man borrows $5000 and agrees to pay $500 plus interest at 4 per cent on the outstanding principal at the end of each year until the debt is retired. Find the total interest paid.

60. A man paid $2800 for a car that depreciated 20 per cent the first year, 18 per cent the second, 16 per cent the third, and so on. How much was the car worth at the end of 5 years?

61. The bottom rung of a ladder is 24 in. long. There are 17 rungs in the ladder and each is $\frac{3}{4}$ in. shorter than the one just below it. Find the total length of the rungs.

62. The 10 north-south streets in a suburban addition are to be paved at a cost of $10 per linear yard. If the first street is 2000 yd. in length, the second 1900 yd., the third 1800 yd., and so on, find the cost of the paving.

63. A total of 231 lengths of pipe are stacked in a pile with the ends in the shape of a triangle. There are 21 lengths in the bottom layer, 20 in the next, 19 in the next, and so on. If the outside diameter of each pipe is 6 in., find the height of the pile.

64. In a potato race, nine potatoes are placed in a row 10 ft. apart, and a basket is placed on the starting line in line with the potatoes and 17 ft. from the nearest. The object of the race is to place the potatoes one at a time in the basket in the shortest possible time. How far will a contestant run before he completes the race?

65. The rungs of a ladder increase uniformly in length from 14 to 26 in., and their total length is 21 ft and 8 in. Find the number of rungs in the ladder and the amount by which two consecutive rungs differ.

66. Several people played 18 holes of golf and made scores varying from 76 to 90 strokes. When arranged in order of magnitude, it was found that there was a uniform difference between the consecutive scores. If the sum of the scores was 664, find the number of players and the score of each.

67. A man saved $10 the first week he worked, and each week thereafter he increased this amount by $1.50 until his weekly saving was $25. He then saved the latter amount regularly each week until his total saving was $442.50. How many weeks were required for this sum to accumulate?

68. In a vacuum a body falls approximately 16.1 ft. the first second, 48.3 ft. the second, 80.5 ft. during the third, and so on.   Neglecting the resistance of air, find, to the nearest second, the time required for a practice bomb to reach the ground if it is dropped from a plane 20,000 ft. high.

91. *Geometric progressions.* DEFINITION.   *A **geometric progression** is a sequence of numbers so related that each one after the first can be obtained from the preceding by multiplying it by a fixed constant called the **common ratio.***

EXAMPLES

Each of the sequences below is a geometric progression with the indicated common ratio.

1. 2,   6,   18,   54,   162;   common ratio 3.
2. 3,   −3,   3,   −3,   3;   common ratio −1.
3. 96,   24,   6, $\frac{3}{2}$, $\frac{3}{8}$;   common ratio $\frac{1}{4}$.

In order to obtain formulas for dealing with a geometric progression we shall let[1]

$$a = \text{the first term,}$$
$$l = \text{the last term,}$$
$$r = \text{the common ratio,}$$
$$n = \text{the number of terms,}$$

and

$$s = \text{the sum of the terms.}$$

92. *The last term of a geometric progression.* In terms of the above notation, the first six terms of a geometric progression in which the first term is a and the common ratio is r are

$$a, \qquad ar, \qquad ar^2, \qquad ar^3, \qquad ar^4, \qquad ar^5.$$

[1] Note that the letters used here can be arranged so as to spell the word "snarl."

We notice here that the exponent of r in the second term is one, and that this exponent increases by one as we proceed from each term to the next. Hence, the exponent of r in any term is one less than the number of that term in the progression. Therefore, the nth term is ar^{n-1}, and we have the formula

(1) $$l = ar^{n-1}.$$

EXAMPLE 1

Find the seventh term of the geometric progression 36, -12, 4, $\cdot\ \cdot\ \cdot\ \cdot$.

Solution

In this progression, each term, after the first, is obtained by multiplying the preceding term by $-\frac{1}{3}$. Hence, $r = -\frac{1}{3}$. Obviously, $a = 36$, $n = 7$, and the seventh term is l. Hence, if we substitute these values in (1), we have

$$l = 36(-\tfrac{1}{3})^{7-1}$$
$$= \frac{36}{(-3)^6}$$
$$= \frac{36}{729}$$
$$= \frac{4}{81}.$$

93. *The sum of a geometric progression.* If we add the terms of the geometric progression

$$a,\ ar,\ ar^2\ \cdot\ \cdot\ \cdot\ ,\ ar^{n-2},\ ar^{n-1},$$

we have

(1) $$s = a + ar + ar^2 + \cdot\ \cdot\ \cdot + ar^{n-2} + ar^{n-1}.$$

However, by use of an algebraic device, we can obtain a more compact formula for s. First, we multiply each member of (1) by r and get

(2) $$rs = ar + ar^2 + ar^3 + \cdot\ \cdot\ \cdot + ar^{n-1} + ar^n.$$

Next we notice that if we subtract the corresponding members of (1) and (2), all the terms on the right cancel except the first term in (1) and the last term in (2). Hence, we have

$$s - rs = a - ar^n,$$

or

$$s(1 - r) = a - ar^n.$$

Solving the last equation for s, we obtain

(3) $$s = \frac{a - ar^n}{1 - r}.$$

EXAMPLE 1

Find the sum of the first six terms of the progression $2, -6, 18, \cdots$.

Solution

In this progression, $a = 2$, $r = -3$, and $n = 6$. Hence, if we substitute these values in (3), we have

$$s = \frac{2 - 2(-3)^6}{1 - (-3)}$$

$$= \frac{2 - 2(729)}{1 + 3}$$

$$= \frac{2 - 1458}{4}$$

$$= \frac{-1456}{4}$$

$$= -364.$$

EXAMPLE 2

The first term of a geometric progression is 3; the fourth term is 24. Find the tenth term and the sum of the first 10 terms.

Solution

In order to find either the tenth term or the sum, we must have the value of r. We may obtain this value by considering the progression made up of the first four terms of the above. Then we have $a = 3$, $n = 4$, and $l = 24$. If we substitute these values in (1), Art. 92, we get

$$24 = 3r^{4-1},$$

or

$$3r^3 = 24.$$

Hence,

$$r^3 = 8,$$

and

$$r = 2.$$

Now, using (1), Art. 92, again with $a = 3$, $r = 2$, and $n = 10$, we get

$$l = 3(2^{10-1})$$
$$= 3(2^9)$$
$$= 3(512)$$
$$= 1536.$$

Hence, the tenth term is 1536.

In order to obtain s, we shall use (3), Art. 93, with $a = 3$, $r = 2$, and $n = 10$ and get

$$s = \frac{3 - 3(2)^{10}}{1 - 2} = \frac{3 - 3(1024)}{-1} = \frac{3 - 3072}{-1} = 3069.$$

94. Geometric means. The terms between the first and last terms of a geometric progression are called the *geometric means.* If the progression contains only three terms, the middle term is called the *geometric mean* of the other two. In order to obtain the geometric means between a and l, we use (1) of Art. 92 to find the value of r, and then the means can be computed. If there are only three terms in the progression, then, by (1), Art. 92,

$$l = ar^2.$$

Hence

$$r = \pm \sqrt{\frac{l}{a}}.$$

Thus, the second term, or the geometric mean between a and l, is

$$a\left(\pm \sqrt{\frac{l}{a}} \right) = \pm \sqrt{\frac{a^2 l}{a}} = \pm \sqrt{al}.$$

Hence, *the geometric means between two quantities are plus and minus the square root of their product.*

EXAMPLE 1

Find two sets of five geometric means between 3 and 192.

Solution

A geometric progression starting with 3 and ending with 192 with five intermediate terms contains seven terms. Hence, $n = 7$, $a = 3$, and $l = 192$. Therefore, by (1), Art. 92,

$$192 = 3(r^{7-1}).$$

Hence,

$$r^6 = \frac{192}{3}$$
$$= 64,$$

and

$$r = \pm \sqrt[6]{64} = \pm 2.$$

Consequently, the two sets of geometric means of five terms each between 3 and 192 are 6, 12, 24, 48, 96, and −6, 12, −24, 48, −96.

EXAMPLE 2

Find the geometric means of $\frac{1}{2}$ and $\frac{1}{8}$.

Solution

By the statement just before Example 1, the geometric means of $\frac{1}{2}$ and $\frac{1}{8}$ are $\pm \sqrt{(\frac{1}{2})(\frac{1}{8})} = \pm \sqrt{\frac{1}{16}} = \pm\frac{1}{4}$.

EXERCISE 53

Determine which of the sequences in Problems 1 to 8 are geometric progressions. State the value of r for each geometric progression.

1. 1, 2, 4, 8, 16.   **2.** 2, 4, 6, 8, 10.   **3.** 2, −2, 2, −2.

4. 12, 6, 3, $1\frac{1}{2}$, $\frac{3}{4}$.   **5.** x, $2x^2$, $3x^3$, $4x^4$.   **6.** a, $2a^2$, $4a^3$, $8a^4$.

7. a, $a^2 + 2a$, $a^3 + 4a^2 + 4a$.

8. $(a^2 - b^2)^2$, $(a - b)^2(a + b)$, $a^2 - 2ab + b^2$.

Write the n terms of the geometric progression that has the elements given in each of Problems 9 to 20.

9. $a = \frac{1}{2}$, $r = 2$, $n = 7$.   **10.** $a = 81$, $r = \frac{1}{3}$, $n = 6$.

11. $a = 128$, $r = -\frac{1}{2}$, $n = 8$.   **12.** $a = \frac{1}{3}$, $r = -3$, $n = 7$.

13. First term, 2; second term, 4; $n = 6$.

14. First term, 256; second term, 64; $n = 5$.

15. First term, 243; third term, 27; $n = 6$.

16. First term, $\frac{1}{8}$; fourth term, 1; $n = 8$.

17. Second term, −1; fifth term, 8; $n = 7$.

18. Third term, 9; sixth term, −243; $n = 8$.

19. Third term, 64; seventh term, 4; $n = 7$.

20. Fifth term, 27; eighth term, −729; $n = 8$.

Determine the value of x so that the sequence in each of Problems 21 to 28 is a geometric progression.

21. x, 2, 6.   **22.** x, 3, 12.   **23.** 1, 3, $4x + 1$.

24. 2, 6, $5x + 3$.   **25.** 1, x, 4.   **26.** 2, $3x$, 18.

27. $x - 5$, 5, $4x + 1$.   **28.** $x - 4$, 5, $6x + 1$.

Find the value of each of the two of the five letters s, n, a, r, and l that is missing in Problems 29 to 44.

29. $n = 5$, $a = 1$, $r = 2$.   **30.** $n = 6$, $a = 1$, $r = 3$.

31. $n = 5$, $r = 2$, $l = 16$.   **32.** $n = 6$, $r = 3$, $l = 243$.

33. $s = 3$, $n = 9$, $r = -1$.   **34.** $s = -170$, $n = 8$, $r = -2$.

35. $s = 364$, $a = 1$, $r = 3$.   **36.** $s = 1093$, $a = 729$, $r = \frac{1}{3}$.

37. $a = 16$, $r = -\frac{1}{2}$, $l = -\frac{1}{2}$.   **38.** $a = 256$, $r = -\frac{3}{4}$, $l = -\frac{243}{4}$.

39. $l = \frac{1}{4}$, $n = 7$, $a = 16$.   **40.** $s = 364$, $r = \frac{1}{3}$, $l = 1$.

41. $s = 189$, $a = 3$, $l = 96$.   **42.** $s = 5460$, $a = 4096$, $l = 4$.

43. $n = 7$, $a = 64$, $l = 729$.   **44.** $a = 16$, $r = -\frac{1}{2}$, $l = \frac{1}{4}$.

45. Insert two geometric means between 2 and 16.

46. Insert three geometric means between 1 and 81.

47. Insert three geometric means between 4 and 1024.

48. Insert five geometric means between 2 and 128.

49. Insert four geometric means between $\frac{4}{9}$ and $\frac{27}{8}$.

50. Insert five geometric means between $\frac{27}{64}$ and $\frac{1}{27}$.

51. Insert five geometric means between $\frac{1}{8}$ and 8.

52. Insert six geometric means between $\frac{81}{16}$ and $\frac{8}{27}$.

53. Find the sum of all integral powers of 2 from 2 to 256, inclusive.

54. Find the sum of all integral powers of 3 from 3 to 243, inclusive.

55. Find the sum of all integral powers of 5 from 5 to 5^6, inclusive.

56. Find the sum of all integral powers of 7 from 7^2 to 7^5, inclusive.

57. A boy receives 1 cent for delivering the first of 10 packages, 2 cents for the second, 4 cents for the third, and so on. Find the total amount received for the 10 deliveries.

58. If there are no duplications, find the number of ancestors that a pair of twins have in the five generations immediately preceding them.

59. If there are n bacteria in a culture, and if the number doubles every 2 hr., find the number in the culture at the end of 16 hr.

60. If a car depreciates 20 per cent of its value each year and cost $2500 when new, find the value at the end of the fifth year.

61. The total volume of five cubes is 4861 cu. ft. If the side of each cube is twice that of the next smaller, find the volume of the largest and of the smallest cube.

62. The board of development of a rapidly growing city estimates that the population will double every 4 years for the next 20 years. If their estimate is correct and the present population is 10,000, what will the population be at the end of the twentieth year?

63. The mid-points of the adjacent sides of a square are joined by straight lines, thus forming a second square whose area is $\frac{1}{2}$ of the original. This procedure is successively repeated with the second square, the third, and so on until a square is obtained whose area is $\frac{1}{256}$ of the original. How many squares, including the first, are in the series?

64. A man deposits $100 at the beginning of each year in a savings bank that pays 2 per cent compounded annually. How much will he have to his credit at the end of 6 years?

65. Twelve men are fishing from a pier. The first has $1000; the second, $2000; the third, $4000; and so on. How many millionaires are fishing from the pier?

66. Suppose it is possible for a person to save 1 cent the first day of the month, 2 cents the second, 4 cents the third, and so on. Find the amount he would save during the first 15 days of the month. How much would his savings be increased if he continued this practice for 5 days longer?

67. During the first 5 years an engineer worked, he received a raise of 10 per cent for each year after the first. During the next 5 years he received a fixed increase of $400 annually. If his salary during the first year was $4000, find his salary during the tenth year and the total sum earned during the 10 years.

68. The sum of three numbers in a geometric progression is 52. If the middle number is increased by 8 and the other two are unchanged, the new set forms an arithmetic progression. Find the original numbers.

95. *Infinite geometric progressions.* If the common ratio is between -1 and 1, the numerical values of the terms in a geometric progression decrease as n increases. Hence, if the number of terms of such a progression is large, we would not expect the addition of more terms to affect the sum very greatly. In fact, we shall show that if $-1 < r < 1$, the sum of the terms in a geometric progression approaches nearer and nearer to a fixed number as n increases.

Formula (3), Art. 93, can be expressed in the form

$$(1) \qquad\qquad s = \frac{a}{1 - r}\,(1 - r^n).$$

If $-1 < r < 1$, then the numerical value of r^n decreases as n increases and can be made arbitrarily small by choosing n sufficiently large. Hence, for increasing values of n, the quantity in the parentheses in (1) approaches nearer and nearer to 1. Thus, s approaches $\frac{a}{1 - r}$. In other words, the greater the value of n, the more nearly the value of s is equal to $\frac{a}{1 - r}$. Consequently, when the ratio in a geometric progression is between -1 and 1 and the number of terms is unlimited, we say that

$$(2) \qquad\qquad s = \frac{a}{1 - r}.$$

EXAMPLE 1

Find the sum of $1 + \frac{1}{2} + \frac{1}{4} + \cdots$, where the dots indicate that there is no end to the progression.

Solution

In this progression, $a = 1$ and $r = \frac{1}{2}$. Hence, by (2),

$$s = \frac{1}{1 - \frac{1}{2}} = \frac{1}{\frac{1}{2}} = 2.$$

A nonterminating, repeating decimal fraction is an illustration of an infinite geometric progression with $-1 < r < 1$. For example,

$$.232323 \cdots = .23 + .0023 + .000023 + \cdots.$$

The sequence of terms on the right is a geometric progression with $a = .23$ and $r = \frac{1}{100}$.

By use of (2), we can express any repeating decimal fraction as a common fraction by the method illustrated in the following example:

EXAMPLE 2

Show that $.333 \cdots = \frac{1}{3}$.

Solution

The decimal fraction $.333 \cdots$ can be expressed as the progression

$$.3 + .03 + .003 + \cdots$$

in which $a = .3$ and $r = .1$. Hence, by (2), the sum s is

$$s = \frac{.3}{1 - .1} = \frac{.3}{.9} = \frac{3}{9} = \frac{1}{3}.$$

EXAMPLE 3

Express .423423 · · · as a common fraction.

Solution

Expressing the given repeating decimal as a progression, we have

$$.423423423 \cdots = .423 + .000423 + .000000423 + \cdots,$$

in which $a = .423$ and $r = .001$. Hence, by (2),

$$s = \frac{.423}{1 - .001} = \frac{.423}{.999} = \frac{423}{999} = \frac{47}{111}.$$

EXERCISE 54

Find the sum of the infinite progression that has the elements in each of Problems 1 to 8.

1. $a = 4, r = \frac{1}{2}$.   **2.** $a = 6, r = \frac{1}{3}$.   **3.** $a = 5, r = \frac{3}{5}$.

4. $a = 3, r = \frac{1}{4}$.   **5.** First term, 2; second term, 1.

6. First term, 7; second term, 5.

7. Second term, 3; fourth term, $\frac{1}{3}$.

8. Third term, $\frac{9}{4}$; seventh term, $\frac{4}{9}$.

Express the repeating decimal fraction in each of Problems 9 to 20 as a common fraction or a mixed number.

9. 444 · · · .   **10.** .555 · · · .   **11.** .777 · · · .

12. .222 · · · .   **13.** .181818 · · · .   **14.** .484848 · · · .

15. .878787 · · · .   **16.** .838383 · · · .

17. 2.135135135 · · · .   **18.** 4.234234234 · · · .

19. 2.162162162 · · · .   **20.** 5.531531531 · · · .

21. Find the sum of all positive integral powers of $\frac{1}{2}$.

22. Find the sum of all positive integral powers of $\frac{2}{3}$.

23. Find the sum of all positive integral powers of $\frac{3}{4}$.

24. Find the sum of all positive integral powers of $\frac{4}{5}$.

25. A ball dropped from a platform rebounded $\frac{2}{3}$ as far as it fell. Approximately how far did it travel before coming to rest if the platform was 12 ft. from the floor?

26. The motion of a ball rolling across a surface is retarded in such a way that it moves $\frac{1}{2}$ as far each second as in the preceding second. If the ball rolled 5 ft. the first second, approximately what distance will it move before coming to rest?

27. A series of squares is formed by starting with one whose side is 12 in. in length and connecting the mid-points of the adjacent sides, repeating the procedure with the second, and so on. What is the limit of the sum of the areas?

28. At the birth of a grandson a man established a fund that would pay the child $100 on his first birthday, $90 on his second, $81 on his third, and so on. What is the maximum amount that the grandson would receive from this source?

29. A bale of cotton weighed 600 lb. after it had been wet in a rainstorm. After a day in the sun the weight decreased by 20 lb., and each day thereafter the decrease in weight was $\frac{4}{5}$ of that of the preceding. What was the approximate weight of the bale after it was dry?

30. A small college received as a bequest the royalty from an oil well. If the royalty was $10,000 the first year, and if each year after the first the royalty was $\frac{2}{3}$ of that of the preceding, what is the maximum amount that could be realized from the bequest? The college sold the royalty right for $25,000 cash and the well was exhausted after 5 years. Neglecting interest, did it gain or lose by the transaction?

31. Suppose that the shrinkage per week in the weight of stored potatoes was $\frac{1}{2}$ of that of the preceding week. If a dealer stored 500 lb. of potatoes when the price was 5 cents per pound and the weight decreased to 480 lb. during the first week, could he afford to hold them until the price rose to 6 cents?

32. In an infinite geometric progression each term is $1\frac{1}{2}$ times the sum of all terms that follow it. Find the ratio.

33. If $x > 1$, find the sum of all positive integral powers of $\dfrac{1}{x}\cdot$

34. If $x > -\frac{1}{3}$, find the sum of $\dfrac{1}{(3x+2)}, \dfrac{1}{(3x+2)^2}, \dfrac{1}{(3x+2)^3}, \cdots$

35. If $x > \frac{3}{2}$, find the sum of $\dfrac{2}{(2x-1)}, \dfrac{2^2}{(2x-1)^2}, \dfrac{2^3}{(2x-1)^3} \cdots$

36. If $x > -1$, find the sum of $\dfrac{1}{(x+2)}, \dfrac{1}{(x+2)^2}, \dfrac{1}{(x+2)^3} \cdots$

CHAPTER 13

THE BINOMIAL THEOREM

96. *The binomial formula.* In this article, we shall develop a formula which enables us to express any power of a binomial as a polynomial. This polynomial is called the expansion of the power of the binomial.

By actual multiplication, we may obtain the following expansions of the first, second, third, fourth, and fifth powers of $x + y$:

$$(x + y)^1 = x + y;$$
$$(x + y)^2 = x^2 + 2xy + y^2;$$
$$(x + y)^3 = x^3 + 3x^2y + 3xy^2 + y^3;$$
$$(x + y)^4 = x^4 + 4x^3y + 6x^2y^2 + 4xy^3 + y^4;$$
$$(x + y)^5 = x^5 + 5x^4y + 10x^3y^2 + 10x^2y^3 + 5xy^4 + y^5.$$

By referring to the above expansions, we may readily verify the fact that the following properties of $(x + y)^n$ exist when $n = 1, 2, 3, 4,$ and 5:

1. The first term in the expansion is x^n;
2. The second term is $nx^{n-1}y$;
3. The exponent of x decreases by one and the exponent of y increases by one as we proceed from term to term;
4. There are $n + 1$ terms in the expansion;
5. The $(n + 1)$st term, or the last term, is y^n;
6. The nth, or the next to the last, term of the expansion is nxy^{n-1};
7. If we multiply the coefficient of any term by the exponent of x in that term and then divide the product by the number of the term in the expansion, we obtain the coefficient of the next term;
8. The sum of the exponents of x and y in any term is n.

If we assume that these properties hold for any integral power of n, we may write the first five terms in the expansion of $(x + y)^n$

as follows:

First term,

x^n.   (by Property 1)

Second term,

$nx^{n-1}y$.   (by Property 2)

Third term,

$\dfrac{n(n-1)}{2}\, x^{n-2}y^2$.   (by Properties 7 and 3)

Fourth term,

$\dfrac{n(n-1)(n-2)}{(3)(2)}\, x^{n-3}y^3$.   (by Properties 7 and 3)

Fifth term,

$\dfrac{n(n-1)(n-2)(n-3)}{(4)(3)(2)}\, x^{n-4}y^4$. (by Properties 7 and 3)

We continue this process until we reach the nth term which is

nth term, nxy^{n-1},   (by Property 6)

and, finally, we reach the last, or the

$(n+1)$st term, y^n.   (by Property 5)

We are now in position to form the sum of the above terms and obtain the binomial formula. However, if we introduce a new notation at this point, we can write the expansion in a slightly more compact form.

DEFINITION. *The product of any positive integer **n** and all the positive integers less than **n** is called **factorial n**, and it is designated by the symbol **n!**.*

EXAMPLES

1. $3! = 3 \times 2 \times 1 = 6$.
2. $5! = 5 \times 4 \times 3 \times 2 \times 1 = 120$.

Now, if we notice that $4 \times 3 \times 2 = 4 \times 3 \times 2 \times 1 = 4!$, $3 \times 2 = 3 \times 2 \times 1 = 3!$, and $2 = 2 \times 1 = 2!$, we may write the expansion of $(x + y)^n$ as follows:

$$(1) \quad (x + y)^n = x^n + nx^{n-1}y + \frac{n(n-1)}{2!} x^{n-2}y^2$$
$$+ \frac{n(n-1)(n-2)}{3!} x^{n-3}y^3$$
$$+ \frac{n(n-1)(n-2)(n-3)}{4!} x^{n-4}y^4 + \cdots + nxy^{n-1} + y^n.$$

Formula (1) is called the *binomial formula*, and the statement that it is true is called the *binomial theorem*.

EXAMPLE 3

Use the binomial formula to obtain the expansion of $(2a + b).^6$

Solution

We shall first apply (1) with $x = 2a$, $y = b$, and $n = 6$. Then we shall simplify each term in the expansion. By (1),

$$(2a + b)^6 = (2a)^6 + 6(2a)^5b + \frac{(6)(5)}{2!} (2a)^4b^2 + \frac{(6)(5)(4)}{3!} (2a)^3b^3$$
$$+ \frac{(6)(5)(4)(3)}{4!} (2a)^2b^4 + \frac{(6)(5)(4)(3)(2)}{5!} (2a)b^5$$
$$+ \frac{(6)(5)(4)(3)(2)(1)}{6!} b^6.$$

Now we shall compute the coefficients and raise $2a$ to the indicated powers and obtain

$$(2a + b)^6 = 64a^6 + 6(32a^5)b + 15(16a^4)b^2 + 20(8a^3)b^3 + 15(4a^2)b^4$$
$$+ 6(2a)b^5 + b^6.$$

Finally, we perform the indicated multiplication in each term above and get

$$(2a + b)^6 = 64a^6 + 192a^5b + 240a^4b^2 + 160a^3b^3 + 60a^2b^4 + 12ab^5 + b^6.$$

The computation of the coefficients can, in most cases, be performed mentally by use of Property 7, and thus we can avoid writing the first step in the expansion in the above example.

EXAMPLE 4

Expand $(a - 3b)^5$.

Solution

The first term in the expansion is a^5, and the second is $5a^4(-3b)$. To get the coefficient of the third, we multiply 5 by 4 and divide the product by 2, obtaining 10. Hence, the third term is $10a^3(-3b)^2$. Similarly, the fourth term is $\frac{30}{3}a^2(-3b)^3 = 10a^2(-3b)^3$. Continuing this process, we obtain the following expansion:

$$(a - 5b)^5 = a^5 + 5a^4(-3b) + 10a^3(-3b)^2 + 10a^2(-3b)^3$$
$$+ 5a(-3b)^4 + (-3b)^5$$
$$= a^5 - 15a^4b + 90a^3b^2 - 270a^2b^3 + 405ab^4 - 243b^5.$$

It should be noted that we carry the second term of the binomial $-3b$ through the first step of the expansion as a single term. Then we raise $-3b$ to the indicated power and simplify the result.

EXAMPLE 5

Expand $(2x - 5y)^4$.

Solution

We shall carry through the expansion with $2x$ as the first term and $-5y$ as the second and get

$$(2x - 5y)^4 = (2x)^4 + 4(2x)^3(-5y) + 6(2x)^2(-5y)^2 + 4(2x)(-5y)^3$$
$$+ (-5y)^4$$
$$= 16x^4 + 4(8x^3)(-5y) + 6(4x^2)(25y^2) + 4(2x)(-125y^3)$$
$$+ 625y^4$$
$$= 16x^4 - 160x^3y + 600x^2y^2 - 1000xy^3 + 625y^4.$$

EXERCISE 55

Expand the binomial in each of Problems 1 to 32 to the indicated power.

1. $(x + y)^5$.
2. $(a - b)^7$.
3. $(m + n)^6$.
4. $(a + c)^8$.
5. $(p - q)^9$.
6. $(a - t)^8$.
7. $(r + u)^{10}$.
8. $(w - z)^{11}$.
9. $(2x - y)^7$.
10. $(x + 3y)^6$.
11. $(a - 3b)^9$.
12. $(2c + d)^8$.
13. $(2x + 3w)^5$.
14. $(3a - 2b)^4$.
15. $(4t - 3u)^5$.
16. $(3r + 5s)^6$.
17. $(x^2 - y)^9$.
18. $(2a + b^3)^7$.
19. $(w^2 - t^3)^6$.
20. $(s^2 - 2y)^{10}$.
21. $(10^2 + 1)^5$.
22. $(10^2 - 1)^4$.
23. 102^6.
24. 98^5.
25. $(1 + .01)^6$.
26. 1.02^4.
27. 1.03^7.
28. 1.05^5.
29. $\left(\dfrac{x}{2} + \dfrac{2}{x}\right)^8$.
30. $\left(\dfrac{x}{3} - \dfrac{1}{x}\right)^5$.
31. $\left(\dfrac{x^2}{2} - \dfrac{3}{x}\right)^6$.
32. $\left(\dfrac{y^3}{2} + \dfrac{4}{y^2}\right)^7$.

Find the first four terms in the expansion of each binomial in Problems 33 to 40.

33. $(a + b)^{50}$.   **34.** $(c - d)^{60}$.   **35.** $(x - 2y)^{30}$.

36. $(c - 3d)^{40}$.   **37.** $(x^2 - 2w)^{25}$.   **38.** $(m^2 - 3n)^{20}$.

39. $(s^2 - t^3)^{60}$.   **40.** $(a^3 - 2b)^{40}$.

97. The rth term of the binomial formula. In the preceding examples, we explained the method for obtaining any term of a binomial expansion from the term just before it. However, by use of this method, it is impossible to obtain any specific term of the expansion without first computing all the terms which precede it. We shall next develop a formula for finding the general, or rth, term without reference to the other terms. Our development is an example of the method of inductive reasoning—a method that is very important in all scientific investigations.

We shall consider the fifth term in (1) of the previous article and note the following properties:

1. The exponent of y in the fifth term is one less than the number 5 of the term in the expansion;

2. The exponent of x is n minus the exponent of y;

3. The denominator of the coefficient is the exponent of y followed by the exclamation point or the factorial of the exponent of y;

4. The first factor in the numerator is n and the last factor is n minus a number that is two less than the number of the term, or $n - (5 - 2)$, and the intervening factors are the consecutive integers between the first and the last factors.

We may also verify the fact that the above properties are true for the other terms of the expansion.

We now assume that the above properties hold for *any* term in the expansion, and hence for the rth term we have

1. The exponent of y is $r - 1$;

2. The exponent of x is $n - (r - 1) = n - r + 1$;

3. The denominator of the coefficient is $(r - 1)!$;

4. The last factor in the numerator is $n - (r - 2) = n - r + 2$, and hence the numerator is $n(n - 1)(n - 2) \cdots (n - r + 2)$. Therefore, we have the formula

(1) **The rth term in the expansion of $(x + y)^n$**

$$= \frac{n(n - 1)(n - 2) \cdots (n - r + 2)}{(r - 1)!} x^{n-r+1}y^{r-1}.$$

It should be noted that this formula is based on the *assumption* that the four properties mentioned in the second paragraph of this article hold for *all* terms in the expansion. The proof of this fact depends upon the method known as mathematical induction which is beyond the scope of this book.

EXAMPLE 1

Find the sixth term in the expansion of $(2a - b)^9$.

Solution

In this problem, $x = 2a$, $y = -b$, $n = 9$, and $r = 6$. Hence, $r - 1 = 5$, $n - r + 1 = 9 - 6 + 1 = 4$, and $n - r + 2 = 5$. Hence, if we substitute these values in (1), we get

$$6\text{th term} = \frac{(9)(8)(7)(6)(5)}{(5)(4)(3)(2)(1)} (2a)^4(-b)^5$$
$$= 126(16a^4)(-b^5)$$
$$= -2016a^4b^5.$$

EXERCISE 56

Find the specified term in the expansion of the binomial in each of the problems below.

1. Fifth term of $(a + b)^8$.
2. Seventh term of $(x - y)^9$.
3. Fourth term of $(m - n)^{10}$.
4. Sixth term of $(c + d)^{11}$.
5. Seventh term of $(2y + w)^7$.
6. Ninth term of $(3x - y)^{11}$.
7. Third term of $(a - 3c)^7$.
8. Fourth term of $(m + 2n)^6$.
9. Fifth term of $(x^2 - 2y)^8$.
10. Eleventh term of $(a - y^3)^{13}$.
11. Seventh term of $\left(x^2 - \dfrac{1}{x}\right)^{10}$.
12. Tenth term of $\left(a - \dfrac{1}{a^2}\right)^{14}$.

ANSWERS

1. 20, 100, 200. **2.** \$1100, \$1295. **3.** 40 gal.; the capacity is multiplied by 8.
5. 540 sq. ft; the area is multiplied by 4. **6.** \$1000, \$250. **7.** 25,132.8 miles, .6 in.
9. Rational, irrational, integer, integer. **10.** Irrational, integer, integer, rational.

11. Integer, rational, integer, rational. **13.** $L = 2\pi rl$. **14.** $V = \dfrac{S^2h}{3}$. **15.** $M = lwhd$.

17. 6, 4, 10, -10, -4. **18.** 3, 9, -6, -9. **19.** 22, -6, 8, -30.
21. $W = (h - 60)5.5 + 110$, 176 lb. **22.** $h = 8 + \frac{1}{2}(18 - a)$, 12.

23. $p = \frac{1}{2}a + 110$, 138. **25.** $S = \dfrac{\pi dr}{12}$, 4π ft. per min. **26.** $L_1d_1 = L_2d_2$, $145\frac{5}{11}$ lb.

27. $C = \dfrac{lwh}{2.5}$, 230.4.

Exercise 2

1. 140. **2.** 236. **3.** 48. **5.** -51. **6.** -181. **7.** -425. **9.** 195. **10.** 64.
11. -32. **13.** -186. **14.** 27. **15.** 19. **17.** 127. **18.** 32. **19.** -40. **21.** -1.
22. 0. **23.** -40. **25.** 32. **26.** 36. **27.** -85. **29.** 99. **30.** 48. **31.** 41.
33. $5a + 6b$. **34.** $12x + 2y$. **35.** $10m + 8n$. **37.** $2a + 2b$. **38.** $7h + 2k$.
39. $5x - 7y$. **41.** $-11x + 7y + 3z$. **42.** $4a + 7b$. **43.** $5e - 8f + 4g$.
45. $24r + 22s - 9t$. **46.** $20x - 6y - 7z$. **47.** $6a - 8b + 10c$. **49.** -72.
50. -72. **51.** 56. **53.** 10. **54.** -8. **55.** -100. **57.** $6a^2$. **58.** $-16b^2$.
59. $63c^2$. **61.** -20. **62.** -100. **63.** 75. **65.** $6a^2b$. **66.** $-60xy^2$. **67.** $-192r^2s$.
69. 4. **70.** -3. **71.** -8. **73.** 11. **74.** 5. **75.** -9. **77.** $-19a$. **78.** $4b$.
79. $-21x$. **81.** 11. **82.** 2. **83.** 0. **85.** 5. **86.** -2. **87.** -11. **89.** $4a^2$.
90. $-10y^2$. **91.** $-6bc$. **93.** -2. **94.** -36. **95.** 12. **97.** -3. **98.** -8.
99. -6.

Exercise 3

1. 4. **2.** -4. **3.** 2. **5.** 8. **6.** 36. **7.** 6. **9.** -2. **10.** 3. **11.** 3. **13.** 2.
14. 2. **15.** 1. **17.** 5. **18.** -1. **19.** -1. **21.** $-\frac{1}{2}$. **22.** $-\frac{1}{2}$. **23.** -1.
25. 4. **26.** 3. **27.** -4. **29.** 2. **30.** -1. **31.** 2. **33.** 3. **34.** 10. **35.** 3.
37. $2\frac{1}{2}$. **38.** 4. **39.** 2. **41.** 6. **42.** 12. **43.** -2. **45.** -7. **46.** 24. **47.** 4.
49. 7. **50.** 27. **51.** -12. **53.** $-\frac{15}{4}$. **54.** 14. **55.** -8. **57.** 2. **58.** 0.
59. -2. **61.** 7. **62.** 50%. **63.** 6 years. **65.** 12 in. **66.** 20. **67.** 8 in.

Exercise 4

1. 12, 24. **2.** 11, 16. **3.** 15, 45. **5.** 4, 8. **6.** 34. **7.** 66.
9. Slide rule \$18, brief case \$22. **10.** 315 miles, 340 miles. **11.** \$70, \$75, \$60.

13. 6, 13, 22. **14.** 25, 40, 50. **15.** John 36, Tom 12, Harry 48.
17. Jack $5, Bill $15. **18.** James 16, Charles 32. **19.** Bob $25, Dick $20.
21. 5 years, 15 years. **22.** 4 years. **23.** 13 years. **25.** 13. **26.** 36. **27.** 45.
29. 390 miles, 110 miles. **30.** 60 miles per hr., 55 miles per hr. **31.** 900 miles.
33. $1.10, $.90. **34.** $75, $90. **35.** Smith $7000, Brown $8000, Jones $10,000.
37. $5000. **38.** 10 quarters, 20 dimes, 30 nickels. **39.** 60 by 150 ft.
41. 25 lb. at 80 cents, 75 lb. at $1. **42.** 10 lb.
43. $37\frac{1}{2}$ lb. of $3 grade, $22\frac{1}{2}$ lb. of $5 grade. **45.** 60 miles per hr., 50 miles per hr.
46. 180 miles. **47.** 53 miles per hr., 43 miles per hr.

Exercise 5

1. $6x^2 - 2x + 4$. **2.** $3a^2 - 4a + 4$. **3.** $x^3 + 3x^2 - x + 7$. **5.** $-a^2 + ab$.
6. $-z^2 + zw + 2w^2$. **7.** $2c^3d + 6cd^3 + d^4$. **9.** $2a^3 - 2ab^2$.
10. $6x^4 + 3x^3 - 2x^2 - x - 2$. **11.** $2b^5 + 4b^3 - b^2 - 2b - 1$.
13. $w^5 + 2w^4 + 2w^3 + 2w^2 + 2w + 2$. **14.** $x^3 + 2x^2y + xy^2$. **15.** $-3a^4b - 2a^3b^2$.
17. $2x^2 + 4x + 4$. **18.** $w^2 + 8w + 1$. **19.** $-4z^3 + 3z^2 - 4z + 3$.
21. $-7a^2 + 10ab + 3b^2$. **22.** $w^2 - 5wz - 4z^2$. **23.** $c^3d + c^2d^2 + cd^3 - 3d^4$.
25. $4x^2 - 4x - 2$. **26.** $-4a^2 + 6a + 2$. **27.** $c^2 - 3cd - d^2$. **29.** $r^2 + 4$.
30. $-3m^3 - 2m^2 + 7m + 2$. **31.** $4p^2$. **33.** $2a^2 + 5a + 4$. **34.** $7b^3 - 10b^2 - b + 2$.
35. $-3c^2 + cd + d^2$. **37.** $x^5 - 6x^4 + 4x^3 + 5x^2 - x - 2$.
38. $6a^6 + 4a^5 - 3a^4 + 2a^3 + a^2 - 5a + 4$. **39.** $4w^5 + 9w^4 - 4w^3 - w^2 - 4w - 1$.

Exercise 6

1. $6x - 1$. **2.** $7x + 1$. **3.** $10x - y$. **5.** $x + 5$. **6.** $-3x - 3$. **7.** $8x - 5$.
9. $3a + b - 1$. **10.** $5a - 7b + 4$. **11.** $-a - 4x + 6$. **13.** $7x$. **14.** $13a + 2b$.
15. $5a - x$. **17.** $7a + 16b$. **18.** $-2x + a$. **19.** $2x + b$. **21.** $8a + 6b - c$.
22. $-4a + x + 8y$. **23.** $-2x^2 - x + 1$. **25.** $4a + b$. **26.** $2a - 2b$. **27.** $4x - y$.
29. $5a - 4b$. **30.** $7x + 20y$. **31.** $37y - 5x$. **33.** $20x + 10$. **34.** $5x - 15$.
35. $3x - 12$. **37.** $18a - 36$. **38.** $-2a - 10$. **39.** $-24x - 21$.
41. $-x^3 + 2x^2 - 2x$. **42.** $x^3 + 6x^2 + 3x$. **43.** $5x^3$. **45.** $-8a^3 + 6a^2$.
46. $12a^2 - 3a^3$. **47.** $-6x^3 + 30x^2 - 6x$. **49.** $32y^3 + 6y$. **50.** $35a^3 - 15a^2 + 10a$.
51. $-2a^3 - 2a^2$. **53.** $-c$. **54.** $5y - 5$. **55.** 0. **57.** $c^2 - d^2$. **58.** $m^2 - mp + n^2$.
59. $x^3 - x^2y + 2xyz + y^3$.

Exercise 7

1. $x^2 + x - 6$. **2.** $a^2 + 3a - 4$. **3.** $b^2 - 3b + 2$. **5.** $6z^2 + z - 2$.
6. $10a^2 - 19a + 6$. **7.** $15w^2 - 11w - 12$. **9.** $acx^2 - 3ax + 2cx - 6$.
10. $2ax^2 - 2x - abx + b$. **11.** $3bx^2 + 2bx + 3cx + 2c$. **13.** $6x^2 + 5xy - 6y^2$.
14. $10a^2 - 19ab + 7b^2$. **15.** $6c^2 + 7cd - 20d^2$. **17.** $abx^2 - 3axy + 2bxy - 6y^2$.
18. $2dp^2 + 6pq - cdpq - 3cq^2$. **19.** $5ax^2 - 2axy + 5bxy - 2by^2$.
21. $2x^3 - 7x^2 + 5x - 1$. **22.** $6x^3 - 5x^2 - 9x - 2$. **23.** $5a^3 - 13a^2 + 16a - 6$.
25. $ax^3 + 2ax^2 + bx^2 + 3ax + 2bx + 3b$. **26.** $2cx^3 - cx^2 - 2dx^2 + 3cx + dx - 3d$.
27. $2ay^3 - 3ay^2 + 2by^2 - 3by + 2cy - 3c$. **29.** $2w^4 - 5w^3 + 11w^2 - 9w + 9$.
30. $6a^4 + 17a^3 - 4a^2 - 22a + 8$. **31.** $7y^4 + 53y^3 - y^2 - 23y + 4$.
33. $2x^4 - x^3y + 2x^2y^2 + 3xy^3 - 2y^4$. **34.** $2b^4 - b^3c - b^2c^2 + 11bc^3 - 3c^4$.
35. $12w^4 - 17w^3z + 25w^2z^2 - 14wz^3 + 4z^4$. **37.** $a - 3$. **38.** $x - 5$.
39. $y - 2$. **41.** $3x + 2$. **42.** $2b + 3$. **43.** $3c - 1$. **45.** $3d + e$. **46.** $3a + 2b$.
47. $3w + 5z$. **49.** $bx + c$. **50.** $dy + c$. **51.** $az - 3$. **53.** $x^2 - x + 3$.
54. $a^2 + 2a - 3$. **55.** $2b^2 + b + 5$. **57.** $2x - 3$. **58.** $3w + 4$. **59.** $2u - 5$.

61. $2y^2 - 3y + 1$. **62.** $z^2 - 5z - 2$. **63.** $3x^2 + 2x + 1$. **65.** $2a^2 - a + 3$.
66. $3b^2 + 2b + 1$. **67.** $c^2 - c + 3$. **69.** $2x^2 + xy - y^2$. **70.** $z^2 - 2zw - w^2$.
71. $5x^2 + xy - y^2$.

Review Exercise, Chapters 1 and 2

1. $2a$. **2.** $6x$. **3.** $-a$. **5.** $4x^2 - 3xy$. **6.** $4b^2 + 4bc$. **7.** $x^2 + x^2y - 3xy^2$.
9. $-17x + 17$. **10.** $-4x - 1$. **11.** $-4x - 3$. **13.** $5x^2 - 19x + 19$.
14. $-9x^2 - 4x - 34$. **15.** $-2x + 8$. **17.** $-10x^2 - 18x - 12$.
18. $15x^2 - 50x - 25$. **19.** $-50x^2 + 34x - 46$. **21.** $-a^3 + 7a^2 - 3a$.
22. $5a^2 - 15a$. **23.** $8a^3 - 30a^2 - 4a$. **25.** $-7a^4 + 9a^3 + 2a^2 + 3a$.
26. $22a^3 - 28a^2 + 14a$. **27.** $-6x^4 - 13x^3 + 16x^2 + 23x - 20$.
29. $6x^4 - 5x^3y - 5x^2y^2 + 5xy^3 - y^4$. **30.** $6x^4 + 5x^3y + 9x^2y^2 + 21xy^3 - 5y^4$.
31. $2x^2 + 3x + 1$. **33.** $5x^2 - 4x + 4$. **34.** $3x^2 - 5x + 4$. **35.** $2J + 5$.
37. $21 + d$. **38.** $300 + m$. **39.** $7w + d$. **41.** $31, 32, 33$. **42.** $186, 351$ acres.
43. 4 miles per hr. **45.** 16 years. **46.** 21 years. **47.** 12 oz.

Exercise 8

1. $3x^2 + 16x + 5$. **2.** $6x^2 + 9x + 3$. **3.** $2x^2 + 8x + 8$. **5.** $5x^2 + 31x + 6$.
6. $2x^2 + 10x + 8$. **7.** $3x^2 + 24x + 21$. **9.** $2c^2 - 7cd + 6d^2$.
10. $3a^2 - 11ab + 6b^2$. **11.** $4u^2 - 27uw + 35w^2$. **13.** $2x^2 - 20xy + 32y^2$.
14. $6r^2 - 9rs + 3s^2$. **15.** $8x^2 - 53xy + 30y^2$. **17.** $3x^2 - xy - 2y^2$.
18. $4r^2 + rs - 3s^2$. **19.** $5f^2 - 4fg - 12g^2$. **21.** $7x^2 + 25xy - 12y^2$.
22. $2c^2 - 10cd - 72d^2$. **23.** $3y^2 - yz - 14z^2$. **25.** $6a^2 + ab - 12b^2$.
26. $20x^2 + 12xy - 8y^2$. **27.** $12r^2 - 38rs + 16s^2$. **29.** $24x^2 + 78xy + 18y^2$.
30. $21u^2 + 37uw + 12w^2$. **31.** $12a^2 - 11ab - 15b^2$. **33.** $4x^2 + 12xy + 9y^2$.
34. $25c^2 - 20cd + 4d^2$. **35.** $9a^2 - 42a + 49$. **37.** $36m^2 + 36mn + 9n^2$.
38. $16x^2 + 48x + 36$. **39.** $49x^2 - 14x + 1$. **41.** $81p^2 - 126pq + 49q^2$.
42. $36x^2 - 48xy + 16y^2$. **43.** $25r^2 + 30rs + 9s^2$. **45.** $x^2 - 16$. **46.** $x^2 - 49$.
47. $x^2 - y^2$. **49.** $9x^2 - 16$. **50.** $36r^2 - 4s^2$. **51.** $4m^2 - 9n^2$. **53.** $25u^2 - 16w^2$.
54. $9c^2 - 36d^2$. **55.** $16x^2 + 34xy - 15y^2$. **57.** $6a^4 + a^2b - 2b^2$.

58. $2x^2 - 2xy^2 - 12y^4$. **59.** $6f^2 - 2fg^2 - 20g^4$. **61.** $\dfrac{x^2}{2} + \dfrac{19}{36}xy - \dfrac{y^2}{3}$.

62. $x^2 - \dfrac{9xy}{20} - y^2$. **63.** $9a^4 - 6a^2b + b^2$. **65.** $25r^4 + 30r^2y + 9y^2$.

66. $4c^2 - 12cd^2 + 9d^4$. **67.** $9g^6 - 24g^3h + 16h^2$. **69.** $36x^4 - 4$. **70.** $16a^2 - 4b^4$.
71. $4m^4 - 16n^2$. **73.** $x^2 + y^2 + z^2 + 2xy + 2xz + 2yz$.
74. $a^2 + b^2 + c^2 - 2ab + 2ac - 2bc$. **75.** $u^2 + v^2 + w^2 - 2uv - 2uw + 2vw$.
77. $4a^2 + 9b^2 + 25c^2 + 12ab - 20ac - 30bc$.
78. $16m^2 + 4n^2 + 9d^2 - 16mn - 24md + 12nd$.
79. $9r^2 + 25s^2 + 49t^2 - 30rs + 42rt - 70st$.
81. $3a^2 + 4ab - 4ac + b^2 - 2bc + c^2$. **82.** $6a^2 + 12ab + 6b^2 - 12ac - 12bc + 6c^2$.
83. $9a^2 + 6ab + b^2 + 9ac + 3bc - 4c^2$. **85.** $8a^2 - 20ab - 20ac + 12b^2 + 24bc + 12c^2$.
86. $9a^2 - 16b^2 - 32bc - 16c^2$. **87.** $36x^2 + 72xy + 36y^2 - 16z^2$.

Exercise 9

1. $(x + 4)(x - 3)$. **2.** $(x - 4)(x + 3)$. **3.** $(a - 5)(a + 4)$. **5.** $(x - 5y)(x - y)$.
6. $(x - 4y)(x - 2y)$. **7.** $(x - 8y)(x - y)$. **9.** $(c + 7d)(c + d)$.
10. $(p + 5q)(p + 2q)$. **11.** $(z - 3w)(z + 2w)$. **13.** $(3m + n)(m + n)$.
14. $2(a + b)(a + b)$. **15.** $(2a + 3b)(a + b)$. **17.** $(3h - k)(h - 3k)$.

18. $(2a - b)(a - b)$.   **19.** $3(x - y)(x - y)$.   **21.** $(2a - b)(a + 2b)$.

22. $(3x + 2y)(x - y)$.   **23.** $(2h - 3k)(h + k)$.   **25.** $(x - 5)(x - 5)$.

26. $(x - 4)(x - 4)$.   **27.** $(a + 3)(a + 3)$.   **29.** $4(x + 2y)(x + 2y)$.

30. $(3x - y)(3x - y)$.   **31.** $9(a - b)(a - b)$.   **33.** $4(c + d)(c + d)$.

34. $(5r + 3s)(5r + 3s)$.   **35.** $(3a - 5b)(3a - 5b)$.   **37.** $(5e + 8f)(5e + 8f)$.

38. $(4x + 9y)(4x + 9y)$.   **39.** $(5h - 7k)(5h - 7k)$.   **41.** $(3x + 2y)(x + 3y)$.

42. $2(a - 2b)(a + b)$.   **43.** $2(3m + n)(m + n)$.   **45.** $(2c - 7d)(2c - d)$.

46. $3(x + 2y)(x - y)$.   **47.** $(3a + 5b)(2a - b)$.   **49.** $2(3c + 4d)(c - d)$.

50. $2(3c - 5d)(c + d)$.   **51.** $6(c + 2d)(c - d)$.   **53.** $2(3x - y)(x + 2y)$.

54. $2(3r - 8s)(r + s)$.   **55.** $2(3m + 2n)(m - 5n)$.   **57.** $(4x + 7)(2x - 3)$.

58. $(5x - 4)(2x + 3)$.   **59.** $(5a + 7b)(2a - 3b)$.   **61.** $(3h + 2k)(4h - 3k)$.

62. $(8x - 3y)(3x + 4y)$.   **63.** $(6c + 5d)(6c - d)$.   **65.** $(2x - y + 3)(2x - y - 2)$.

66. $(2a - 2b - 5)(2a - 2b - 3)$.   **67.** $(8u + 12v - 1)(6u + 9v - 4)$.

69. $(2a - 3b + 9c)(a + 2b - 6c)$.   **70.** $(3x + 8y - 12z)(2x - 2y + 3z)$.

71. $(4p - 4q + 3r)(2p + 20q - 15r)$.

Exercise 10

1. $(x + 1)(x - 1)$.   **2.** $(x + 4)(x - 4)$.   **3.** $(x + 3y)(x - 3y)$.

5. $(3x + 2y)(3x - 2y)$.   **6.** $(4a + 2b)(4a - 2b)$.   **7.** $(3m + 4n)(3m - 4n)$.

9. $(6x + 2y)(6x - 2y)$.   **10.** $(4x + 5y)(4x - 5y)$.   **11.** $(a^2 + 2b)(a^2 - 2b)$.

13. $(4x^2 + 3y^3)(4x^2 - 3y^3)$.   **14.** $(6a^3 + 2b^2)(6a^3 - 2b^2)$.   **15.** $(5c^3 + 4a)(5c^3 - 4a)$.

17. $(6p^2 + q)(6p^2 - q)$.   **18.** $(4r^3 + 3s^2)(4r^3 - 3s^2)$.   **19.** $(5a^4 + 2b^2)(5a^4 - 2b^2)$.

21. $(x - 1)(x^2 + x + 1)$.   **22.** $(x + 1)(x^2 - x + 1)$.   **23.** $(a + 2)(a^2 - 2a + 4)$.

25. $(x - 3y)(x^2 + 3xy + 9y^2)$.   **26.** $(3a + b)(9a^2 - 3ab + b^2)$.

27. $(2x - y)(4x^2 + 2xy + y^2)$.   **29.** $(4x + 2y)(16x^2 - 8xy + 4y^2)$.

30. $(5a + 3b)(25a^2 - 15ab + 9b^2)$.   **31.** $(3m - 4n)(9m^2 + 12mn + 16n^2)$.

33. $(3a - 5b)(9a^2 + 15ab + 25b^2)$.   **34.** $(4c + 5d)(16c^2 - 20cd + 25d^2)$.

35. $(x^2 + y^2)(x^4 - x^2y^2 + y^4)$.   **37.** $(m^3 - 2n)(m^6 + 2m^3n + 4n^2)$.

38. $(3c^2 + 2d^3)(9c^4 - 6c^2d^3 + 4d^6)$.   **39.** $(z^4 - 2y)(z^8 + 2z^4y + 4y^2)$.

41. $(x + 3y + z)(x + 3y - z)$.   **42.** $(2a - b + c)(2a - b - c)$.

43. $(c + 4d + f)(c + 4d - f)$.   **45.** $(r + 3s + 2t)(r - 3s - 2t)$.

46. $(2x + 2y - 4z)(2x - 2y + 4z)$.   **47.** $(4a + 5b + 3c)(4a - 5b - 3c)$.

49. $(x + y - z)(x^2 + 2xy + y^2 + xz + yz + z^2)$.

50. $(x + 3y + 3)(x^2 + 6xy + 9y^2 - 3x - 9y + 9)$.

51. $(z + x + y)(z^2 - zx - zy + x^2 + 2xy + y^2)$.   **53.** $(a + 1)(a - 1)(a^2 + 1)$.

54. $(x^2 + 2)(x^2 - 2)(x^4 + 4)$.   **55.** $(a^2 + b)(a^2 - b)(a^4 + b^2)$.

57. $(x + y)(x - y)(x^2 - xy + y^2)(x^2 + xy + y^2)$.   **58.** $(u^3 + v^2)(u^3 - v^2)(u^6 + v^4)$.

59. $(c + d)(c^2 - cd + d^2)(c^6 - c^3d^3 + d^6)$.

Exercise 11

1. $2(x + 3)$.   **2.** $3(a - 2)$.   **3.** $2(c + 4)$.   **5.** $y(y + 4)$.   **6.** $b(b - 5)$.

7. $d(2d + 3)$.   **9.** $2(x + 2)(x + 4)$.   **10.** $3(a + 3)(a - 2)$.   **11.** $2(r + 5)(r + 1)$.

13. $(x - y)(a + b)$.   **14.** $(3 - b)(a - c)$.   **15.** $(y + 3z)(x + 2)$.   **17.** $(r + 2)(s - t)$.

18. $(3c + d)(2a - b)$.   **19.** $(x - y)(4z - 3)$.   **21.** $(3x - 1)(x + 2y)$.

22. $(2a - 3c)(a + 2b)$.   **23.** $(3w - 5z)(3x^2 - 2y)$.   **25.** $(a + 4)(a - 2)(a + 2)$.

26. $(x - 3)(x + 1)(x - 1)$.   **27.** $(2b + 5)(b + 3)(b - 3)$.   **29.** $2y(3y + 2)(y - 1)$.

30. $3a(2a + 3)(a - 4)$.   **31.** $2c(3c + 2)(2c - 3)$.   **33.** $2x(x - 3)^2$.   **34.** $3b(2b + 1)^2$.

35. $5m(m - 2)^2$.   **37.** $(2x + y + 2)(2x + y - 2)$.   **38.** $(a + 3b + 3)(a + 3b - 3)$.

39. $(2b + 3c + 2d)(2b + 3c - 2d)$.   **41.** $(2p + m - n)(2p - m + n)$.

42. $(2a - 2b - c)(2a + 2b + c)$.   **43.** $(x + y + 3z)(x - y - 3z)$.
45. $(a + b)(a - b)(a^2 + b^2 - 1)$.   **46.** $(x - y)(x^3 + x^2y + xy^2 + y^3 - x + y)$.
47. $(c - d)(c^2 + cd + d^2 - c - d)$.   **49.** $(x^2 + 3x + 1)(x^2 - 3x + 1)$.
50. $(a^2 + 2a - 2)(a^2 - 2a - 2)$.   **51.** $(y^2 + 2y + 3)(y^2 - 2y + 3)$.
53. $(a^2 + 2ab - 4b^2)(a^2 - 2ab - 4b^2)$.   **54.** $(m^2 + 3mn + 3n^2)(m^2 - 3mn + 3n^2)$.
55. $(x^2 + 3xy - 2y^2)(x^2 - 3xy - 2y^2)$.   **57.** $(3c^2 + 3cd + 4d^2)(3c^2 - 3cd + 4d^2)$.
58. $(5x^2 + 2xy - 3y^2)(5x^2 - 2xy - 3y^2)$.   **59.** $(4m^2 + 3mn - 3n^2)(4m^2 - 3mn - 3n^2)$.

Review Exercise for Chapter 3

1. $4x^2 - 5xy - 6y^2$.   **2.** $7r^2 + 26rs - 8s^2$.   **3.** $5m^2 - 14mn - 3n^2$.
5. $24p^2 + 2pq - 15q^2$.   **6.** $8c^2 + 22cd - 6d^2$.   **7.** $50x^2 + 55xy - 40y^2$.
9. $4x^2 + 28xy + 49y^2$.   **10.** $25a^2 - 30ab + 9b^2$.   **11.** $16c^2 + 8cd + d^2$.
13. $64m^2 + 32mn + 4n^2$.   **14.** $9p^2 - 36pq + 36q^2$.   **15.** $4r^2 + 16rs + 16s^2$.
17. $9a^2 - 9b^2$.   **18.** $64c^2 - 16d^2$.   **19.** $16m^2 - 4n^2$.   **21.** $144r^2 - 4s^2$.
22. $49a^2 - 9b^2$.   **23.** $25x^2 - 36y^2$.   **25.** $a^2 + 2ab + b^2 - 9$.
26. $9x^2 + 6xy + y^2 - 4z^2$.   **27.** $c^2 - 6cd + 9d^2 - e^2$.
29. $4r^2 + 9s^2 + t^2 - 12rs + 4rt - 6st$.   **30.** $16x^2 + 4y^2 + 9z^2 + 16xy - 24xz - 12yz$.
31. $25a^2 + 4b^2 + 4c^2 + 20ab - 20ac - 8bc$.   **33.** $(2x - 1)(x - 3)$.
34. $(3x - 2)(x + 1)$.   **35.** $(3a + 2)(a - 2)$.   **37.** $(2x + 3y)(x + 2y)$.
38. $(5m + 3n)(m - 2n)$.   **39.** $2(4x - 9y)(x + y)$.   **41.** $(r + 6s)^2$.
42. $(2a + 3b)^2$.   **43.** $(4x + 3y)^2$.   **45.** $(5x + 3y)(5x - 3y)$.   **46.** $(4a + 9b)(4a - 9b)$.
47. $(8c + 10)(8c - 10)$.   **49.** $(x + 3y + z)(x - 3y - z)$.
50. $(4a + 4b - 2c)(4a - 4b + 2c)$.   **51.** $(2x + y + 5z)(2x + y - 5z)$.
53. $(2x + y)(a + b)$.   **54.** $(2y + z)(2w - x)$.   **55.** $(3c - d)(a + 2b)$.
57. $(x - 2y)(x + y - 2)$.   **58.** $(a + 2b)(a - 2b + 3)$.   **59.** $(m - 3n)(m + 3n + 1)$.
61. $(2x - 4y)(4x^2 + 8xy + 16y^2)$.   **62.** $(3a + 5b)(9a^2 - 15ab + 25b^2)$.
63. $(5r - 4s)(25r^2 + 20rs + 16s^2)$.   **65.** $(x - y - z)(x^2 - 2xy + y^2 + xz - yz + z^2)$.
66. $(a + b - c)(a^2 - ab + ac + b^2 - 2bc + c^2)$.   **67.** $2xy(x - 2y)(x^2 + 2xy + 4y^2)$.
69. $(2x - y)(2x + y)(4x^2 + y^2)$.   **70.** $(a - b)(a + b)(a^2 + ab + b^2)(a^2 - ab + b^2)$.
71. $(m + n)(m - n)(m^2 + n^2)(m^4 + n^4)$.   **73.** $(4r + 2s - t)(4r - 2s + t)$.
74. $(3t + 4m + 2n)(3t - 4m - 2n)$.   **75.** $(5a + b + 3c)(5a - b - 3c)$.
77. $(s^2 + 4t^2 + 2st)(s^2 + 4t^2 - 2st)$.   **78.** $(a^2 + 3ab - 3b^2)(a^2 - 3ab - 3b^2)$.
79. $(x^2 + 2xy + 5y^2)(x^2 - 2xy + 5y^2)$.

Exercise 12

1. $\dfrac{x}{y}$.   **2.** $\dfrac{2ab}{5b^2c}$.   **3.** $\dfrac{3r^2s}{4t^2}$.   **5.** $\dfrac{a - b}{a^2(a + b)}$.   **6.** $\dfrac{x + y}{x(x - y)}$.   **7.** $\dfrac{c}{d^2}$.   **9.** $\dfrac{y^3}{xz^2}$.

10. $-\dfrac{rs}{t^4}$.   **11.** $-\dfrac{x}{y}$.   **13.** $\dfrac{4}{6xy^3}$.   **14.** $\dfrac{6x^3}{14x^2y^2}$.   **15.** $\dfrac{a^2 - b^2}{c(a + b)}$.   **17.** $\dfrac{cd}{c - d}$.

18. $\dfrac{y - x}{x - y}$.   **19.** $\dfrac{3t + s - 2r}{t + 2s - r}$.   **21.** $\dfrac{x}{x - y}$.   **22.** $\dfrac{2}{a + 2b}$.   **23.** $\dfrac{m - n}{m + n}$.

25. $\dfrac{2r^2 + 2rs}{6r^2}$.   **26.** $\dfrac{-4ab^2 + 2b^3}{-10b^3}$.   **27.** $\dfrac{x^2 - y^2}{x^3 - y^3}$.   **29.** $\dfrac{c}{c + 1}$.   **30.** $\dfrac{a^2 + ab + b^2}{3a + 2b}$.

31. $\dfrac{2r - s}{3r + 2s}$.   **33.** $\dfrac{x - 2}{x + 2}$.   **34.** $\dfrac{a + 3b}{a + b}$.   **35.** $\dfrac{2p - 3q}{3p + 2q}$.   **37.** $\dfrac{c + d}{c + 2d}$.   **38.** $\dfrac{2r + s}{r - 3s}$.

39. $\dfrac{x + 2y}{x + 3y}$.   **41.** $\dfrac{x + y}{y - x}$.   **42.** $\dfrac{y - 2z}{2y + z}$.   **43.** $\dfrac{c - d}{2c - 3d}$.   **45.** $\dfrac{x + y}{x^2 + xy + y^2}$.

46. $\dfrac{m-n}{m^2-mn+n^2}$. **47.** $\dfrac{a^2+b^2}{a^4+a^2b^2+b^4}$. **49.** $\dfrac{x^2+xy+y^2}{x+y}$. **50.** $\dfrac{1}{a^2-b^2}$.

51. $\dfrac{m^2+2m+4}{m+2}$. **53.** $\dfrac{1}{3x+1}$. **54.** $\dfrac{1}{2y+1}$. **55.** $\dfrac{1}{3m+1}$. **57.** $\dfrac{1}{x+4}$.

58. $\dfrac{1}{2b+1}$. **59.** 1.

Exercise 13

1. $\dfrac{3}{2}$. **2.** 4. **3.** $\dfrac{4}{7}$. **5.** $\dfrac{5}{3}$. **6.** 1. **7.** $\dfrac{3}{2}$. **9.** $\dfrac{8b^2}{5}$. **10.** $\dfrac{5y^2}{2}$. **11.** $\dfrac{2d}{c}$.

13. wxy. **14.** ad. **15.** $\dfrac{2abc^2d}{3}$. **17.** $\dfrac{ab^3}{d^2}$. **18.** $\dfrac{wy}{z}$. **19.** $7c^2$. **21.** 10. **22.** $\dfrac{2x}{x-y}$.

23. $\dfrac{1}{a}$. **25.** $\dfrac{2x}{5y}$. **26.** $\dfrac{3z}{4w}$. **27.** $x+2y$. **29.** 1. **30.** a^3b. **31.** q. **33.** $\dfrac{x+1}{x-2}$.

34. $\dfrac{a-2b}{a+b}$. **35.** $\dfrac{2c+3d}{c-2d}$. **37.** $\dfrac{a(a-2b)}{3(a+2b)}$. **38.** $\dfrac{x(x+2y)}{x-3y}$. **39.** $\dfrac{1}{c+2d}$.

41. $\dfrac{a+b}{a+3b}$. **42.** $\dfrac{2m+n}{m-3n}$. **43.** $\dfrac{x-4y}{x+y}$. **45.** $\dfrac{1}{x-1}$. **46.** $\dfrac{2a-1}{a+3}$. **47.** $\dfrac{y-1}{y+3}$.

49. x^2+y^2. **50.** $\dfrac{a-1}{1-b}$. **51.** $\dfrac{b+1}{2b+1}$. **53.** $x-y$. **54.** 2. **55.** $\dfrac{x-1}{x+2}$.

57. $\dfrac{z+1}{z-1}$. **58.** 1. **59.** $\dfrac{3-b}{b-4}$.

Exercise 14

1. $\dfrac{1}{8}$. **2.** $-\dfrac{2}{15}$. **3.** $\dfrac{1}{2}$. **5.** $\dfrac{3}{4}$. **6.** $\dfrac{4}{5}$. **7.** $-\dfrac{5}{8}$. **9.** $\dfrac{18x^2z-8xy^2+3yz^2}{12xyz}$.

10. $\dfrac{24a^2-4b^2-45c^2}{18abc}$. **11.** $\dfrac{12c^2+10d^2-7e^2}{28cde}$. **13.** $\dfrac{3x}{5y}$. **14.** $\dfrac{5a}{4b}$. **15.** $-\dfrac{2c}{3d}$.

17. $\dfrac{4y^2+5z^2}{5xyz}$. **18.** $\dfrac{15a^3-20b^3}{12a^2b^2}$. **19.** $\dfrac{3e^3+d^3}{2d^3e^2}$. **21.** $\dfrac{3y^2-2x^2}{y(2x+y)}$. **22.** $\dfrac{15p^2-8q^2}{2q(5p+2q)}$.

23. $\dfrac{2a^2+b^2}{3b(a-3b)}$. **25.** $\dfrac{a}{b}$. **26.** $\dfrac{3x}{4y}$. **27.** $\dfrac{2h}{3k}$. **29.** $\dfrac{2x}{x+y}$. **30.** $\dfrac{a}{2a-b}$. **31.** $\dfrac{-u}{u-v}$.

33. $\dfrac{3x^3+2y^3}{xy(x+y)}$. **34.** $\dfrac{5a^3-3b^3}{ab(a+b)}$. **35.** $\dfrac{27d^3-32c^3}{12cd(3d-4c)}$. **37.** $\dfrac{1}{x}$. **38.** $\dfrac{3}{a}$. **39.** $\dfrac{4}{y}$.

41. $\dfrac{1}{x}$. **42.** $\dfrac{1}{a}$. **43.** $\dfrac{w}{z(2w-3z)}$. **45.** $\dfrac{1}{x-1}$. **46.** $\dfrac{3}{x+3}$. **47.** $\dfrac{1}{2x-1}$.

49. $\dfrac{6ab}{(a+b)(a-b)(2a-1)}$. **50.** $\dfrac{9v^2}{(u+v)(2u-v)(u-2v)}$.

51. $\dfrac{20x^2}{(x-2)(x+3)(x-1)}$. **53.** $\dfrac{1}{(u+2v)(u+v)}$. **54.** $\dfrac{1}{(2z-w)(z-2w)}$.

55. $\dfrac{1}{(4x+3y)(2x+y)}$. **57.** $\dfrac{x+3y}{(x+y)(x-y)}$. **58.** $\dfrac{5(2a-b)}{(3a-4b)(3a+4b)}$.

59. $\dfrac{7(z+w)}{(z-2w)(z+2w)}$.

Exercise 15

1. $\frac{3}{5}$. 2. $\frac{5}{2}$. 3. $\frac{3}{2}$. 5. $\frac{1}{3}$. 6. $\frac{1}{2}$. 7. $\frac{3}{2}$. 9. $\frac{5}{3x^2}$. 10. $3x$. 11. $\frac{4a}{b}$.

13. $x + 1$. 14. $a - 3$. 15. $\frac{1}{u + v}$. 17. $\frac{b + c}{b - c}$. 18. $\frac{p - 2q}{p + 2q}$. 19. $\frac{3x - 4y}{3x + 5y}$.

21. $a + 1$. 22. $x + 2$. 23. $y - 4$. 25. $x + y$. 26. $3 - t$. 27. $3s + 2r$.

29. $\frac{x - 1}{x - 3}$. 30. $\frac{1}{2}$. 31. $\frac{b - a}{b + a}$. 33. $\frac{c - 2d}{c + 2d}$. 34. $\frac{u - 2v}{u + 2v}$. 35. $\frac{a + b}{a - b}$. 37. $\frac{5}{8}$.

38. $\frac{5}{7}$. 39. x.

Exercise 16

1. 2. 2. -2. 3. 2. 5. 5. 6. 6. 7. -3. 9. 2. 10. 6. 11. 6. 13. -2.

14. 3. 15. -3. 17. -2. 18. 2. 19. -1. 21. -5. 22. -6. 23. 1.

25. 2. 26. 7. 27. -1. 29. $-\frac{1}{2}$. 30. -3. 31. $-\frac{3}{2}$. 33. $\frac{4}{5}$. 34. 4. 35. $\frac{3}{4}$.

37. 2. 38. 5. 39. -4. 41. 29. 42. 8. 43. -21. 45. 1. 46. 2. 47. -5.

49. 4. 50. -2. 51. -9. 53. -2. 54. 3. 55. $\frac{2}{3}$. 57. $\frac{5}{3}$. 58. -7.

59. -2.

Exercise 17

1. 30. 2. 12. 3. 72. 5. 48, 72. 6. 24. 7. 10. 9. $4\frac{4}{5}$ hr. 10. 6 hr.

11. $18\frac{2}{3}$ hr. 13. 50 min. 14. 8 hr. 15. 24 min. 17. 5:50 P.M. 18. $\frac{1}{4}$ day.

19. 24 hr. 21. 900 miles. 22. 4 miles. 23. 80 miles. 25. 2 hr. 26. 120 miles.

27. 1 mile. 29. 60 miles per hr. 30. 60 miles. 31. 4 miles per hr. 33. $2\frac{1}{2}$ qt.

34. $2\frac{6}{7}$ qt. 35. $2\frac{2}{3}$ qt. 37. 150 lb., 50 lb. 38. 38 lb. 39. 45%.

41. $7\frac{1}{2}$ lb., $22\frac{1}{2}$ lb. 42. 10 cc. 43. 3 bu. 45. \$600. 46. 30. 47. 24 ft.

48. 750, 1250. 50. 1280 acres, \$20 per acre. 51. 20, 10. 53. \$36.

54. 50 by 150 ft., 60 by 100 ft. 55. 12 days, \$40 per day.

Exercise 18

1. 11, 2, 0, -7. 2. 11, 8, 7, 1. 3. 9, -4, -21. 5. 0, $\frac{3}{4}$, 6. 6. 41, 1, 1.

7. 150, -2, 0. 9. $-\frac{2}{5}$, 0, -20. 10. 0, $\frac{1}{2}$, $-\frac{8}{29}$. 11. 0, 1, $-\frac{13}{2}$.

13. $2a + 1$, $6b + 1$, $-4k + 1$. 14. $15a - 2$, $-5a - 2$, $a - 2$.

15. $3x - 4$, $6b - 4$, $-9c - 4$. 17. $2x + 1$, $4y - 3$, $2w - 1$.

18. $7t + 10$, $7a + 3$, $7k + 3$. 19. $5 - 3b$, $-3k - 4$, $-3a - 1$. 21. $\frac{5}{8}$. 22. -54.

23. $\frac{2x + 1}{6x - 3}$. 25. $y^2 - 5y + 5$, $4y^2 - 2y - 1$, $x^2 - x - 1$.

26. $2x^2 - 7x + 5$, $8y^2 - 22y + 14$, $2h^2 - 3h$.

27. $3b^2 + 2b + 1$, $3y^2 - 16y + 22$, $3a^2 + 14a + 17$. 29. $\frac{t}{2(2t - 3)}$. 30. $\frac{a - 2}{2(2a - 1)}$.

31. $\frac{x - 5}{5(5x - 1)}$.

Exercise 19

3. First, fourth, first, second, fourth, third.

Exercise 21

1. $x = 3$, $y = 1$. 2. $x = 3$, $y = -2$. 3. $x = -1$, $y = 3$. 5. $x = \frac{1}{2}$, $y = 2$.

6. $x = 2$, $y = 1\frac{1}{2}$. 7. $x = 1$, $y = \frac{1}{2}$. 9. $x = 9$, $y = -1.3$. 10. $x = 3.7$, $y = -1.3$.

11. Inconsistent. **13.** Dependent. **14.** Dependent. **15.** $x = -.5$, $y = 2.3$.
17. Inconsistent. **18.** Inconsistent. **19.** $x = 1.3$, $y = 2.3$. **21.** $x = 1.4$, $y = 1.1$.
22. $x = 4.8$, $y = 1.6$. **23.** Dependent. **25.** $x = -.5$, $y = 1$. **26.** $x = -2.5$, $y = 2$.
27. $x = 2.3$, $y = 1.3$. **29.** $x = 1.1$, $y = -1.6$. **30.** Inconsistent.
31. $x = .4$, $y = -.02$.

Exercise 22

1. $x = 1$, $y = 3$. **2.** $x = 2$, $y = 1$. **3.** $x = 3$, $y = 2$. **5.** $x = 2$, $y = 5$.
6. $x = 3$, $y = 4$. **7.** $x = 5$, $y = 3$. **9.** $x = 1\frac{1}{2}$, $y = 1$. **10.** $x = \frac{8}{3}$, $y = \frac{7}{4}$.
11. $x = \frac{5}{2}$, $y = \frac{7}{3}$. **13.** $x = 4$, $y = 3$. **14.** $x = 5$, $y = 4$. **15.** $x = 12$, $y = 2$.
17. $x = 4$, $y = 3$. **18.** $x = -8$, $y = 3$. **19.** $x = 3$, $y = 1$. **21.** $x = 2$, $y = -1$.
22. $x = -2$, $y = 3$. **23.** $x = 3$, $y = -2$. **25.** $x = \frac{4}{3}$, $y = \frac{5}{6}$. **26.** $x = \frac{3}{4}$, $y = \frac{2}{3}$.
27. $x = \frac{3}{2}$, $y = \frac{7}{3}$. **29.** $x = 6$, $y = 4$. **30.** $x = 5$, $y = 3$. **31.** $x = 4$, $y = 5$.
33. $x = 2$, $y = 4$. **34.** $x = 3$, $y = 1$. **35.** $x = 5$, $y = 3$. **37.** $x = 7$, $y = 3$.
38. $x = 2$, $y = 6$. **39.** $x = 5$, $y = 4$. **41.** $x = 2$, $y = 3$. **42.** $x = -3$, $y = 4$.
43. $x = -2$, $y = 5$. **45.** $x = 2$, $y = -2$. **46.** $x = 1$, $y = 3$. **47.** $x = -2$, $y = 1$.

49. $x = 1$, $y = 0$. **50.** $x = 0$, $y = \frac{r}{b}$. **51.** $x = 2$, $y = 0$. **53.** $x = 6$, $y = 2$.

54. $x = 5$, $y = 3$. **55.** $x = 3$, $y = \frac{3}{4}$. **57.** $x = 7$, $y = 6$. **58.** $x = \frac{1}{3}$, $y = -\frac{3}{4}$.
59. $x = \frac{1}{7}$, $y = \frac{1}{8}$.

Exercise 23

1. $x = 2$, $y = 3$, $z = -2$. **2.** $x = 3$, $y = 1$, $z = 4$. **3.** $x = 4$, $y = -3$, $z = 2$.
5. $x = 4$, $y = 6$, $z = 3$. **6.** $x = -6$, $y = 7$, $z = 4$. **7.** $x = -2$, $y = 6$, $z = 5$.
9. $x = 2$, $y = 1$, $z = 3$. **10.** $x = -2$, $y = 3$, $z = 1$. **11.** $x = 5$, $y = -4$, $z = 2$.
13. $x = \frac{2}{3}$, $y = \frac{3}{4}$, $z = \frac{1}{2}$. **14.** $x = \frac{3}{5}$, $y = \frac{1}{3}$, $z = \frac{5}{6}$. **15.** $x = \frac{1}{6}$, $y = -\frac{2}{5}$, $z = -\frac{1}{4}$.
17. $x = \frac{2}{3}$, $y = \frac{2}{5}$, $z = \frac{3}{4}$. **18.** $x = \frac{4}{3}$, $y = \frac{3}{2}$, $z = \frac{5}{4}$. **19.** $x = \frac{3}{5}$, $y = \frac{1}{4}$, $z = \frac{1}{2}$.
21. $x = -\frac{3}{4}$, $y = \frac{4}{3}$, $z = \frac{5}{2}$. **22.** $x = \frac{2}{5}$, $y = \frac{3}{5}$, $z = \frac{1}{4}$. **23.** $x = \frac{5}{6}$, $y = \frac{2}{3}$, $z = \frac{7}{4}$.
25. $x = 4$, $y = 5$, $z = -7$. **26.** $x = 4$, $y = 3$, $z = 5$. **27.** $x = 1$, $y = 2$, $z = 4$.
29. $x = 4$, $y = 3$, $z = 5$. **30.** $x = 3$, $y = -3$, $z = 4$. **31.** $x = 4$, $y = 2$, $z = 5$.

Exercise 24

1. 35 students, 40 students. **2.** Essays, $4.50; grammar, $3.75.
3. Camera, $50; camping equipment, $30. **5.** 96 by touchdowns, 12 by conversions.
6. 25 days at $8, 35 days at $10. **7.** 310 theatre tickets, 54 buffet tickets.
9. $35, $45. **10.** Dress, $18; shoes, $7. **11.** 2 miles per hr., 4 miles per hr.
13. Rider, 5 miles per hr.; hiker, 3 miles per hr. **14.** 40 by bus, 20 by car.
15. Harry, $350; Tom, $400. **17.** 40 miles per hr., 20 miles per hr.
18. 5 doz. of each. **19.** Old developer, 1800 liters; replenisher, 600 liters.
21. Student, 9 hr.; professor, $4\frac{1}{2}$ hr. **22.** 36,000 acres, 30,000 acres.
23. Gum balls, 375; prizes, 125. **25.** Luggage, $80; camera, $40; clothes, $100.
26. A, 4; B, 16; C, 10. **27.** A, 3 hr.; B, 2 hr.; C, 11 hr.
29. 18 years, 9; 19 years, 6; 20 years, 5. **30.** $\frac{1}{2}$ hr. walking, 1 hr. by bus, 2 hr. by plane.
31. Tom, 4 hr.; Dick, 6 hr.; Harry, 3 hr.

Exercise 25

1. 243. **2.** 128. **3.** 256. **5.** 7. **6.** 625. **7.** 27. **9.** 64. **10.** 729.

11. 390,625. **13.** 5184. **14.** 20,736. **15.** 25. **17.** $\frac{81}{64}$. **18.** $\frac{15,625}{256}$. **19.** 8.

21. $\dfrac{a^8b^4}{c^{12}}$.　**22.** $\dfrac{a^9b^6}{c^{12}}$.　**23.** $\dfrac{-32u^{20}}{243w^{10}}$.　**25.** $6a^5b^3$.　**26.** $-8x^5y^7$.　**27.** $10x^7y^5z^3$.

29. $\dfrac{3a^4}{2b^2}$.　**30.** $\dfrac{4d^2}{3c^2}$.　**31.** $\dfrac{3p^2}{4q^2}$.　**33.** ab^2c^4.　**34.** $x^4y^2z^2$.　**35.** $\dfrac{rs}{t}$.　**37.** $r^9s^{14}t^4$.

38. $12a^6b^5c^8$.　**39.** $16x^{14}y^9$.　**41.** $\dfrac{u^4}{vw^2}$.　**42.** $\dfrac{x}{v}$.　**43.** $a^{10}y^8$.　**45.** $\dfrac{3ab^7}{2}$.　**46.** $\dfrac{8b^3}{s^2u^7}$.

47. $\dfrac{3vt}{5}$.　**49.** bc.　**50.** $\dfrac{n}{3m^2p^4}$.　**51.** $\dfrac{2x}{t^2}$.　**53.** $\dfrac{y^6}{8x^3}$.　**54.** $\dfrac{b^4}{16a^4}$.　**55.** $\dfrac{27w^{12}}{64v^9}$.　**57.** $\dfrac{27}{8b^3}$.

58. $\dfrac{y^{16}}{81x^4}$.　**59.** $\dfrac{c^{20}d^{10}}{1024}$.　**61.** 4.　**62.** 81.　**63.** 16.　**65.** 81^n.　**66.** 64^n.　**67.** 125^n.

69. a^3.　**70.** a^m.　**71.** r^{2c+3}.　**73.** s^{2t+4}.　**74.** b^{4r-4}.　**75.** c^{3n+9}.　**77.** a^8b^{2x}.

78. a^2b^{2y}.　**79.** m^9n^{4x}.

Exercise 26

1. $\dfrac{1}{9}$.　**2.** $\dfrac{1}{4}$.　**3.** $\dfrac{1}{125}$.　**5.** $\dfrac{1}{8}$.　**6.** $\dfrac{1}{9}$.　**7.** $\dfrac{1}{625}$.　**9.** $\dfrac{1}{3}$.　**10.** $\dfrac{1}{8}$.　**11.** 343.

13. $\dfrac{1}{64}$.　**14.** 9.　**15.** 25.　**17.** $\dfrac{9}{4}$.　**18.** $\dfrac{5}{3}$.　**19.** $\dfrac{125}{8}$.　**21.** $\dfrac{3}{4}$.　**22.** 64.

23. $\dfrac{625}{4}$.　**25.** $4x^2y^{-3}$.　**26.** $3a^3b^{-4}$.　**27.** $2c^5d^{-1}e^{-2}$.　**29.** $2^{-13}a^2bcd^{-2}$.

30. $4x^2y^3w^2z^{-1}$.　**31.** $3^{-1}r^3s^2t^3v^3$.　**33.** $\dfrac{2}{a^3}$.　**34.** $\dfrac{4}{c^2}$.　**35.** $\dfrac{6}{x^5}$.　**37.** $\dfrac{1}{x}$.　**38.** x^5.

39. y^4.　**41.** $p^2d^2q^2$.　**42.** $\dfrac{st^5}{r}$.　**43.** $\dfrac{e^2}{p^3n^3}$.　**45.** $\dfrac{9a^3}{2r^4t}$.　**46.** $\dfrac{8e^2r^2}{9p^2}$.　**47.** $\dfrac{3ae^4}{4r^2}$.

49. $\dfrac{6a^4c^5}{b^3}$.　**50.** $\dfrac{16z^6}{x^4y^6}$.　**51.** $\dfrac{q^5}{5p^3r}$.　**53.** $\dfrac{x^3}{y^5}$.　**54.** $\dfrac{b^8}{m^4}$.　**55.** $a^{12}m^6$.　**57.** $\dfrac{y^6}{8x^6}$.

58. $\dfrac{81b^{12}}{a^{12}}$.　**59.** $\dfrac{d^2}{25c^{10}}$.　**61.** $-x^a$.　**62.** $-\dfrac{1}{x^a}$.　**63.** $\dfrac{x^a}{2}$.　**65.** $\dfrac{2a}{b}$.　**66.** $\dfrac{a^2+b^2}{ab}$.

67. $\dfrac{a^2b^2+1}{ab}$.　**69.** $\dfrac{ab+a^2}{b}$.　**70.** $\dfrac{a^2b-a^3}{b}$.　**71.** $\dfrac{b+a}{ab}$.　**73.** $-\dfrac{(x+1)(x+5)}{(x-1)^4}$.

74. $\dfrac{2(2x+1)^2(x+5)}{(x+2)^3}$.　**75.** $\dfrac{(2x-3)^3(6x+11)}{(x+1)^2}$.　**77.** $\dfrac{3(2x-3)}{(2x+3)^3(3-x)^2}$.

78. $\dfrac{9x-13}{(3x-1)^3(2-x)^2}$.　**79.** $\dfrac{2(2x+5)^2(x+4)}{(x+3)^3}$.

Exercise 27

1. 2.　**2.** 5.　**3.** 3.　**5.** $.1$.　**6.** $.6$.　**7.** $.5$.　**9.** 9.　**10.** 8.　**11.** $.027$.　**13.** $\dfrac{1}{3}$.

14. $\dfrac{1}{4}$.　**15.** $\dfrac{1}{8}$.　**17.** 3.　**18.** 4.　**19.** 2.　**21.** $6a$.　**22.** $3b^2$.　**23.** $2x^2$.　**25.** $\dfrac{x^2}{y^3}$.

26. $\dfrac{2x}{3y^4}$.　**27.** $\dfrac{2y^3}{3a^2}$.　**29.** $a^{\frac{3}{2}}$.　**30.** $b^{\frac{2}{3}}$.　**31.** $b^{\frac{1}{2}}$.　**33.** $2^{\frac{5}{2}}$.　**34.** $2^{\frac{4}{3}}$.　**35.** $2^{\frac{2}{3}}$.

37. $2a^{\frac{3}{2}}b^2$.　**38.** $2x^2y^{\frac{2}{3}}z^{\frac{1}{3}}$.　**39.** $2a^{\frac{2}{3}}b^2c^{\frac{1}{2}}$.　**41.** $\dfrac{2a^{\frac{2}{3}}}{3b^{\frac{1}{3}}}$.　**42.** $\dfrac{b^{\frac{3}{4}}}{2w^2}$.　**43.** $\dfrac{4a^{\frac{2}{3}}}{3a^{\frac{5}{3}}}$.　**45.** $\sqrt[3]{a^2}$.

46. $\sqrt[4]{b^3}$.　**47.** $\sqrt[5]{c^2}$.　**49.** $\dfrac{1}{\sqrt{x}}$.　**50.** $\dfrac{1}{\sqrt[3]{y^2}}$.　**51.** $\dfrac{1}{\sqrt[5]{z^3}}$.　**53.** $\sqrt[3]{a^2b^2}$.

54. $\sqrt[5]{x^2y^3}$.　**55.** $\sqrt[7]{y^2w^4}$.　**57.** $2\sqrt[3]{a^2}$.　**58.** $9y\sqrt{xy}$.　**59.** $8\sqrt[4]{zw^3}$.　**61.** $\dfrac{4}{\sqrt[3]{b}}$.

62. $\dfrac{8}{\sqrt[4]{y}}$.　63. $3\sqrt[3]{\dfrac{a^2}{y}}$.　65. $\sqrt[4]{x^2y}$.　66. $\sqrt[6]{a^3b^2}$.　67. $\sqrt[12]{p^8q^9}$.　69. $3\sqrt[15]{c^5y^6}$.

70. $2\sqrt[6]{x^3y^4}$.　71. $\sqrt[30]{a^{15}y^{12}w^{10}}$.　73. $2\sqrt[4]{ab^2}$.　74. $2\sqrt[6]{x^9y^2}$.　75. $2\sqrt[6]{c^2d^5e^3}$.

Exercise 28

1. a.　2. x^2.　3. c.　5. $a^{\frac{5}{4}}$.　6. $d^{\frac{11}{12}}$.　7. $z^{\frac{1}{2}}$.　9. b.　10. m.　11. $r^{\frac{1}{4}}$.

13. $6b^{\frac{1}{2}}$.　14. $2xy^{\frac{1}{3}}$.　15. $12w^{\frac{1}{5}}z^{\frac{1}{2}}$.　17. $2ab^{\frac{1}{3}}$.　18. $3m^{\frac{1}{4}}n^2$.　19. $2x^2y^{\frac{1}{3}}z^{\frac{1}{6}}$.　21. $\dfrac{a^2}{y^{\frac{1}{2}}}$.

22. $\dfrac{1}{p^{\frac{1}{3}}t}$.　23. $\dfrac{m^{\frac{3}{4}}}{e^{\frac{1}{2}}}$.　25. $\dfrac{a^2}{16b^3}$.　26. $\dfrac{x^2}{2y^3}$.　27. $\dfrac{3a^3}{x^5}$.　29. $a^{\frac{1}{3}}b$.　30. $\dfrac{x^{\frac{1}{2}}y^{\frac{1}{2}}}{3}$.　31. $\dfrac{d}{c^{\frac{1}{5}}}$.

33. $\dfrac{v}{25u^2}$.　34. $\dfrac{3r}{s}$.　35. $\dfrac{b}{a^2}$.　37. x.　38. $\dfrac{3^{\frac{3}{2}}n^{\frac{5}{8}}}{m^{\frac{1}{4}}}$.　39. $\dfrac{1}{q^{\frac{1}{2}}p^{\frac{1}{2}}}$.　41. $\dfrac{1}{2^{\frac{3}{2}}}$.　42. d^3.

43. $\dfrac{1}{16}$.　45. $\dfrac{4}{v^{\frac{5}{3}}}$.　46. $\dfrac{54x^{\frac{5}{4}}}{y^{\frac{13}{2}}}$.　47. $\dfrac{64s^3y^6}{3}$.　49. $\dfrac{1}{2}a^{\frac{1}{4}}b^2c^{\frac{1}{2}}$.　50. $\dfrac{s^{\frac{3}{5}}}{r}$.　51. $\dfrac{x^{\frac{5}{7}}}{y}$.

53. $\dfrac{y^{\frac{1}{3}}x^{\frac{1}{5}}}{a^2}$.　54. $\dfrac{1}{2sx}$.　55. $\dfrac{d^{\frac{2}{3}}q}{p}$.　57. $\dfrac{d^{\frac{1}{6}}}{y^{\frac{1}{10}}}$.　58. $\dfrac{y^{\frac{4}{15}}}{m^{\frac{7}{6}}}$.　59. $\dfrac{s^{\frac{1}{6}}}{x^{\frac{11}{12}}}$.　61. $\dfrac{3}{2b^5}$.

62. $9s^2a^{\frac{17}{2}}$.　63. $b^{\frac{1}{2}}c^{\frac{3}{2}}$.　65. $a^{\frac{1}{3}}b^{\frac{2}{5}}$.　66. $e^{10}f^{\frac{9}{5}}$.　67. $ty^{\frac{9}{2}}$.　69. $\dfrac{b+a}{b-a}$.　70. $\dfrac{ab}{a+b}$.

71. $\left(\dfrac{ab}{b-a}\right)^2$.　73. x.　74. x^a.　75. y^{n-m}.　77. $\dfrac{5x-5}{(2x-1)^{\frac{1}{2}}(3x-4)^{\frac{2}{3}}}$.

78. $\dfrac{17x-3}{(4x-3)^{\frac{1}{4}}(3x+1)^{\frac{1}{3}}}$.　79. $\dfrac{9x-8}{(2x-3)^{\frac{1}{2}}(5x-2)^{\frac{2}{5}}}$.

Exercise 29

1. 4.　2. 7.　3. 16.　5. $5\sqrt{2}$.　6. $3\sqrt{6}$.　7. $7\sqrt{3}$.　9. $8\sqrt{2}$.

10. $10\sqrt{2}$.　11. $8\sqrt{3}$.　13. $2\sqrt[3]{3}$.　14. $3\sqrt[3]{3}$.　15. $3\sqrt[3]{11}$.　17. $3\sqrt[4]{2}$.

18. $5\sqrt[4]{3}$.　19. $3\sqrt[4]{5}$.　21. $5ay\sqrt{2y}$.　22. $3ay^2\sqrt{2a}$.　23. $3x^3y^3\sqrt{3y}$.

25. $3xy\sqrt[3]{2x}$.　26. $2t^2\sqrt[3]{3a^2}$.　27. $2mr\sqrt[4]{3m^3r}$.　29. $uvw^2\sqrt[5]{u^2v^4w}$.

30. $mnw^2\sqrt[5]{n^2w^2}$.　31. $ghk^2\sqrt[6]{gh^3k}$.　33. $2ab^3c\sqrt[3]{2ac^2}$.　34. $2xy^2z^2\sqrt[4]{3x^3z}$.

35. $2c^2de\sqrt[5]{2de^3}$.　37. $3xy\sqrt{5}$.　38. $4x^2\sqrt{5xy}$.　39. $7as^2\sqrt{2s}$.　41. $\dfrac{2ac^2\sqrt{2a}}{3b^2}$.

42. $\dfrac{2mp\sqrt[3]{3p}}{5n^2}$.　43. $\dfrac{2rs\sqrt[3]{rs}}{3t^2}$.　45. 12.　46. 9.　47. 18.　49. 4.　50. 5.

51. 2.　53. $4r^2t^3$.　54. $6ab^2\sqrt{a}$.　55. $10x^4y\sqrt{y}$.　57. $2x^2y$.　58. $6a^3c^2$.

59. $a^2b^2c\sqrt[4]{a^3c}$.　61. 8.　62. 3.　63. 6.　65. $\dfrac{3y}{x}$.　66. $\dfrac{3y}{x^3}$.　67. $\dfrac{7x^3}{5y}$.

69. $2b^2c\sqrt{ac}$.　70. $\dfrac{y^2\sqrt{2z}}{x^3}$.　71. $\dfrac{2u^3\sqrt{u}}{vz^2}$.　73. $\dfrac{3\sqrt{2}}{2}$.　74. 6.　75. $\dfrac{2\sqrt{7}}{3}$.

77. $2y^3$.　78. $14a^2b^3\sqrt{a}$.　79. $12w^3\sqrt{2z}$.

Exercise 30

1. $\dfrac{\sqrt{6}}{2}$. **2.** $\dfrac{\sqrt{35}}{7}$. **3.** $\dfrac{\sqrt{15}}{5}$. **5.** $\dfrac{\sqrt{14}}{4}$. **6.** $\dfrac{\sqrt{10}}{6}$. **7.** $\dfrac{\sqrt{15}}{10}$. **9.** $\dfrac{2\sqrt{6}}{9}$.

10. $\dfrac{2\sqrt{35}}{21}$. **11.** $\dfrac{4\sqrt{10}}{15}$. **13.** $\dfrac{\sqrt[3]{2}}{2}$. **14.** $\dfrac{\sqrt[3]{12}}{2}$. **15.** $\dfrac{\sqrt[3]{50}}{5}$. **17.** $\dfrac{3\sqrt[3]{12}}{4}$.

18. $\dfrac{2\sqrt[3]{21}}{7}$. **19.** $\dfrac{3\sqrt[3]{10}}{5}$. **21.** $\dfrac{\sqrt{10}}{5}$. **22.** $\dfrac{\sqrt{14}}{4}$. **23.** $\dfrac{\sqrt{30}}{5}$. **25.** $\dfrac{\sqrt{ac}}{c}$.

26. $\dfrac{x\sqrt{2xy}}{y}$. **27.** $\dfrac{s\sqrt{3t}}{3t}$. **29.** $\dfrac{a\sqrt{2b}}{3b}$. **30.** $\dfrac{a\sqrt{15b}}{3b^2}$. **31.** $\dfrac{2\sqrt{5}}{5xy}$. **33.** $\dfrac{\sqrt{cxy}}{cxy}$.

34. $\dfrac{x\sqrt{6a}}{3a}$. **35.** $\dfrac{4x\sqrt{3d}}{3}$. **37.** $\dfrac{\sqrt[3]{2bcd^2}}{cd}$. **38.** $\dfrac{\sqrt[3]{6xy^2}}{2y}$. **39.** $\dfrac{a\sqrt[3]{15ab^2}}{3b}$.

41. $\dfrac{2a\sqrt{3x}}{3x^2}$. **42.** $\dfrac{2\sqrt{3a}}{b}$. **43.** $\dfrac{m\sqrt[3]{as^2}}{ab}$. **45.** $(a+b)\sqrt{a-b}$. **46.** $\dfrac{\sqrt{a+b}}{a-b}$.

47. $\dfrac{(x-y)\sqrt{x+y}}{x+y}$. **49.** $\sqrt{2}+1$. **50.** $\sqrt{3}-1$. **51.** $-1-\sqrt{5}$.

53. $5+2\sqrt{6}$. **54.** $3+2\sqrt{2}$. **55.** $5-2\sqrt{6}$. **57.** $3+2\sqrt{2}$.

58. $7-4\sqrt{3}$. **59.** $6+\sqrt{35}$.

Exercise 31

1. $6\sqrt{3}$. **2.** $2\sqrt{2}$. **3.** 0. **5.** $8\sqrt{2}-3\sqrt{3}$. **6.** $-3\sqrt{2}-2\sqrt{5}$.

7. $\sqrt{7}+3\sqrt{3}$. **9.** 0. **10.** $6\sqrt[3]{3}$. **11.** $6\sqrt[3]{6}$. **13.** $5a^2\sqrt{b}$.

14. $(m+p)^2\sqrt{p}$. **15.** $4xy\sqrt{xy}$. **17.** $5c^3d^3\sqrt{cd}$. **18.** $u^2v^2\sqrt{uv}$.

19. $-2w^3z^2\sqrt{wz}$. **21.** $\dfrac{23xy\sqrt{y}}{24}$. **22.** $\dfrac{4b\sqrt{2a}}{3a}$. **23.** $\dfrac{\sqrt{5xy}}{5}\left(\dfrac{4}{y}-\dfrac{1}{x}\right)$.

25. $xy\sqrt{x}$. **26.** $y\sqrt{xy}$. **27.** $\sqrt[4]{a^2b^3}$. **29.** $\sqrt[3]{3xy^2}$. **30.** $2\sqrt[3]{xy^2}$. **31.** $\sqrt[3]{2ab^2}$.

33. $3y\sqrt{x}$. **34.** $\dfrac{\sqrt{6mn}}{3}$. **35.** $\sqrt{2xy}$. **37.** $\dfrac{\sqrt{6ab}}{2a}$. **38.** $\dfrac{\sqrt[3]{100n}}{5m}$. **39.** $\dfrac{\sqrt{6xy}}{2y}$.

41. $\sqrt{x},\ y\sqrt{xy}$. **42.** $\sqrt[3]{a^2b},\ \sqrt[3]{a^2b}$. **43.** $\sqrt[6]{p^4q^2},\ \sqrt[6]{pq^2}$. **45.** $\sqrt[6]{x^6y^3},\ \sqrt[6]{4x^2y^4}$.

46. $\sqrt[12]{27a^3b^9},\ \sqrt[12]{4a^4b^4}$. **47.** $\sqrt[24]{16z^8w^{12}},\ \sqrt[24]{27z^3w^3}$. **49.** $\sqrt[6]{a^3},\ \sqrt[6]{a^2},\ \sqrt[6]{a}$.

50. $\sqrt[12]{64x^6y^6},\ \sqrt[12]{27x^9y^6},\ \sqrt[12]{4x^{10}y^6}$. **51.** $\sqrt[24]{a^{12}b^{12}},\ \sqrt[24]{a^{16}b^8},\ \sqrt[24]{a^9b^{15}}$. **53.** $4x^2\sqrt[12]{32x^5}$.

54. $2s^2t\sqrt[12]{2st^6}$. **55.** $9by\sqrt[12]{3b^7y^5}$.

Exercise 32

1. $\pm\frac{3}{2}$. **2.** $\pm\frac{4}{5}$. **3.** $\pm\frac{7}{3}$. **5.** ±2. **6.** ±3. **7.** ±5. **9.** $\pm\dfrac{4\sqrt{3}}{3}$.

10. $\pm\dfrac{2\sqrt{6}}{3}$. **11.** $\pm\dfrac{2\sqrt{15}}{5}$. **13.** $\pm2i$. **14.** $\pm5i$. **15.** $\pm3i$. **17.** $\pm\sqrt{7}\,i$.

18. $\pm\sqrt{5}\,i$. **19.** $\pm\sqrt{3}\,i$. **21.** $1,-3$. **22.** $5,-1$. **23.** $2,-4$. **25.** $5,-2$.

26. $5,-4$. **27.** $-5,3$. **29.** $\frac{3}{2},-2$. **30.** $2,-\frac{2}{3}$. **31.** $1,-\frac{3}{5}$. **33.** $\frac{5}{2},-1$.

34. $\frac{1}{7}, -2.$ **35.** $-\frac{2}{5}, 2.$ **37.** $-\frac{1}{2}, -\frac{3}{4}.$ **38.** $\frac{5}{3}, -\frac{1}{2}.$ **39.** $\frac{1}{2}, \frac{3}{4}.$ **41.** $-\frac{4}{3}, \frac{3}{2}.$

42. $\frac{3}{2}, -\frac{3}{4}.$ **43.** $\frac{1}{3}, -\frac{3}{2}.$ **45.** $\frac{3}{4}, -\frac{4}{3}.$ **46.** $\frac{3}{2}, -\frac{5}{4}.$ **47.** $-\frac{3}{5}, \frac{2}{3}.$ **49.** $\frac{9}{7}, -\frac{2}{3}.$

50. $\frac{6}{5}, -\frac{3}{2}.$ **51.** $\frac{7}{5}, \frac{3}{4}.$ **53.** $\frac{8}{7}, -\frac{5}{6}.$ **54.** $-\frac{10}{9}, -\frac{3}{4}.$ **55.** $-\frac{8}{9}, \frac{7}{6}.$ **57.** $\frac{8}{9}, -\frac{4}{3}.$

58. $\frac{8}{7}, -\frac{4}{5}.$ **59.** $-\frac{3}{10}, -\frac{9}{2}.$ **61.** $\dfrac{-3m}{2}, -m.$ **62.** $\dfrac{4r}{3}, -2r.$ **63.** $\dfrac{-3b}{2a}, \dfrac{4b}{a}.$

65. $m, n.$ **66.** $\dfrac{d}{c}, d.$ **67.** $\dfrac{a}{2}, 2b.$

Exercise 33

1. $2, -8.$ **2.** $3, -5.$ **3.** $-7, -1.$ **5.** $-4, 1.$ **6.** $4, 1.$ **7.** $6, 1.$ **9.** $\frac{7}{2}, -\frac{3}{2}.$

10. $\frac{1}{2}, -\frac{7}{2}.$ **11.** $\frac{8}{3}, -\frac{2}{3}.$ **13.** $4, -\frac{3}{2}.$ **14.** $\frac{5}{2}, -1.$ **15.** $3, -\frac{4}{3}.$ **17.** $\frac{1}{2}, \frac{1}{3}.$

18. $\frac{1}{2}, -\frac{1}{3}.$ **19.** $1, -\frac{3}{8}.$ **21.** $\frac{3}{2}, \frac{3}{4}.$ **22.** $2, \frac{1}{2}.$ **23.** $2, \frac{1}{8}.$ **25.** $2 \pm \sqrt{6}.$

26. $1 \pm \sqrt{5}.$ **27.** $3 \pm \sqrt{3}.$ **29.** $\dfrac{-2 \pm \sqrt{5}}{2}.$ **30.** $\dfrac{3 \pm \sqrt{2}}{2}.$ **31.** $\dfrac{2 \pm \sqrt{5}}{3}.$

33. $\dfrac{1 \pm \sqrt{2}}{3}.$ **34.** $\dfrac{-2 \pm \sqrt{2}}{3}.$ **35.** $\dfrac{1 \pm \sqrt{5}}{6}.$ **37.** $2 \pm 2i.$ **38.** $-1 \pm 2i.$

39. $3 \pm i.$ **41.** $\dfrac{1 \pm 5i}{2}.$ **42.** $\dfrac{-2 \pm 3i}{2}.$ **43.** $\dfrac{2 \pm 2i}{3}.$ **45.** $\dfrac{3 \pm \sqrt{19}\,i}{6}.$

46. $\dfrac{3 \pm \sqrt{2}\,i}{3}.$ **47.** $\dfrac{2 \pm \sqrt{5}\,i}{2}.$ **49.** $2b, -b.$ **50.** $2a, -6a.$ **51.** $b, -2a.$

53. $1, -\dfrac{b+a}{a}.$ **54.** $-\dfrac{1}{ab}, -\dfrac{1}{a}.$ **55.** $-b, \dfrac{2b-a}{4}.$ **57.** $\dfrac{-b}{a}, \dfrac{-a}{b}.$

58. $\dfrac{2a-b}{3}, -a.$ **59.** $\dfrac{-1}{a}, -1.$

Exercise 34

1. $-4, 2.$ **2.** $2, -6.$ **3.** $-5, -1.$ **5.** $2, \frac{1}{2}.$ **6.** $\frac{2}{3}, -2.$ **7.** $1, -\frac{5}{2}.$ **9.** $\frac{1}{3}, -\frac{3}{2}.$

10. $-\frac{5}{4}, \frac{1}{2}.$ **11.** $\frac{2}{3}, -\frac{3}{4}.$ **13.** $\frac{1}{4}, -\frac{6}{7}.$ **14.** $-\frac{3}{7}, \frac{1}{6}.$ **15.** $-\frac{5}{9}, \frac{1}{6}.$ **17.** $-1 \pm \sqrt{5}.$

18. $3 \pm \sqrt{3}.$ **19.** $4 \pm 2\sqrt{3}.$ **21.** $\dfrac{5 \pm \sqrt{5}}{4}.$ **22.** $\dfrac{2 \pm \sqrt{2}}{3}.$ **23.** $\dfrac{3 \pm \sqrt{5}}{4}.$

25. $\dfrac{-2 \pm \sqrt{7}}{3}.$ **26.** $\dfrac{5 \pm 2\sqrt{10}}{5}.$ **27.** $\dfrac{-7 \pm 4\sqrt{7}}{7}.$ **29.** $\dfrac{15 \pm 3\sqrt{5}}{10}.$

30. $\dfrac{3 \pm \sqrt{2}}{7}.$ **31.** $\dfrac{-2 \pm 2\sqrt{6}}{5}.$ **33.** $-1 \pm 2i.$ **34.** $3 \pm 4i.$ **35.** $4 \pm i.$

37. $\dfrac{2 \pm i}{2}.$ **38.** $\dfrac{1 \pm 4i}{3}.$ **39.** $\dfrac{-1 \pm 2i}{2}.$ **41.** $\dfrac{-2 \pm \sqrt{2}\,i}{3}.$ **42.** $\dfrac{3 \pm \sqrt{6}\,i}{5}.$

43. $\dfrac{-2 \pm \sqrt{3}\,i}{7}.$ **45.** $\dfrac{-1 \pm \sqrt{2}\,i}{6}.$ **46.** $\dfrac{-2 \pm \sqrt{26}\,i}{10}.$ **47.** $\dfrac{1 \pm \sqrt{5}\,i}{4}.$

49. $-m, -n.$ **50.** $-1, rs.$ **51.** $\dfrac{-2b}{a}, \dfrac{-b}{a}.$ **53.** $m + 2n, -2m - n.$

54. $\dfrac{2b}{a}, \dfrac{-2a}{b}$. **55.** $\dfrac{cd}{2}, \dfrac{2}{cd}$. **57.** $\dfrac{-p+1}{p}, \dfrac{-p-1}{p}$. **58.** $\dfrac{1}{m-1}, \dfrac{1}{m+1}$.

59. $\dfrac{a}{a+b}, \dfrac{-a}{a-b}$.

Exercise 35

1. Irrational and unequal; $-6, -3$. **2.** Irrational and unequal; $-3, -2$.
3. Irrational and unequal; $-7, 4$. **5.** Rational and unequal; $-4, 3$.
6. Rational and unequal; $3, 2$. **7.** Rational and equal; $-6, 9$.
9. Rational and unequal; $-\frac{5}{2}, 1$. **10.** Rational and unequal; $-\frac{8}{3}, -1$.
11. Rational and unequal; $-\frac{3}{2}, \frac{1}{2}$. **13.** Imaginary; $-\frac{3}{4}, \frac{1}{2}$. **14.** Imaginary; $-\frac{5}{3}, \frac{4}{3}$.
15. Imaginary; $\frac{7}{5}, \frac{3}{5}$. **17.** Rational and unequal; $-\frac{7}{4}, -\frac{1}{2}$.
18. Rational and unequal; $-\frac{7}{3}, \frac{2}{3}$. **19.** Rational and unequal; $-\frac{4}{5}, -\frac{1}{5}$.
21. Irrational and unequal; $-\frac{5}{3}, -1$. **22.** Irrational and unequal; $-\frac{3}{2}, \frac{1}{4}$.
23. Irrational and unequal; $\frac{5}{2}, -1$. **25.** Imaginary; $\frac{7}{2}, \frac{7}{2}$. **26.** Imaginary; $-\frac{5}{7}, \frac{6}{7}$.
27. Imaginary; $\frac{9}{8}, \frac{3}{4}$. **29.** Irrational and unequal; $-\frac{10}{3}, \frac{2}{3}$.
30. Irrational and unequal; $\frac{13}{5}, -\frac{4}{5}$. **31.** Imaginary; $-\frac{12}{7}, \frac{8}{7}$.

Exercise 36

1. 2. **2.** 3. **3.** 7. **5.** $\frac{1}{4}$. **6.** $-\frac{1}{16}$. **7.** 6. **9.** $2, -\frac{3}{2}$. **10.** $3, -\frac{4}{3}$.
11. $\frac{5}{2}, -3$. **13.** 4. **14.** 2. **15.** -2. **17.** $3, \frac{1}{2}$. **18.** 2. **19.** 4. **21.** $3, -1$.
22. $2, 6$. **23.** 4. **25.** 2. **26.** 2. **27.** -3. **29.** 5. **30.** 1. **31.** 3. **33.** 1.
34. -2. **35.** $2, \frac{22}{35}$. **37.** 3. **38.** $2, 6$. **39.** -1. **41.** a. **42.** $2b$. **43.** c^2.

Exercise 37

1. $\pm 2, \pm 4$. **2.** $\pm 3, \pm 5$. **3.** $\pm \frac{1}{2}, \pm 3$. **5.** $\pm 2, \pm \sqrt{3}$. **6.** $\pm 3, \pm \sqrt{5}$.
7. $\pm \frac{3}{2}, \pm \sqrt{2}$. **9.** $\pm \sqrt{2}, \pm 2i$. **10.** $\pm \sqrt{2}, \pm 3i$. **11.** $\pm i, \pm \sqrt{3}$.
13. $\pm \frac{1}{2}i, \pm \dfrac{\sqrt{6}}{2}$. **14.** $\pm 3i/2, \pm \sqrt{3}$. **15.** $\pm \dfrac{\sqrt{6}}{2}, \pm \dfrac{\sqrt{6}\,i}{3}$. **17.** $2, -3$.
18. $2, -\frac{1}{2}$. **19.** $3, 1$. **21.** $3, 1$. **22.** $\frac{3}{2}, -1$. **23.** $\pm 3, \pm 1, \pm 3i, \pm i$.
25. $\pm 3, \pm 2$. **26.** $\pm 2, \pm 1$. **27.** $\pm 2, \pm 3$. **29.** $-3, 1, -1 \pm \sqrt{2}$.
30. $\frac{1}{2}, -1, \frac{3}{2}, -2$. **31.** $\pm 1, 2, 4$. **33.** $3, -1, 1 \pm \sqrt{3}$. **34.** $1, -4, \frac{1}{2}(-3 \pm \sqrt{17})$.
35. $1, -\frac{1}{2}, \frac{1}{4}(1 \pm \sqrt{17})$. **37.** $\frac{3}{2}, \frac{2}{3}$. **38.** $-3, -\frac{9}{5}$. **39.** $-1, -2$. **41.** $\frac{4}{5}, 2$.
42. $-8, -\frac{1}{2}$. **43.** $-\frac{3}{2}, -\frac{5}{2}$. **45.** $-\frac{1}{3}, \frac{2}{3}$. **46.** $\frac{5}{2}$. **47.** $1, \frac{5}{2}$.

Exercise 38

1. 34. **2.** $9, 10$. **3.** 4. **5.** $14, 8$. **6.** $17, 7$. **7.** $15, 6$. **9.** 3. **10.** 1. **11.** 4.
13. 10 ft., 6 ft. **14.** 30 by 75 ft. **15.** 9 by 12 ft. **17.** 30 by 40 ft. **18.** 20 by 30 ft.
19. 12 by 12 in., 8 by 9 in. **21.** 60 miles per hr. **22.** 45 miles per hr., 60 miles per hr.
23. 50 miles per hr., 40 miles per hr. **25.** $1\frac{1}{2}$ hr., 3 hr. **26.** 5 hr., $7\frac{1}{2}$ hr.
27. $75, 100$. **29.** 50. **30.** 40 cu. ft. per min. **31.** \$40 per month, \$30 per month.

Exercise 40

1. $x = 1, y = -1; x = 5, y = -9$. **2.** $x = -1, y = 3; x = -25, y = -9$.
3. $x = 1, y = 2; x = \frac{11}{4}, y = -\frac{3}{2}$. **5.** $x = 2, y = 3; x = -\frac{6}{5}, y = -\frac{17}{5}$.
6. $x = 3, y = -1; x = -\frac{13}{5}, y = \frac{9}{5}$. **7.** $x = 5, y = 0; x = 4, y = 3$.

9. $x = 2, y = -2; x = -\frac{2}{3}, y = \frac{10}{3}.$ **10.** $x = 1, y = -3; x = \frac{7}{3}, y = -\frac{1}{3}.$

11. $x = 2, y = -5; x = -\frac{3}{2}, y = \frac{11}{2}.$ **13.** $x = 1, y = 0; x = 5, y = 6.$

14. $x = 2, y = 1; x = 7, y = -4.$ **15.** $x = 3, y = 1; x = 11, y = 9.$

17. $x = 1, y = 0; x = -6, y = 21.$ **18.** $x = 3, y = -1; x = -\frac{4}{5}; y = \frac{13}{25}.$

19. $x = 3, y = -2; x = -\frac{3}{2}, y = -\frac{1}{2}.$ **21.** $x = 1, y = -1; x = -\frac{2}{3}, y = \frac{7}{3}.$

22. $x = 2, y = 3; x = \frac{1}{8}, y = -\frac{3}{4}.$ **23.** $x = \frac{5}{7}, y = \frac{2}{7}; x = 5, y = 6.$

25. $x = a, y = a; x = -4a, y = -14a.$ **26.** $x = 2a, y = -b; x = -2a, y = 2a - b.$

27. $x = a, y = -3a; x = \dfrac{-9a}{5}, y = \dfrac{13a}{5}.$ **29.** $x = a, y = \dfrac{b}{a}; x = -a, y = \dfrac{-b}{a}.$

30. $x = b, y = a; x = -b, y = -a.$ **31.** $x = \dfrac{-b}{m}, y = 0; x = 0, y = b.$

Exercise 41

1. $x = 2, y = 1; x = 2, y = -1; x = -2, y = 1; x = -2, y = -1.$

2. $x = 3, y = 2; x = 3, y = -2; x = -3, y = 2; x = -3, y = -2.$

3. $x = 1, y = 1; x = 1, y = -1; x = -1, y = 1; x = -1, y = -1.$

5. $x = 4, y = 1; x = 4, y = -1; x = -4, y = 1; x = -4, y = -1.$

6. $x = 2, y = 1; x = 2, y = -1; x = -2, y = 1; x = -2, y = -1.$

7. $x = 1, y = 0; x = 1, y = 0; x = -1, y = 0; x = -1, y = 0.$

9. $x = 2, y = 1; x = 2, y = -1; x = 5, y = 4\sqrt{2}\,i; x = 5, y = -4\sqrt{2}\,i.$

10. $x = 1, y = 2i; x = 1, y = -2i; x = -2, y = 2i; x = -2, y = -2i.$

11. $x = 1, y = 2\sqrt{3}; x = 1, y = -2\sqrt{3}; x = -\frac{3}{4}, y = \dfrac{3\sqrt{5}}{4}; x = -\frac{3}{4}, y = \dfrac{-3\sqrt{5}}{4}.$

13. $x = 1, y = \sqrt{2}; x = 1, y = -\sqrt{2}; x = 3, y = 4; x = 3, y = -4.$

14. $x = 0, y = \frac{1}{2}; x = 0, y = -\frac{1}{2}; x = 2, y = \frac{1}{2}; x = 2, y = -\frac{1}{2}.$

15. $x = 3, y = \frac{1}{2}; x = -3, y = \frac{1}{2}; x = \dfrac{\sqrt{29}}{2}, y = -\frac{5}{4}; x = \dfrac{-\sqrt{29}}{2}, y = -\frac{5}{4}.$

17. $x = 2, y = 1; x = -2, y = 1; x = \dfrac{\sqrt{267}}{8}, y = -\frac{3}{8}; x = \dfrac{-\sqrt{267}}{8}, y = -\frac{3}{8}.$

18. $x = 3, y = 2; x = -3, y = 2; x = \dfrac{\sqrt{41}}{7}, y = -\frac{2}{7}; x = \dfrac{-\sqrt{41}}{7}, y = -\frac{2}{7}.$

19. $x = 1, y = -1; x = -1, y = -1; x = \dfrac{\sqrt{2}}{10}, y = \frac{2}{5}; x = \dfrac{-\sqrt{2}}{10}, y = \frac{2}{5}.$

21. $x = 4, y = 1; x = -1, y = -4.$ **22.** $x = 2, y = 1; x = -3, y = \frac{8}{3}.$

23. $x = 1, y = 0.$ **25.** $x = 2, y = 1; x = -\frac{3}{2}, y = -\frac{1}{6}.$ **26.** $x = 3, y = 4.$

27. $x = -\frac{1}{2}, y = 2; x = \frac{5}{2}, y = -2.$ **29.** $x = 3, y = 4; x = -\frac{31}{28}, y = -\frac{7}{4}.$

30. $x = 2, y = \frac{1}{2}; x = \frac{34}{5}, y = -\frac{5}{2}.$ **31.** $x = 3, y = \frac{1}{2}; x = \frac{7}{4}, y = -2.$

Exercise 42

1. $x = 1, y = 1; x = -1, y = -1; x = 4, y = -2; x = -4, y = 2.$

2. $x = 1, y = -1; x = -1, y = 1; x = 6, y = 2; x = -6, y = -2.$

3. $x = 3, y = -1; x = -3, y = 1; x = 4, y = 2; x = -4, y = -2.$

5. $x = 2, y = -1; x = -2, y = 1; x = 2, y = -2; x = -2, y = 2.$

6. $x = 3, y = 1; x = -3, y = -1; x = 2, y = -3; x = -2, y = 3.$

7. $x = 1\frac{1}{2}, y = \frac{1}{2}; x = -1\frac{1}{2}, y = -\frac{1}{2}; x = 1, y = 2; x = -1, y = -2.$

9. $x = \frac{1}{2}, y = 1; x = -\frac{1}{2}, y = -1; x = \frac{3}{4}, y = \frac{1}{4}; x = -\frac{3}{4}, y = -\frac{1}{4}.$

10. $x = \frac{1}{4}, y = \frac{1}{2}; x = -\frac{1}{4}, x = -\frac{1}{2}; x = \frac{1}{2}, y = 2; x = -\frac{1}{2}, y = -2.$

11. $x = \frac{2}{3}, y = 2; x = -\frac{2}{3}, y = -2; x = \frac{1}{4}, y = 1; x = -\frac{1}{4}, y = -1.$

13. $x = 5, y = -3; x = -5, y = 3; x = \frac{1}{3}, y = \frac{5}{3}; x = -\frac{1}{3}, y = -\frac{5}{3}.$

14. $x = 5, y = -4; x = -5, y = 4; x = \sqrt{2}, y = \dfrac{3\sqrt{2}}{2}; x = -\sqrt{2}, y = \dfrac{-3\sqrt{2}}{2}.$

15. $x = 8, y = -5; x = -8, y = 5; x = 1, y = 2; x = -1, y = -2.$

17. $x = 1, y = 0; x = -1, y = 0; x = 1, y = \frac{1}{2}; x = -1, y = -\frac{1}{2}.$

18. $x = 0, y = \frac{1}{3}; x = 0, y = -\frac{1}{3}; x = \frac{1}{3}, y = \frac{2}{9}; x = -\frac{1}{3}, y = -\frac{2}{9}.$

19. $x = 3, y = -2; x = -3, y = 2; x = i, y = i; x = -i, y = -i.$

21. $x = 0, y = i; x = 0, y = -i; x = 2i, y = i; x = -2i, y = -i.$

22. $x = i, y = 0; x = -i, y = 0; x = i, y = 2i; x = -i, y = -2i.$

23. $x = \frac{9}{7}, y = -\frac{4}{7}; x = -\frac{9}{7}, y = \frac{4}{7}; x = i, y = i; x = -i, y = -i.$

25. $x = i, y = i; x = -i, y = -i; x = 2i, y = -i; x = -2i, y = i.$

26. $x = 2, y = 3; x = -2, y = -3; x = \sqrt{3}, y = 3\sqrt{3}; x = -\sqrt{3}, y = -3\sqrt{3}.$

27. $x = 3, y = 1; x = -3, y = -1; x = \sqrt{2}, y = 4\sqrt{2}; x = -\sqrt{2}, y = -4\sqrt{2}.$

29. $x = 3, y = -1; x = -3, y = 1; x = \dfrac{2i}{3}, y = \dfrac{5i}{3}; x = -\dfrac{2i}{3}, y = \dfrac{-5i}{3}.$

30. $x = 2i\sqrt{3}, y = 3i\sqrt{3}; x = -2i\sqrt{3}, y = -3i\sqrt{3}; x = 2, y = 1; x = -2, y = -1.$

31. $x = \frac{1}{4}, y = -\frac{1}{2}; x = -\frac{1}{4}, y = \frac{1}{2}; x = \dfrac{\sqrt{5}}{5}, y = \dfrac{-\sqrt{5}}{5}; x = \dfrac{-\sqrt{5}}{5}, y = \dfrac{\sqrt{5}}{5}.$

Exercise 43

1. $x = 2, y = 1; x = -2, y = 1.$

2. $x = 3, y = -2; x = -3, y = -2; x = \sqrt{14}, y = 3; x = -\sqrt{14}, y = 3.$

3. $x = 1, y = 1; x = 1, y = -1; x = 7, y = 2; x = 7, y = -2.$

5. $x = 3, y = 1; x = -3, y = 1; x = 2\sqrt{2}, y = 0; x = -2\sqrt{2}, y = 0.$

6. $x = 2, y = -5; x = -2, y = -5; x = 2i, y = 3; x = -2i, y = 3.$

7. $x = -3, y = 3; x = -3, y = -3; x = 3, y = \sqrt{3}; x = 3, y = -\sqrt{3}.$

9. $x = 3, y = 1; x = -3, y = -1; x = 1, y = 3; x = -1, y = -3.$

10. $x = 1, y = -2; x = -1, y = 2; x = 3, y = -\frac{2}{3}; x = -3, y = \frac{2}{3}.$

11. $x = 2, y = 2; x = -2, y = -2; x = 2\sqrt{2}, y = \sqrt{2}; x = -2\sqrt{2}, y = -\sqrt{2}.$

13. $x = 3, y = 2; x = 7, y = -2.$ **14.** $x = -1, y = -\frac{1}{2}; x = 2, y = 1.$

15. $x = 1, y = 0; x = \frac{13}{5}, y = -\frac{2}{3}.$ **17.** $x = 2, y = 1; x = -1, y = -2.$

18. $x = -2, y = -3; x = -3\frac{1}{2}, y = -1\frac{1}{2}.$ **19.** $x = 0, y = 1; x = -3, y = 4.$

21. $x = 2, y = -1; x = -2, y = 1; x = 1, y = -2; x = -1, y = 2.$

22. $x = 1, y = 1; x = -1, y = -1.$

23. $x = 2, y = 1; x = -2, y = -1; x = 1, y = 2; x = -1, y = -2.$

25. $x = 3, y = 2; x = -3, y = -2; x = 2, y = 3; x = -2, y = -3.$

26. $x = 1, y = 1; x = -1, y = -1.$

27. $x = 2, y = -1; x = -2, y = 1; x = 1, y = -2; x = -1, y = 2.$

29. $x = 3, y = -2; x = -2, y = 3; x = -2 - \sqrt{5}, y = -2 + \sqrt{5}; x = -2 + \sqrt{5},$
$y = -2 - \sqrt{5}.$ **30.** $x = 1, y = -1; x = -1, y = 1; x = 0, y = -1; x = -1, y = 0.$

31. $x = 1, y = -2; x = -2, y = 1; x = 4, y = -1; x = -4, y = 1.$

Exercise 44

1. 14, 9. **2.** ± 6, ± 18. **3.** 7, 8. **5.** 15 ft., 7 ft. **6.** 9 ft., 12 ft. **7.** 12 ft., 5 ft.
9. 6, $\frac{1}{3}$. **10.** 34. **11.** 53. **13.** 30 ft., 50 ft. **14.** 17 in., 13 in.
15. 3 by 8 in. or 6 by 4 in. **17.** 5 in., 2 in. **18.** 4 ft., 8 ft. **19.** 3 cm., 4 cm.
21. $3600, 4%. **22.** First, 30 bales, $160; second, 40 bales, $150.
23. 4 miles per hr., $1\frac{1}{2}$ miles per hr.

Exercise 45

1. $\frac{16}{3}$. **2.** $\frac{9}{2}$. **3.** $\frac{45}{2}$. **5.** $\frac{7}{2}$. **6.** $\frac{8}{3}$. **7.** $\frac{28}{3}$. **9.** ab^2. **10.** ax. **11.** $\frac{c}{c \pm d}$.
13. 45 miles per hr. **14.** $.75 per pound. **15.** $525 per month. **17.** 1. **18.** 1.
19. 6. **21.** 0. **22.** 3. **23.** $\frac{9}{2}$. **25.** ± 4. **26.** ± 9. **27.** ± 2. **29.** $\pm x^3$.
30. $\pm xy^{-3}$. **31.** $\pm (y - 1)$. **33.** 12. **34.** 32. **35.** $\frac{25}{3}$. **37.** 9. **38.** 10. **39.** 1.
41. $x = 6, y = 8$. **42.** $x = 2, y = 10$. **43.** $x = 14, y = 6$. **45.** 24, 16.
46. 65°, 25°. **47.** $6300, $8400. **49.** 27, 57. **50.** 20 ft. **51.** 40°, 60°, 80°.
53. $\frac{5}{12}$. **54.** $\frac{1}{20}$. **55.** 7.8.

Exercise 46

1. (a) $y = kx$, (b) $s = \dfrac{k}{t}$, (c) $m = kpq$. **2.** (a) $v = ke^3$, (b) $I = krt$, (c) $y = \dfrac{k}{z^2}$.

3. (a) $F = \dfrac{k}{s^2}$, (b) $I = ks$, (c) $F = km_1m_2$. **5.** 3, 21. **6.** 14, 56. **7.** 36, 6. **9.** $70.

10. The circumference of the smaller is $\frac{2}{3}$ that of the other. **11.** 40.8 lb.
13. The volume of the first is $\frac{8}{9}$ of the second. **14.** 190 lb. **15.** 5 foot candles.
17. 80,000 ft.-lb. **18.** .45 sec. **19.** 2.9 lb. **21.** 24 sec. **22.** .01 sec.
23. $10 \sqrt{15}$ miles. **25.** The first has $\frac{1}{4}$ the power of the second.
26. First volume $\frac{4}{5}$ of the second. **27.** 1225. **29.** 36 ft. **30.** 17.28 lb.
31. 1.8 years. **33.** 32 amp. **34.** They are the same.

35. The pitch of the first is $\dfrac{\sqrt{2}}{2}$ times that of the second.

Exercise 47

1. $6^2 = 36$. **2.** $2^4 = 16$. **3.** $4^3 = 64$. **5.** $2^{-2} = \frac{1}{4}$. **6.** $3^{-3} = \frac{1}{27}$. **7.** $8^{-2} = \frac{1}{64}$.
9. $9^{\frac{3}{2}} = 27$. **10.** $4^{\frac{5}{2}} = 32$. **11.** $25^{\frac{3}{2}} = 125$. **13.** $a^2 = a^2$. **14.** $(a^2)^3 = a^6$.
15. $(a^3)^2 = a^6$. **17.** $\log_5 25 = 2$. **18.** $\log_6 216 = 3$. **19.** $\log_2 32 = 5$.
21. $\log_2 \frac{1}{2} = -1$. **22.** $\log_3 \frac{1}{9} = -2$. **23.** $\log_{\frac{1}{2}} 4 = -2$. **25.** $\log_8 2 = \frac{1}{3}$.
26. $\log_{64} 2 = \frac{1}{6}$. **27.** $\log_{27} \frac{1}{3} = -\frac{1}{3}$. **29.** $\log_8 4 = \frac{2}{3}$. **30.** $\log_{32} 8 = \frac{3}{5}$.
31. $\log_{64} \frac{1}{32} = -\frac{5}{6}$. **33.** 2. **34.** 3. **35.** 3. **37.** 3. **38.** 5. **39.** 3. **41.** $\frac{1}{2}$.
42. $\frac{1}{3}$. **43.** $\frac{1}{5}$. **45.** -2. **46.** -3. **47.** -2. **49.** $\frac{2}{3}$. **50.** $\frac{2}{3}$. **51.** $\frac{3}{2}$. **53.** 3.
54. $\frac{3}{2}$. **55.** 4. **57.** 2. **58.** 3. **59.** $\frac{1}{3}$. **61.** 8. **62.** 27. **63.** 3. **65.** 9.
66. 2. **67.** 16.

Exercise 48

1. 0. **2.** 0. **3.** 0. **5.** 1. **6.** 1. **7.** 3. **9.** -1. **10.** 0. **11.** -1. **13.** -2.
14. -3. **15.** -3. **17.** 0.3692. **18.** 0.7627. **19.** 0.6618. **21.** 1.7657.
22. 1.9159. **23.** 2.8774. **25.** 2.5694. **26.** 1.9304. **27.** 2.7860. **29.** $9.5119 - 10$.
30. $9.8463 - 10$. **31.** $9.5051 - 10$. **33.** $8.1959 - 10$. **34.** $7.3979 - 10$.
35. $8.4771 - 10$. **37.** 3.4116. **38.** 3.3979. **39.** 3.7559. **41.** 0.5100. **42.** 0.7568.

43. 0.4650. **45.** 1.9922. **46.** 1.8595. **47.** 2.8071. **49.** 3.8270. **50.** 3.5166.
51. 3.7651. **53.** 9.5128 − 10. **54.** 9.8923 − 10. **55.** 9.9923 − 10.
57. 8.3120 − 10. **58.** 2.8348. **59.** 0.0915.

Exercise 49

1. 14.1. **2.** 1.49. **3.** 157. **5.** 257. **6.** 35.0. **7.** 4570. **9.** 4.17. **10.** 237.
11. 2450. **13.** .753. **14.** .0797. **15.** .00868. **17.** .999. **18.** .0196. **19.** .00164.
21. 11.1. **22.** 9.74. **23.** 163. **25.** 20.3. **26.** 92.8. **27.** 2640. **29.** 33.7.
30. 817. **31.** 3.78. **33.** .424. **34.** .0736. **35.** .00488. **37.** .0529. **38.** .637.
39. .000553. **41.** 1.889. **42.** 30.36. **43.** 202.1. **45.** 387.1. **46.** 4.889.
47. 5926. **49.** 16.30. **50.** 150.5. **51.** 1448. **53.** .1550. **54.** .01554.
55. .002478. **57.** .2543. **58.** .05216. **59.** .0004641.

Exercise 50

1. 20.6. **2.** 11.3. **3.** 7.28. **5.** 3.46. **6.** 1110. **7.** 6.60. **9.** 1.77. **10.** 1.41.
11. 3.12. **13.** 114. **14.** 737. **15.** 2.04. **17.** 4.16. **18.** 3.06. **19.** 1.05.
21. .565. **22.** .751. **23.** .0819. **25.** .893. **26.** .652. **27.** .480. **29.** 3.453.
30. 4.232. **31.** 122.2. **33.** 29.67. **34.** 5.431. **35.** 1.205. **37.** 1.168. **38.** 1.448.
39. 1.367. **41.** 2.058. **42.** 7.660. **43.** 2.467. **45.** .06557. **46.** .4505.
47. .9036. **49.** .1842. **50.** .8764. **51.** .4896.

Exercise 51

1. 4.069. **2.** 2.019. **3.** −.2194. **5.** 2.138. **6.** 3.041. **7.** 4722. **9.** −.9631.
10. 2.049. **11.** 2.136. **13.** 1.801. **14.** 1.920. **15.** 3.097. **17.** 3.583. **18.** 4.540.
19. 4.120. **21.** 4.419. **22.** 5.067. **23.** .8692. **25.** −10.32. **26.** 3.608.
27. 1.447. **29.** 0, −5. **30.** 1, −4. **31.** 0, −4. **33.** $-2\frac{1}{2}$. **34.** −2. **35.** $-\frac{2}{5}$.
37. 3. **38.** 22. **39.** 5, −1. **41.** $x = .7153, y = .7153$. **42.** $x = 2.096, y = 0$.
43. $x = 3.213, y = .6426$. **45.** $x = 1.719, y = 1.088$. **46.** $x = 1.107, y = 0.1513$.
47. $x = 1.404, y = 0.798$.

Exercise 52

1. AP, $d = 4$. **2.** AP, $d = 3$. **3.** Not an AP. **5.** AP, $d = 2$. **6.** AP, $d = b + 1$.
7. Not an AP. **9.** 7, 9, 11, 13, 15. **10.** 1, 4, 7, 10, 13, 16.
11. 8, 5, 2, −1, −4, −7, −10. **13.** 3, 5, 7, 9, 11, 13. **14.** 8, 7, 6, 5, 4, 3.
15. 4, 5, 6, 7, 8. **17.** −13, −10, −7, −4, −1. **18.** 13, 11, 9, 7, 5, 3, 1, −1.
19. 9, 7, 5, 3, 1, −1, −3, −5, −7. **21.** 3. **22.** 3. **23.** 0. **25.** $1\frac{1}{2}$, 1. **26.** 2, 1.
27. −3, −1. **29.** $l = 14, s = 56$. **30.** $l = 10, s = 52$. **31.** $a = 4, s = 50$.
33. $d = −2, s = 15$. **34.** $d = 3, l = 13$. **35.** $n = 8, s = −32$. **37.** $d = 2, n = 7$.
38. $a = 3, d = 1$. **39.** $a = 4, l = 16$. **41.** $a = 7, n = 5$. **42.** $a = −2, n = 6$.
43. $n = 8, l = 3; n = 4, l = −5$. **45.** 7, 10, 13. **46.** 1, 3, 5. **47.** 1, 4, 7, 10.
49. −6, −5, −4, −3, −2. **50.** 1, −1, −3, −5, −7, −9.
51. 5, 8, 11, 14, 17, 20, 23. **53.** 126. **54.** 520. **55.** 459. **57.** $252.50.
58. $7600, $58,000. **59.** $1100. **61.** 306 in. **62.** $155,000. **63.** 126 in.
65. 13, 1 in. **66.** 8 people; 76, 78, 80, 82, 84, 86, 88, 90. **67.** 21 weeks.

Exercise 53

1. GP, $r = 2$. **2.** Not a GP. **3.** GP, $r = −1$. **5.** Not a GP. **6.** GP, $r = 2a$.
7. GP, $r = a + 2$. **9.** $\frac{1}{2}$, 1, 2, 4, 8, 16, 32. **10.** 81, 27, 9, 3, 1, $\frac{1}{3}$.
11. 128, −64, 32, −16, 8, −4, 2, −1. **13.** 2, 4, 8, 16, 32, 64. **14.** 256, 64, 16, 4, 1.

15. 243, ±81, 27, ±9, 3, ±1.   **17.** $\frac{1}{2}$, −1, 2, −4, 8, −16, 32.

18. 1, −3, 9, −27, 81, −243, 729, −2187.   **19.** 256, ±128, 64, ±32, 16, ±8, 4.

21. $\frac{2}{3}$.   **22.** $\frac{3}{4}$.   **23.** 2.   **25.** ±2.   **26.** ±2.   **27.** 6, $-\frac{5}{4}$.   **29.** $l = 16, s = 31$.

30. $l = 243, s = 364$.   **31.** $a = 1, s = 31$.   **33.** $a = 3, l = 3$.   **34.** $a = 2, l = -256$.

35. $n = 6, l = 243$.   **37.** $n = 6, s = \frac{21}{2}$.   **38.** $n = 6, s = 120\frac{1}{4}$.   **39.** $r = \frac{1}{2}, s = \frac{127}{4}$.

41. $n = 6, r = 2$.   **42.** $r = \frac{1}{4}, n = 6$.   **43.** $r = -\frac{3}{2}, s = 463$.   **45.** 4, 8.

46. ±3, 9, ±27.   **47.** ±16, 64, ±256.   **49.** $\frac{2}{3}$, 1, $\frac{3}{2}$, $\frac{9}{4}$.   **50.** $\pm\frac{3}{32}, \frac{3}{16}, \pm\frac{1}{8}, \frac{1}{12}, \pm\frac{1}{18}$.

51. $\pm\frac{1}{4}, \frac{1}{2}, \pm 1, 2, \pm 4$.   **53.** 510.   **54.** 363.   **55.** 19,530.   **57.** $10.23.   **58.** 62.

59. 256n.   **61.** 4096 cu ft., 1 cu. ft.   **62.** 160,000.   **63.** 9.   **65.** 2.

66. $327.67, $10,158.08.   **67.** $7856.40, $59,702.40.

Exercise 54

1. 8.   **2.** 9.   **3.** $12\frac{1}{2}$.   **5.** 4.   **6.** $24\frac{1}{2}$.   **7.** $13\frac{1}{2}$.   **9.** $\frac{4}{9}$.   **10.** $\frac{5}{9}$.   **11.** $\frac{7}{9}$.

13. $\frac{2}{11}$.   **14.** $\frac{16}{33}$.   **15.** $\frac{29}{33}$.   **17.** $\frac{79}{37}$.   **18.** $4\frac{26}{111}$.   **19.** $2\frac{6}{37}$.   **21.** 1.   **22.** 2.

23. 3.   **25.** 60 ft.   **26.** 10 ft.   **27.** 288 sq. in.   **29.** 500 lb.

30. $30,000; lost $1049.38.   **31.** Yes, he would gain at least $2.60 by holding.

33. $\dfrac{1}{x-1}$.   **34.** $\dfrac{1}{3x+1}$.   **35.** $\dfrac{2}{2x-3}$.

Exercise 55

1. $x^5 + 5x^4y + 10x^3y^2 + 10x^2y^3 + 5xy^4 + y^5$.   **2.** $a^7 - 7a^6b + 21a^5b^2 - 35a^4b^3 + 35a^3b^4 - 21a^2b^5 + 7ab^6 - b^7$.   **3.** $m^6 + 6m^5n + 15m^4n^2 + 20m^3n^3 + 15m^2n^4 + 6mn^5 + n^6$.   **5.** $p^9 - 9p^8q + 36p^7q^2 - 84p^6q^3 + 126p^5q^4 - 126p^4q^5 + 84p^3q^6 - 36p^2q^7 + 9pq^8 - q^9$.   **6.** $a^8 - 8a^7t + 28a^6t^2 - 56a^5t^3 + 70a^4t^4 - 56a^3t^5 + 28a^2t^6 - 8at^7 + t^8$.   **7.** $r^{10} + 10r^9u + 45r^8u^2 + 120r^7u^3 + 210r^6u^4 + 252r^5u^5 + 210r^4u^6 + 120r^3u^7 + 45r^2u^8 + 10ru^9 + u^{10}$.   **9.** $128x^7 - 448x^6y + 672x^5y^2 - 560x^4y^3 + 280x^3y^4 - 84x^2y^5 + 14xy^6 - y^7$.   **10.** $x^6 + 18x^5y + 135x^4y^2 + 540x^3y^3 + 1215x^2y^4 + 1458xy^5 + 729y^6$.   **11.** $a^9 - 27a^8b + 324a^7b^2 - 2268a^6b^3 + 10,206a^5b^4 - 30,618a^4b^5 + 61,236a^3b^6 - 78,732a^2b^7 + 59,049ab^8 - 19,683b^9$.   **13.** $32x^5 + 240x^4w + 720x^3w^2 + 1080x^2w^3 + 810xw^4 + 243w^5$.   **14.** $81a^4 - 216a^3b + 216a^2b^2 - 96ab^3 + 16b^4$.   **15.** $1024t^5 - 3840t^4u + 5760t^3u^2 - 4320t^2u^3 + 1620tu^4 - 243u^5$.   **17.** $x^{18} - 9x^{16}y + 36x^{14}y^2 - 84x^{12}y^3 + 126x^{10}y^4 - 126x^8y^5 + 84x^6y^6 - 36x^4y^7 + 9x^2y^8 - y^9$.   **18.** $128a^7 + 448a^6b^3 + 672a^5b^6 + 560a^4b^9 + 280a^3b^{12} + 84a^2b^{15} + 14ab^{18} + b^{21}$.   **19.** $w^{12} - 6w^{10}t^3 + 15w^8t^6 - 20w^6t^9 + 15w^4t^{12} - 6w^2t^{15} + t^{18}$.   **21.** $10,000,000,000 + 500,000,000 + 10,000,000 + 100,000 + 500 + 1 = 10,510,100,501$.   **22.** 96,059,601.   **23.** 1,126,162,419,264.   **25.** 1,061,520,150,601.   **26.** 1.08,243,216.

27. 1.22,987,386,542,487.   **29.** $\dfrac{x^8}{256} + \dfrac{x^6}{8} + \dfrac{7x^4}{4} + 14x^2 + 70 + \dfrac{224}{x^2} + \dfrac{448}{x^4} + \dfrac{512}{x^6} + \dfrac{256}{x^8}$.

30. $\dfrac{x^5}{243} - \dfrac{5x^3}{81} + \dfrac{10x}{27} - \dfrac{10}{9x} + \dfrac{5}{3x^3} - \dfrac{1}{x^5}$.   **31.** $\dfrac{x^{12}}{64} - \dfrac{9x^9}{16} + \dfrac{135x^6}{16} - \dfrac{135x^3}{2} + \dfrac{1215}{2} - \dfrac{729}{x^3} + \dfrac{729}{x^6}$.   **33.** $a^{50} + 50a^{49}b + 1225a^{48}b^2 + 19,600a^{47}b^3$.   **34.** $c^{60} - 60c^{59}d + 1770c^{58}d^2 + 34,220c^{57}d^3$.   **35.** $x^{30} - 60x^{29}y + 1740x^{28}y^2 - 32,480x^{27}y^3$.   **37.** $x^{50} - 50x^{48}w + 1200x^{46}w^2 - 18,400x^{44}w^3$.   **38.** $m^{40} - 60m^{38}n + 1710m^{36}n^2 - 30,780m^{34}n^3$.   **39.** $s^{120} - 60s^{118}t^3 + 1770s^{116}t^6 - 34,220s^{114}t^9$.

Exercise 56

1. $70a^4b^4$.   **2.** $84x^3y^6$.   **3.** $-120m^7n^3$.   **5.** $14yw^6$.   **6.** $4455x^3y^8$.   **7.** $189a^5c^2$.

9. $1120x^8y^4$.   **10.** $286a^3y^{30}$.   **11.** $210x^2$.

APPENDIX

INTERMEDIATE ALGEBRA

TABLE I.—COMMON LOGARITHMS

N	0	1	2	3	4	5	6	7	8	9
10	0000	0043	0086	0128	0170	0212	0253	0294	0334	0374
11	0414	0453	0492	0531	0569	0607	0645	0682	0719	0755
12	0792	0828	0864	0899	0934	0969	1004	1038	1072	1106
13	1139	1173	1206	1239	1271	1303	1335	1367	1399	1430
14	1461	1492	1523	1553	1584	1614	1644	1673	1703	1732
15	1761	1790	1818	1847	1875	1903	1931	1959	1987	2014
16	2041	2068	2095	2122	2148	2175	2201	2227	2253	2279
17	2304	2330	2355	2380	2405	2430	2455	2480	2504	2529
18	2553	2577	2601	2625	2648	2672	2695	2718	2742	2765
19	2788	2810	2833	2856	2878	2900	2923	2945	2967	2989
20	3010	3032	3054	3075	3096	3118	3139	3160	3181	3201
21	3222	3243	3263	3284	3304	3324	3345	3365	3385	3404
22	3424	3444	3464	3483	3502	3522	3541	3560	3579	3598
23	3617	3636	3655	3674	3692	3711	3729	3747	3766	3784
24	3802	3820	3838	3856	3874	3892	3909	3927	3945	3962
25	3979	3997	4014	4031	4048	4065	4082	4099	4116	4133
26	4150	4166	4183	4200	4216	4232	4249	4265	4281	4298
27	4314	4330	4346	4362	4378	4393	4409	4425	4440	4456
28	4472	4487	4502	4518	4533	4548	4564	4579	4594	4609
29	4624	4639	4654	4669	4683	4698	4713	4728	4742	4757
30	4771	4786	4800	4814	4829	4843	4857	4871	4886	4900
31	4914	4928	4942	4955	4969	4983	4997	5011	5024	5038
32	5051	5065	5079	5092	5105	5119	5132	5145	5159	5172
33	5185	5198	5211	5224	5237	5250	5263	5276	5289	5302
34	5315	5328	5340	5353	5366	5378	5391	5403	5416	5428
35	5441	5453	5465	5478	5490	5502	5514	5527	5539	5551
36	5563	5575	5587	5599	5611	5623	5635	5647	5658	5670
37	5682	5694	5705	5717	5729	5740	5752	5763	5775	5786
38	5798	5809	5821	5832	5843	5855	5866	5877	5888	5899
39	5911	5922	5933	5944	5955	5966	5977	5988	5999	6010
40	6021	6031	6042	6053	6064	6075	6085	6096	6107	6117
41	6128	6138	6149	6160	6170	6180	6191	6201	6212	6222
42	6232	6243	6253	6263	6274	6284	6294	6304	6314	6325
43	6335	6345	6355	6365	6375	6385	6395	6405	6415	6425
44	6435	6444	6454	6464	6474	6484	6493	6503	6513	6522
45	6532	6542	6551	6561	6571	6580	6590	6599	6609	6618
46	6628	6637	6646	6656	6665	6675	6684	6693	6702	6712
47	6721	6730	6739	6749	6758	6767	6776	6785	6794	6803
48	6812	6821	6830	6839	6848	6857	6866	6875	6884	6893
49	6902	6911	6920	6928	6937	6946	6955	6964	6972	6981
50	6990	6998	7007	7016	7024	7033	7042	7050	7059	7067
51	7076	7084	7093	7101	7110	7118	7126	7135	7143	7152
52	7160	7168	7177	7185	7193	7202	7210	7218	7226	7235
53	7243	7251	7259	7267	7275	7284	7292	7300	7308	7316
54	7324	7332	7340	7348	7356	7364	7372	7380	7388	7396
N	0	1	2	3	4	5	6	7	8	9

TABLE I.—COMMON LOGARITHMS.—(*Continued*)

N	0	1	2	3	4	5	6	7	8	9
55	7404	7412	7419	7427	7435	7443	7451	7459	7466	7474
56	7482	7490	7497	7505	7513	7520	7528	7536	7543	7551
57	7559	7566	7574	7582	7589	7597	7604	7612	7619	7627
58	7634	7642	7649	7657	7664	7672	7679	7686	7694	7701
59	7709	7716	7723	7731	7738	7745	7752	7760	7767	7774
60	7782	7789	7796	7803	7810	7818	7825	7832	7839	7846
61	7853	7860	7868	7875	7882	7889	7896	7903	7910	7917
62	7924	7931	7938	7945	7952	7959	7966	7973	7980	7987
63	7993	8000	8007	8014	8021	8028	8035	8041	8048	8055
64	8062	8069	8075	8082	8089	8096	8102	8109	8116	8122
65	8129	8136	8142	8149	8156	8162	8169	8176	8182	8189
66	8195	8202	8209	8215	8222	8228	8235	8241	8248	8254
67	8261	8267	8274	8280	8287	8293	8299	8306	8312	8319
68	8325	8331	8338	8344	8351	8357	8363	8370	8376	8382
69	8388	8395	8401	8407	8414	8420	8426	8432	8439	8445
70	8451	8457	8463	8470	8476	8482	8488	8494	8500	8506
71	8513	8519	8525	8531	8537	8543	8549	8555	8561	8567
72	8573	8579	8585	8591	8597	8603	8609	8615	8621	8627
73	8633	8639	8645	8651	8657	8663	8669	8675	8681	8686
74	8692	8698	8704	8710	8716	8722	8727	8733	8739	8745
75	8751	8756	8762	8768	8774	8779	8785	8791	8797	8802
76	8808	8814	8820	8825	8831	8837	8842	8848	8854	8859
77	8865	8871	8876	8882	8887	8893	8899	8904	8910	8915
78	8921	8927	8932	8938	8943	8949	8954	8960	8965	8971
79	8976	8982	8987	8993	8998	9004	9009	9015	9020	9025
80	9031	9036	9042	9047	9053	9058	9063	9069	9074	9079
81	9085	9090	9096	9101	9106	9112	9117	9122	9128	9133
82	9138	9143	9149	9154	9159	9165	9170	9175	9180	9186
83	9191	9196	9201	9206	9212	9217	9222	9227	9232	9238
84	9243	9248	9253	9258	9263	9269	9274	9279	9284	9289
85	9294	9299	9304	9309	9315	9320	9325	9330	9335	9340
86	9345	9350	9355	9360	9365	9370	9375	9380	9385	9390
87	9395	9400	9405	9410	9415	9420	9425	9430	9435	9440
88	9445	9450	9455	9460	9465	9469	9474	9479	9484	9489
89	9494	9499	9504	9509	9513	9518	9523	9528	9533	9538
90	9542	9547	9552	9557	9562	9566	9571	9576	9581	9586
91	9590	9595	9600	9605	9609	9614	9619	9624	9628	9633
92	9638	9643	9647	9652	9657	9661	9666	9671	9675	9680
93	9685	9689	9694	9699	9703	9708	9713	9717	9722	9727
94	9731	9736	9741	9745	9750	9754	9759	9763	9768	9773
95	9777	9782	9786	9791	9795	9800	9805	9809	9814	9818
96	9823	9827	9832	9836	9841	9845	9850	9854	9859	9863
97	9868	9872	9877	9881	9886	9890	9894	9899	9903	9908
98	9912	9917	9921	9926	9930	9934	9939	9943	9948	9952
99	9956	9961	9965	9969	9974	9978	9983	9987	9991	9996
N	0	1	2	3	4	5	6	7	8	9

TABLE II.—POWERS AND ROOTS

No.	Sq.	Sq. Root	Cube	Cube Root	No.	Sq.	Sq. Root	Cube	Cube Root
1	1	1.000	1	1.000	51	2,601	7.141	132,651	3.708
2	4	1.414	8	1.260	52	2,704	7.211	140,608	3.733
3	9	1.732	27	1.442	53	2,809	7.280	148,877	3.756
4	16	2.000	64	1.587	54	2,916	7.348	157,464	3.780
5	25	2.236	125	1.710	55	3,025	7.416	166,375	3.803
6	36	2.449	216	1.817	56	3,136	7.483	175,616	3.826
7	49	2.646	343	1.913	57	3,249	7.550	185,193	3.849
8	64	2.828	512	2.000	58	3,364	7.616	195,112	3.871
9	81	3.000	729	2.080	59	3,481	7.681	205,379	3.893
10	100	3.162	1,000	2.154	60	3,600	7.746	216,000	3.915
11	121	3.317	1,331	2.224	61	3,721	7.810	226,981	3.936
12	144	3.464	1,728	2.289	62	3,844	7.874	238,328	3.958
13	169	3.606	2,197	2.351	63	3,969	7.937	250,047	3.979
14	196	3.742	2,744	2.410	64	4,096	8.000	262,144	4.000
15	225	3.873	3,375	2.466	65	4,225	8.062	274,625	4.021
16	256	4.000	4,096	2.520	66	4,356	8.124	287,496	4.041
17	289	4.123	4,913	2.571	67	4,489	8.185	300,763	4.062
18	324	4.243	5,832	2.621	68	4,624	8.246	314,432	4.082
19	361	4.359	6,859	2.668	69	4,761	8.307	328,509	4.102
20	400	4.472	8,000	2.714	70	4,900	8.367	343,000	4.121
21	441	4.583	9,261	2.759	71	5,041	8.426	357,911	4.141
22	484	4.690	10,648	2.802	72	5,184	8.485	373,248	4.160
23	529	4.796	12,167	2.844	73	5,329	8.544	389,017	4.179
24	576	4.899	13,824	2.884	74	5,476	8.602	405,224	4.198
25	625	5.000	15,625	2.924	75	5,625	8.660	421,875	4.217
26	676	5.099	17,576	2.962	76	5,776	8.718	438,976	4.236
27	729	5.196	19,683	3.000	77	5,929	8.775	456,533	4.254
28	784	5.291	21,952	3.037	78	6,084	8.832	474,552	4.273
29	841	5.385	24,389	3.072	79	6,241	8.888	493,039	4.291
30	900	5.477	27,000	3.107	80	6,400	8.944	512,000	4.309
31	961	5.568	29,791	3.141	81	6,561	9.000	531,441	4.327
32	1,024	5.657	32,768	3.175	82	6,724	9.055	551,368	4.344
33	1,089	5.745	35,937	3.208	83	6,889	9.110	571,787	4.362
34	1,156	5.831	39,304	3.240	84	7,056	9.165	592,704	4.380
35	1,225	5.916	42,875	3.271	85	7,225	9.220	614,125	4.397
36	1,296	6.000	46,656	3.302	86	7,396	9.274	636,056	4.414
37	1,369	6.083	50,653	3.332	87	7,569	9.327	658,503	4.431
38	1,444	6.164	54,872	3.362	88	7,744	9.381	681,472	4.448
39	1,521	6.245	59,319	3.391	89	7,921	9.434	704,969	4.465
40	1,600	6.325	64,000	3.420	90	8,100	9.487	729,000	4.481
41	1,681	6.403	68,921	3.448	91	8,281	9.539	753,571	4.498
42	1,764	6.481	74,088	3.476	92	8,464	9.592	778,688	4.514
43	1,849	6.557	79,507	3.503	93	8,649	9.644	804,357	4.531
44	1,936	6.633	85,184	3.530	94	8,836	9.695	830,584	4.547
45	2,025	6.708	91,125	3.557	95	9,025	9.747	857,375	4.563
46	2,116	6.782	97,336	3.583	96	9,216	9.798	884,736	4.579
47	2,209	6.856	103,823	3.609	97	9,409	9.849	912,673	4.595
48	2,304	6.928	110,592	3.634	98	9,604	9.899	941,192	4.610
49	2,401	7.000	117,649	3.659	99	9,801	9.950	970,299	4.626
50	2,500	7.071	125,000	3.684	100	10,000	10.000	1,000,000	4.642

INDEX

303

$$x+y+z=220$$
$$x+z=20+y$$
$$y+z=-20+2x$$

$$15x - 15y = 22y$$
$$-5\tfrac{5}{8}x + 9\tfrac{3}{8}y = 0$$